PREF

GW00647312

A living language must keep ~~pace with improvement in~~
knowledge and with the multiplicauo.. ...

Noah Webster in a letter to John Pickering, ~~181~~/

Pharmacology is concerned with the discovery of new drugs and with studies of the interactions between living cells and drugs: what drugs do, how they do it, and what happens to them in the body. As such, pharmacology freely borrows its techniques and terminology from other disciplines. People who divert their energies to pharmacology and who describe themselves as pharmacologists might originally have been trained as chemists, biochemists, biologists, physiologists, immunologists, microbiologists, pharmacists, veterinarians, or doctors; a few have been specifically trained as pharmacologists. It is probably this immensely broad input into the subject that leads to the continuously accelerating increase in the development of new drugs, and in our knowledge about their mechanisms of action. In turn, and consequently, we learn more about cellular control mechanisms, pathological processes, toxicity, and the body's capacity to deal with foreign chemicals. It is therefore obvious that the compilation of a glossary of pharmacological terms, such as this, is an open-ended task; there is virtually no limit to the list of terms that might be used by, and useful to, pharmacologists. Necessarily, therefore, we have had to be selective. We have not included drug names in our alphabetical list. Many excellent texts already undertake this huge task, e.g. E. E. J. Marler's *Pharmacological and Chemical Synonyms* (1985, Elsevier, Amsterdam), and the various national pharmacopoeias and related reference books. We have, however, included as separate items drug classes, both chemical (e.g. benzodiazepines) and therapeutic (e.g. diuretics, antidepressants), with named examples, and we have included prototype drugs (e.g. atropine-like drug, curare-like drug). Such terms would surely be regarded as specifically pharmacological. But what about terms such as *cholinergic nerve fibre* or *cyclic AMP*? Do these belong exclusively to physiology and biochemistry respectively, or are they pharmacological words also? We have included such terms, and many others, because pharmacologists need and use them, and this—whether we think that pharmacologists need and use them—has been one of our main criteria for inclusion, along with our personal prejudices.

In defining the terms and trying to explain their origins, we have, as far as possible, stuck to the originators' intended meanings, partly out of respect for the workers and partly because embroidering an original meaning often leads to confusion. The jargon attached to any science is useful, indeed almost essential, for short-hand communication between cognoscenti. In its use, one is, however, treading the narrow path between gobbledegook and excessive pedantry, and some care is needed.

We appeal to our colleagues not to use terms loosely, not because we wish to interfere with their personal liberty, but because once the terms become widened in their application, their value is debased through loss of precision. (See, for example, Sir Henry Dale's comment on his own paper concerned with the nomenclature of fibres in the autonomic nervous system: Dale (1965) *Adventures in Physiology*, p. 529. The Wellcome Trust, London.)

Only occasionally have we expressed a preference for one of a number of synonyms. Usually, we have simply tried to give the accepted meaning. Where we have qualified a term as 'preferred', we have explained why it is preferred, and we mean of course preferred by us. We have not entered into the rather futile arguments concerning the plural forms of words of foreign origin. Insistence on a Greek or Latin plural form seems to be just as much a pedantic affectation as the converse, when a word has been adopted into the English language, especially when common usage exhibits total inconsistency. Thus, it is common usage to say *enemas* and *fetuses*, rather than *enemata* and *fetūs*. On the other hand, *corpora* and *stigmata* are in more common usage than *corpuses* and *stigmas*. There is no logical reason why *criterions* and *datums* should be less acceptable than *criteria* and *data*, but common usage currently dictates the use of the latter. What does seem to be unacceptable is anglicized plural forms of foreign plurals (*criterias* and *datas!*). In general, we should best be guided by whatever happens to have the euphony derived from current practice, but no one need be concerned about, or protest against, a gradual change to anglicized plural forms of all adopted foreign words.

In many cases, rather than simply defining terms in isolation, as would a conventional dictionary, we have tried to put the matter in context by giving the background picture, and indicating the relevance to other aspects of the subject. In this way, we hope not only to have made the text less boring to read, but also to have provided a synopsis of pharmacology that might be readable and of value during odd free moments, such as while waiting for a bus or a *viva voce* examination. One of us is still a student and feels particularly that a slim book such as this will help to foster an improved sense of security (not false we trust) in the minutes leading up to an oral exam.

PREFACE

One of us is co-author of a textbook (Bowman & Rand (1980) *Textbook of Pharmacology*, 2nd Edition. Blackwell Scientific Publications, Oxford). Where we have been satisfied with definitions given therein, we have not seen fit to change them, and we are grateful to our colleague Michael Rand for permitting this.

Finally, we would warn our readers, especially the younger ones, against the concept that something called a dictionary has a divine authority that makes its contents totally true. Undoubtedly we will have made mistakes, and we will be pleased to hear about them, and any omissions, if you can spare the time to write.

W. C. Bowman
Anne Bowman
Alison Bowman

abortifacient   A substance that causes abortion, i.e. that induces premature delivery of the conceptus as an embryo or non-viable fetus (Latin: *abortus*, death, i.e. taken away from life; *faciens*, doing). **Prostaglandin** $F_{2\alpha}$ is an example of a drug that may be used as an abortifacient.

abreaction   A term used in psychiatry to describe a very rapid release of buried fears and tensions in a neurotic patient. Certain drugs may be used to induce an abreaction, which is considered by many psychiatrists to have a beneficial effect in some neurotic patients. Drugs capable of producing an abreaction include amphetamine and certain psychotogenic drugs (e.g. lysergide).

abrin   Also called agglutinin; a toxic glycoprotein obtained from seeds of jequirity (*Abrus precatorius*, Leguminosae). The molecule is composed of two portions: an acidic chain (mol. wt. *c.* 30000 daltons) that inhibits protein synthesis, and a neutral chain (mol. wt. *c.* 35000 daltons) that serves to bind the molecule to the cell surface. The two portions of the molecule are joined through S–S bonds.
   Olsnes (1973) *Europ. J. Biochem.* **35**, 179

absinthe   A spirit drink containing 68% ethanol and flavoured with wormwood (*Artemisia absinthum*) and other herbs. The chief constituent of the essential oil of wormwood is thujone, which produces convulsions in large doses. Overindulgence in absinthe was thought to produce brain damage, and for this reason production of the drink has been prohibited for 50 years or more in most countries. Imitation absinthe, flavoured with aniseed and liquorice, is available under a number of names.

absorption   Generally, the process whereby a substance penetrates into another substance. In pharmacology, the word refers to the process through which a **drug** enters the blood from its site of administration (Latin: *ab*, away from; *sorbere*, to suck).

abstinence syndrome   *See* **withdrawal syndrome**.

acaricide drug   A drug used to kill mites, especially the scabies mite (*Sarcoptes scabiei*). The term is derived from the fact that the scabies mite was formerly called *Acarus scabiei*. Monosulfiram is an example of a drug with acaricide activity.

Acceleranstoff   The name coined by Otto Loewi (1921) to denote the substance released from the sympathetic nerve (the nervus accelerans) to the frog heart. It is now known that Acceleranstoff is **adrenaline**, which is the transmitter of cardiac sympathetic nerves in frogs and toads (**noradrenaline** in mammals). *See also* **Vagusstoff**.

accentuated antagonism This term, which is not widely used, and indeed is not particularly useful, is most easily defined by the use of an example. **Agonists** that act on **muscarinic cholinoceptors** decrease the force of contraction of atrial muscle, but not of mammalian ventricular muscle. However, if the force of contraction of the ventricular muscle has been increased by a β-**adrenoceptor** agonist, a negative **inotropic action** of muscarinic agonists becomes apparent. This interaction has been described as 'accentuated antagonism'.
Levy (1971) *Circulat. Res.* **29**, 437

acceptor sites A term used to denote sites of drug binding other than those that are directly concerned in the pharmacodynamic response. For example, many drugs are bound to plasma albumin, and the binding site on the albumin may be described as an acceptor site. Such binding may affect the rate or duration of drug action, but does not directly produce the drug effect.

acetylcholine The acetyl ester of choline. Acetylcholine is the transmitter of **cholinergic nerve fibres**.

$$H_3C-{}^+\overset{\overset{\displaystyle CH_3}{|}}{\underset{\underset{\displaystyle CH_3}{|}}{N}}-CH_2-CH_2-O-\overset{\overset{\displaystyle O}{\|}}{C}-CH_3$$

acetylcholine receptors *See* **cholinoceptors.**

acetylcholinesterase Also called acetylcholine acetylhydrolase (EC 3.1.1.7), and formerly called true or specific cholinesterase. An enzyme present in nervous tissue, skeletal muscle and erythrocytes. Its main function is to catalyse the hydrolysis of the neurotransmitter, **acetylcholine,** yielding choline and acetate.

acidifying salts Salts that produce acidosis. They may have a limited use as oral **diuretic drugs**. Ammonium chloride is the main example. After absorption, the ammonium ion is converted to urea in the liver and partly excreted. The chloride ion displaces bicarbonate which is converted to H_2O and CO_2, the latter being eliminated in the lungs. There is thus a loss of blood buffer (i.e. an acidosis) in exchange for chloride. Increased chloride ion with accompanying cation (mainly sodium) is filtered in the glomeruli, and a mild diuresis results.

acne Adolescent pimples or pustules (acne vulgaris) arising from blockade of the terminal ducts of pilosebaceous units of the skin. The term is probably derived either from the Greek word *akhne*, a particle, or the Greek word *akme*, a point. The hormonal changes associated with puberty (especially **androgen** production or a fall in **oestrogen** level) increase sebum secretion and produce follicular hyperkeratosis. These changes lead to the formation of **comedones** and then papules, which if they become infected form pustules.

acnegenic activity Activity that exacerbates or causes **acne**. For example, **androgens** such as dihydrotestosterone are acnegenic.

acneiform reaction A skin reaction, resembling **acne**, which is a side-effect of some drugs, including bromides, iodides, troxidone and isoniazid.

addiction *See* **drug dependence**.

additive effect *See* **synergistic action**.

adenosine receptors *See* **purinoceptors**.

adenylate cyclase An enzyme which is present in the membranes of most cells and which catalyses an intramolecular condensation of adenosine triphosphate in the cytoplasm to produce cyclic adenosine 3,5-

The formation and inactivation of cyclic AMP.

monophosphate (abbreviated to **cyclic AMP** or cAMP). Cyclic AMP acts as a **second messenger** in mediating the actions of several **hormones** and neurotransmitters. Cyclic AMP is hydrolysed to 5'-AMP, and thereby inactivated, under the influence of cyclic nucleotide **phosphodiesterases**.

Many hormones and other endogenous chemical mediators (the first messengers) produce at least some of their effects by activating adenylate cyclase (e.g. **adrenaline** and **noradrenaline** via β-**adrenoceptors**, thyroid stimulating hormone, corticotrophin, leutinizing hormone, parathormone, vasopressin, glucagon, **vasoactive intestinal peptide**, some **prostaglandins**, **serotonin, histamine** via H_2-receptors, adenosine via A_2-**purinoceptors**). The ability of a particular hormone to stimulate adenylate cyclase depends upon the cell membrane possessing specific **receptors** for that hormone that are coupled to the enzyme. The receptor and the enzyme are separate proteins that functionally interact when a conformational change is produced in the receptor by a specific **agonist**. However, the receptor and the enzyme are insufficient by themselves. In addition, a GTP-binding protein (G-protein or N_s-protein) is necessary. The sequence of events in the coupling process is not totally clear, but it may be that the agonist induces a conformational change in the receptor protein that allows it to interact with the GTP-binding protein. A consequent conformational change in the GTP-binding protein then induces a conformational change in adenylate cyclase that converts it from the inactive to the active form. A single activated receptor protein may float laterally through the membrane and activate many G-protein and enzyme molecules, thus amplifying the single agonist–receptor interaction. The GTP-binding protein is a GTPase which hydrolyses the bound GTP to GDP. This immediately terminates the adenylate cyclase activation.

Adenylate cyclase activity in some cells is actually controlled by two GTP-binding proteins, the stimulant (N_s) protein already referred to and an inhibitory (N_i) protein in addition. Some receptors may be coupled only to the inhibitory GTP-binding protein, and receptor activation then results in inactivation of the enzyme and a fall in the basal level of cyclic AMP being produced. Such inhibitory agonists include **acetylcholne** at some muscarinic **cholinoceptors**, **opiates** and **opioids** at some **opiate receptors**, agonists at α_2-adrenoceptors, and adenosine at A_1-purinoceptors.

Some agents are able to bypass receptors in activating the GTP-binding protein (e.g. **cholera toxin** and sodium fluoride), and **forskolin** is able to bypass both receptors and GTP-binding proteins and activate the enzyme directly. The so-called **islet-activating protein** stimulates adenylate cyclase by disinhibition; it stabilizes the N_i protein in its inactive state. Adenylate cyclase may also be activated physiologically by the Ca^{2+}—**calmodulin** complex.

adjuvant arthritis An experimental arthritis induced in experimental animals by **Freund's complete adjuvant**. **Intradermal injection** of Freund's complete adjuvant elicits, within 24–48 hours, a local inflammatory response that persists for some weeks. The injected site is invaded by reticuloendothelial macrophages and polymorphonuclear leucocytes, and there is redness, swelling and pain. Widespread secondary responses, termed adjuvant arthritis, develop subsequently. There is inflammation of joints, enlargement of the spleen, conjunctivitis and granulomatous nodules in the skin. The course of events suggests a cell-mediated, **delayed hypersensitivity reaction** directed against autoantigens, the development of which has been facilitated by adjuvant. The model is used to evaluate new **anti-inflammatory drugs** of potential use in human arthritis.

adrenaline   One of two hormones released from the adrenal medulla (the other being **noradrenaline**). Adrenaline also serves as the neurotransmitter of some **adrenergic nerve fibres**. The (−)-isomer (l-isomer) is the naturally occurring and biologically active isomer. In the USA, 'adrenaline' is a registered trade mark and the official name for the hormone is epinephrine (Latin: *ad*, near; *renes*, kidneys. Greek: *epi*, upon; *nephros*, kidney).

$$HO-C_6H_3(OH)-CH(OH)-CH_2-NH-CH_3$$

adrenaline reversal   Refers to the fact that a formerly pressor dose of **adrenaline** produces a fall in blood pressure after administration of an α-**adrenoceptor antagonist**. The fall in pressure is the result of unmasking the stimulant action of adrenaline on β-**adrenoceptors** that mediate vasodilatation. Henry Dale (1913, *J. Physiol.* **46**, 291) first drew attention to adrenaline reversal after injection of ergotoxine (α-adrenoceptor antagonist) in the pithed cat.

adrenergic blocking drug   Synonymous with **adrenoceptor antagonist** which is the preferred term (*see* **adrenergic nerve fibre**).

adrenergic nerve fibre   A nerve fibre that works (Greek: *ergon*, work) by releasing an **adrenaline**-like substance as a neurotransmitter. The adjective adrenergic (along with cholinergic) was coined by H. H. Dale, who subsequently made repeated pleas that for the sake of precision the ending '-ergic' should be restricted to its original intended meaning, and not debased by being used merely to mean 'pertaining to'. (*See also* Trendelenburg (1983) *Trends pharmacol. Sci.* **42**, 49.) In fact the term is now frequently used in a loose sense, often by scientists who should know better. Adrenergic receptor and adrenergic drug are common examples of its incorrect use in terms of Dale's intention, and this leads to imprecision and confusion, since adrenergic drug, for example, might refer to an adrenoceptor agonist, an **adrenoceptor antagonist** or an **adrenergic neurone blocking drug**. It is not too late to change back to the original meaning and this should be done if for no reason other than respect for Dale. Nowadays, the identities of transmitters are known with more certainty than in Dale's time, and more precise descriptions of nerve fibres, such as noradrenergic or dopaminergic, do not offend the spirit of Dale's intention. Strictly speaking, the suffix '-ergic' should be attached to a chemical only when there is evidence beyond reasonable doubt that the nerve fibre being so qualified does in fact release that substance as a neurotransmitter. The evidence is sound for most **noradrenergic** and **cholinergic nerve fibres**, but in many other cases the transmitter is, at best, putative. It is not enough merely to demonstrate the presence of the chemical within the nerve endings.

adrenergic neurone blocking drug　A drug that prevents the release of **noradrenaline** from sympathetic **adrenergic nerve fibre** endings. Examples include guanethidine and bethanidine.

adrenergic receptors　*See* **adrenoceptors**. *See also* **adrenergic nerve fibre** for a discussion of the restricted use of the suffix '-ergic'.

adrenoceptor antagonist　A drug that blocks **adrenoceptors** (α or β, or both). Examples of such drugs include phentolamine (α), propranolol (β), labetolol (both).

α-adrenoceptors　*See* **adrenoceptors**.

β-adrenoceptors　*See* **adrenoceptors**.

adrenoceptors　Receptors specifically sensitive to and operated by **adrenaline** and/or **noradrenaline** and related **sympathomimetic drugs**. Adreno-receptors is an alternative name. They are not homogeneous. H. H. Dale laid the foundation for the concept of subtypes of adrenoceptors in 1913 when he showed in the pithed cat that 'adrenine' (adrenaline) produced a rise in blood pressure before the administration of ergotoxine but a fall thereafter (*see* **adrenaline reversal**). He concluded that ergotoxine selectively paralysed (i.e. blocked) motor (i.e. vasoconstrictor) junctions in the smooth muscle of the blood vessels, thereby unmasking the action at inhibitory (i.e. vasodilator) junctions. We now know that ergotoxine blocks what came to be called α-adrenoceptors which mediate vasoconstriction, leaving functional the β-adrenoceptors which mediate vasodilatation. R. P. Ahlquist (1948) classified adrenoceptors into α- and β-types on the basis of a systematic study of the rank orders of potency of a number of sympathomimetic amines on different organs. (For a retrospective discussion, see Ahlquist (1979) *Trends pharmacol. Sci.* **1**, 16.) The fact that two main and different orders of potency were evident suggested that there are two different receptor types. For the sake of simplicity, we refer here only to the three common sympathomimetic amines adrenaline (A), noradrenaline (N) and isoprenaline (I, isoproterenol in USA). On the basis of their activities, Ahlquist designated as β those adrenoceptors at which isoprenaline was most potent and noradrenaline least (I > A > N), whereas α-adrenoceptors were those at which isoprenaline had little or no activity (A $\geqslant$ N > I). Ahlquist's classification has been generally accepted and has been corroborated by the subsequent development of selective **agonists** at α-adrenoceptors (e.g. methoxamine) and antagonists at β-adrenoceptors (e.g. propranolol). Selective α-**adrenoceptor antagonists** (e.g. phenoxybenzamine and phentolamine) and β-adrenoceptor agonists had existed for several years before Ahlquist's work. Relatively recently, a third main class of adrenoceptors, designated γ-adrenoceptors, has been proposed by G. D. S. Hirst and T. O. Neild to account for the resistance to known blocking agents of the junctional potentials evoked in the smooth muscle of blood vessels by sympathetic nerve stimulation. However, there is controversy as to whether any kind of adrenoceptor is involved. An alternative explanation is that the junctional potentials are not evoked by noradrenaline at all, but rather by ATP or **neuropeptide Y**, one of which may be released as a **co-transmitter** at this site.

In most, and perhaps all, cases β-adrenoceptors are coupled to **adenylate cyclase**, and **cyclic AMP** acts as the **second messenger**. The β-adrenoceptor is a single polypeptide which has been isolated in a pure form and inserted into receptor-deficient cells. The procedure confers responsiveness to isoprenaline to the adenylate cyclase of the acceptor cell. Activation of adenylate cyclase also requires interaction with a guanine nucleotide regulatory protein present in the cell membrane.

α-Adrenoceptors may function in one of several ways. In some tissues they are coupled to the **phospholipase** C involved in the **PI response**. In others, they are coupled to membrane Ca^{2+} channels. Influx of Ca^{2+} may activate the contractile mechanism, or it may cause the opening of Ca^{2+}-operated K^+ channels, whereupon K^+ efflux hyperpolarizes the membrane and thereby inhibits cellular activity. In some tissues, α-adrenoceptors are coupled to Na^+ channels. Na^+ influx produces membrane depolarization and cell excitation.

Both α- and β-adrenoceptors have been further subdivided, again on the basis of rank orders of potency of agonists, into α_1- and α_2- and β_1- and β_2-adrenoceptors. α_1-Adrenoceptors are situated post-junctionally. Phenylephrine is an example of a relatively selective agonist and prazosin an antagonist. α_2-Adrenoceptors are situated on the sympathetic (and at least some parasympathetic) nerve endings, but not exclusively so. There are also post-junctional α_2-adrenoceptors. The prejunctional α_2-adrenoceptors negatively modulate transmitter release (*see also* **autoreceptors**). Clonidine is a relatively selective agonist at α_2-adrenoceptors, and yohimbine and rauwolsine are relatively selective antagonists.

The heart and intestine are important tissues possessing β_1-adrenoceptors. Examples of relatively selective agonists and antagonists include prenalterol and atenolol respectively. β_2-Adrenoceptors are present in the airways and blood vessels, and in skeletal muscle. Examples of relatively selective agonists include salbutamol (albuterol in USA) and terbutaline. Relatively selective antagonists for β_2-adrenoceptors are available (e.g. ICI 118551) but have no proven therapeutic use, except perhaps in the relief of certain types of muscle tremor. *See* Malta *et al.* (1985) *Trends pharmacol. Sci.* **6**, 400.

adrenolytic drug A drug that blocks actions of **adrenaline**. Objections to this term are made on the grounds that the suffix '-lytic' should be reserved to convey the sense of destruction. The term is synonymous with the preferable term **adrenoceptor antagonist**.

adrenoreceptors *See* **adrenoceptors**.

adsorbent A substance with the property of adsorbing gases or toxic substances, especially from the intestine: activated charcoal is an example. Adsorbents may sometimes be applied to external ulcerating surfaces.

aequorin A photoprotein extracted from a luminous jelly fish (*Aequorea forskalea*). It glows with a bluish light when it combines with free calcium ions. The purified protein has been injected in minute amounts into muscle cells. When muscle contraction is evoked, a transient bluish glow is seen, indicating a rise in the sarcoplasmic free Ca^{2+} concentration.

aetiocholanone *See* **pyrogens**.

AF64A Ethylcholine mustard aziridinium ion. A compound that damages **cholinergic nerve fibre** endings and depletes **acetylcholine**. It has been injected into hippocampus and frontal cortex in attempts to produce an animal model of **Alzheimer's disease**.

affinity The tendency of a drug to bind to a binding site including a specific **receptor**. Affinity may be measured at equilibrium by the affinity or association constant (sometimes given the symbol K), which is the reciprocal of the dissociation constant (K_D), or it can be measured in pD_2 units. The pD_2 for an **agonist** is the negative logarithm of the concentration of agonist drug that produces half of the maximal response. The concentration of agonist (mol/l) producing half of the maximal response $[D_2]$ is the dissociation constant of that agonist. Therefore, the pD_2 is the negative logarithm of the dissociation constant (i.e. $-\log K_D$) or the logarithm of the reciprocal of the dissociation constant (i.e. $\log 1/K_D$).

affinity constant *See* **affinity**.

affinity labelling A technique involving the chemical attachment of an identifiable substance to specific submolecular groups, such as active centres of enzymes and **receptor** sites, so as to allow the location of the specific groups to be determined in the organized tissue, in cell fractions, or in purified molecular fractions. For example, radiotracer atoms may be incorporated into a label such as α-**bungarotoxin**, which has high and specific **affinity** for motor endplate **cholinoceptors**. The location of the cholinoceptors (i.e. of the affinity label) can then be determined by autoradiography and electronmicroscopy. Immunological techniques might also be used.

aflatoxins Toxins elaborated by the mould *Aspergillus flavus* which may contaminate ground nuts. A major epidemic of disease in turkeys in the USA in 1960 was traced to feeding with contaminated ground nuts. The toxins are hepatotoxic and may produce liver tumours. The term aflatoxin is an abbreviation of *Aspergillus flavus* **toxin**.

Agent Orange *See* **2,4,5-T.**

AGEPC *See* **PAF-acether.**

agonist A drug that acts on **receptors** to elicit a response, which may be an increase or a decrease in a particular manifestation of the activity of the cell with which the receptors are associated. For example, **acetylcholine** is an agonist that acts on **muscarinic cholinoceptors**. The agonist–receptor interaction results in contraction of intestinal smooth muscle, but in relaxation of arteriolar smooth muscle, and in slowing of the heart. Since it corrects a common error, it is worth emphasizing that the word agonist does not indicate the direction of the response (positive or negative) but only that the drug produces a response by interacting with its receptors.

A full agonist is capable of producing a maximal response. It has high **efficacy**; that is to say that every drug–receptor interaction is capable of contributing to the response. A **partial agonist** is only capable of producing less than the maximal response no matter how high the concentration (Greek: *agein*, to lead).

agonist–receptor interaction The simplest assumption about the formation of an **agonist** drug–**receptor** complex may be expressed thus:

$$\text{Drug} + \text{receptor} \rightleftharpoons \text{drug–receptor complex}$$

or

$$\text{D} + \text{R} \underset{k_2}{\overset{k_2}{\rightleftharpoons}} \text{DR}$$

where k_1 and k_2 are the rate constants for association and dissociation, respectively, of the complex.

A. J. Clark was impressed by Langmuir's kinetic mass action treatment of adsorption, and he applied it to drug–receptor interactions in this way.

According to the law of mass action, the rate of the forward reaction is given by $k_1[D][R]$, and the rate of the reverse reaction by $k_2[DR]$.

At equilibrium, the rates of association and dissociation are equal. That is:

$$k_1[D][R] = k_2[DR]$$

therefore

$$\frac{k_2}{k_1} = \frac{[D][R]}{[DR]} = K_D$$

The ratio k_2/k_1 is given the symbol K_D and is the dissociation constant.

The total number of receptors (R_T) is the sum of the receptors engaged in forming the complex (DR), plus the free receptors (R), or:

$$[R] = [R_T] - [DR]$$

Substituting for $[R]$ in the previous equation, and rearranging, gives:

$$\frac{[DR]}{[R_T]} = \frac{[D]}{[D] + K_D}$$

$[DR]/[R_T]$, the proportion of receptors occupied by agonist, is given the symbol r.

Rearranging the above equation in terms of r gives

$$[D] = \frac{r}{1 - r}(K_D)$$

which is the same as the equation derived from the Langmuir adsorption isotherm in which $[D]$ is the concentration of adsorbable **ligand** and r is the proportion of the potential sites of complex formation that is occupied by ligand, assuming a 1:1 relationship.

If two molecules of ligand (or drug) combine simultaneously with each adsorption site (or receptor), the equation has the form:

$$[D]^2 = \frac{r}{1 - r}(K)$$

and in general:

$$[D]^n = \frac{r}{1 - r}(K)$$

where n is the number of molecules of ligand or drug that combine with each adsorption site or receptor. K is a constant.

aldosterone antagonist drugs Drugs that block the action of aldosterone on the distal tubule of the nephron, hence preventing the exchange of Na^+ for K^+ or H^+. Such drugs therefore cause retention of K^+ at the expense of Na^+, which is lost in the urine. Spironolactone, a **potassium-sparing diuretic drug**, is an example of an aldosterone antagonist.

algesia   The sensation of pain (Greek: *algos*, pain).

algogen   A substance that produces pain (Greek: *algos*, pain). Examples include **histamine, serotonin, bradykinin** and potassium chloride when applied, for example, to a cantharidin-induced blister base.

alkaloid   A term applied loosely to all organic bases of plant origin containing one or more heterocyclic nitrogen atoms in their molecules. The etymology is complex. The word alkali is derived from Arab words meaning to heat in a pan. Soda ash is obtained by heating marine plants in a pan. Hence, the term alkali was used to mean a substance with the properties of soda, and an alkaloid a substance resembling an alkali in its properties. A pharmacist, W. Meissner, first used the word in 1819 to cover a group of natural substances that were 'vegetable alkalis'. Eventually, the term alkaloid acquired the use given at the beginning of this paragraph. Many alkaloids possess pharmacological activity, e.g. **morphine** from the **opium** poppy, quinine from cinchona bark, physostigmine from the **Calabar bean**. The convention is to end the names of alkaloids with '-ine'.
Phillipson (1983) *Pharm. J.*, Jan. 29, 102

alkylating agent   A **drug** that readily forms stable covalent linkages with various nucleophilic cell constituents so that an alkyl group becomes attached. Cytotoxic alkylating agents (e.g. nitrogen mustards such as mustine) alkylate the 7N of guanine in DNA. Other alkylating agents may alkylate drug **receptor** sites to produce a long-lasting (irreversible) receptor block (e.g. the delayed interaction of phenoxybenzamine with α-**adrenoceptors**).

allelopathic agents   Agents involved in what might be termed chemical warfare between plants, whereby one plant releases chemicals that have an adverse effect on neighbouring plants. The release of allelopathic agents accounts for, or at least contributes to, the ability of sorghum to control the growth of certain weeds, and the appearance and disappearance of plant species in a particular order in cut-down forests or disused fields.
Pulman (1983) *Chem. Eng. News* **61** (14), 34

allergens   Substances that can elicit reaginic **antibody** (i.e. immunoglobulins of the E class) formation. Most IgE is bound to the membranes of basophils and **mast cells**. Reaction with allergen leads to disruption of these cells and liberation of the contents of their granules. This effect is responsible for certain **hypersensitivity reactions**. Commonly occurring allergens include pollen, moulds, particles of house dust mites, fur, feathers, food proteins (especially from milk, eggs, fish and shellfish), insect stings and some drugs.

allosteric modifier A substance that binds to an enzyme, at a regulator site which is not the active site, and induces a conformational change such that the interaction of the enzyme with its substrate is modified (Greek: *allos*, different; *stereos*, solid shape). The process is called heterotrophic regulation. Many enzymes are regulated in the body in this way. If the enzymatic activity is impaired, the modifier is called an allosteric inhibitor; if enhanced, an allosteric activator. Examples of allosteric activation and inhibition occur with the enzyme isocitrate dehydrogenase, which catalyses one of the reactions in the tricarboxylic acid cycle. ADP is an allosteric activator, and ATP an allosteric inhibitor, of this enzyme. Thus, the two modifiers provide a sensitive device for regulating the production of ATP by the tricarboxylic acid cycle.

alloxan A compound with the property of causing selective degeneration of the β-cells of the islets of Langerhans, and thereby inducing **insulin-**

deficiency diabetes. It is often used in animal experiments to produce a model of the disease diabetes mellitus. *See also* **streptozotocin**.

alpha-adrenoceptors *See* **adrenoceptors**.

alpha-latrotoxin The major toxic protein constituent from black widow spider venom. It causes an initial increase in transmitter release followed by subsequent depletion of transmitter at a number of types of nerve ending, e.g. **cholinergic** and **noradrenergic nerve fibre** endings and nerve endings that release gamma-aminobutyric acid (**GABA**).

Alzheimer's disease One of the primary degenerative dementias accounting for about half of the patients suffering from such dementias. The disease is characterized by senile plaques and intraneuronal fibrillary tangles and cell loss in the brain, especially the neocortex, hippocampus and amygdala. There is memory loss, due to failure to encode new information into long-term memory, deterioration of personality, disorientation, paranoia and aphasia. At least one form of Alzheimer's disease can be inherited as an autosomal dominant. There is a reduced level of choline acetyltransferase, and cholinergic dysfunction, especially in the nucleus of Meynert, but there is also dysfunction in other neurotransmitter systems (noradrenergic, dopaminergic, GABAergic, **somatostatin** and **substance P**). Attempted therapies have been disappointing. Some success has been achieved with choline plus piracetam, or with 4-aminopyridine.

Attempts are being made to produce animal models of the disease in order to study drug action. (Alois Alzheimer was the German neurologist, 1864–1915, who first described the disease.)

Amanita muscaria A poisonous toadstool (red with white spots), extracts of which have been used to kill flies (Latin: *musca*, a fly; the toadstool is also known as fly agaric). It is important in pharmacology because it contains the **alkaloids, muscarine** and muscimol. The latter is a **GABAmimetic drug**.

Ames test Currently generally recognized as the primary short-term screening test for the detection of potentially oncogenic chemicals. The test was devised and brought to prominence by the American microbial geneticist, B. N. Ames, and his colleagues; it is based on an observation by H. V. Malling that dimethyl**nitrosamine** (a known mutagen) was mutagenic (causing reverse mutation) in two sensitive strains of the bacterium *Salmonella typhimurium* when incubated together with a preparation of rodent liver microsomes. The test is also known as the *Salmonella*–microsome test. The liver microsomes are present as a drug metabolizing system, so that both parent drug and metabolites are tested.

Most chemicals that are oncogenic give a positive result in the Ames' test, but not all substances that give a positive Ames' test are necessarily oncogenic.

γ-aminobutyric acid *See* **GABA.**

aminoglycoside antibiotics As the name implies, the molecules of these **antibiotics** contain amino sugars in glycosidic linkage. The medicinally useful ones include streptomycin, tobramycin, amikacin, kanamycin, neomycin and gentamicin. They act mainly by inhibiting protein synthesis at the level of the 30 S ribosomal subunit.

6-aminopenicillanic acid This compound may be regarded as the parent compound of all **penicillins**. In the structure below, it is the compound in which R = H. The compound can be obtained in large quantities by omitting side-chain precursors from the medium in which

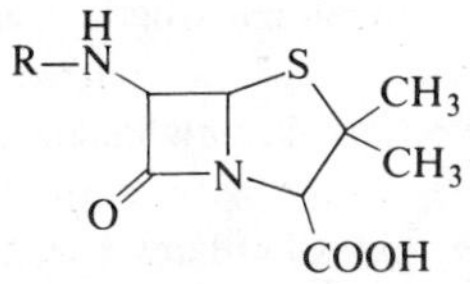

Penicillium chrysogenum is grown, or by the use of enzymes (**penicillin amidases**) to remove the side-chains from penicillins. New penicillins can then be synthesized by adding different side-chains at R.

13

amoebicidal drugs   Drugs used in the therapy of amoebiasis to kill the causative organism, *Entamoeba histolytica*. Examples of amoebicidal drugs include emetine (an **alkaloid** from *Cephaëlis* species) and metronidazole.

anabolic agents   Steroidal compounds that produce retention of nitrogen, potassium and phosphate. They increase protein anabolism and decrease amino acid catabolism, which results in weight gain and muscular development, providing the nutritional status is adequate. They are used therapeutically to hasten recovery from protein deficiency disorders, to enhance wound healing, and in the treatment of advanced metastatic carcinoma of the breast. They may also be used to enhance the performance of athletes, racehorses and racing dogs. Such use is illegal in most countries. The site of action of these agents is at the level of the transfer of amino acids from tRNA to the ribosomes.

They are synthetic **drugs** designed to have low androgenic and high anabolic activities. Examples include nandrolone, stanozolol, methandriol and testolactone.

anaesthesia (anesthesia in the USA)   A state of reversible unconsciousness induced by a **general anaesthetic drug** (Greek: *an*, without; *aesthes*, sensation). The terms *anaesthesia* and *anaesthetic* were devised and suggested by Oliver Wendell Holmes (Professor of Anatomy at Harvard, and a poet) in November, 1846, after learning of the success of his friend, William Morton, in demonstrating the anaesthetic properties of ether in the 'ether dome' of the Massachusetts General Hospital of the University of Harvard on October 16th, 1846. The techniques of anaesthetic practice may be said to have been born on that day.

The exchange of the diphthong (æ) for 'e' in the American spelling follows the pattern of Noah Webster's suggestions in his desire that American spelling should be recognizably different from English. Interestingly, the diphthong is retained in the names of departments, etc. at Harvard University.

An earlier name for anaesthetic was *letheon*, from the River Lethe of Greek mythology, a draught of whose waters expunged all painful memories. However, Holmes' suggestions were soon generally adopted and the term letheon dropped out of use.

anaesthetic drug   *See* **general anaesthetic drug**.

anaesthetic hyperthermia   *See* **malignant hyperpyrexia**.

analeptic drug   A drug that stimulates the respiratory and vasomotor centres in the medulla of the brain. Such drugs are so called because of their ability to revive temporarily a dying person (Greek: *analeptikos*, restorative). In larger doses they stimulate other areas of the brain also, and give rise to clonic convulsions. Examples of analeptic drugs include nikethamide and leptazol (pentylenetetrazol). Analeptic drugs have little place in present-day therapeutics. *See also* **respiratory stimulant drugs**.

analgesic drug   A **drug** with the property of relieving pain (Greek: *an*, without; *algesis*, pain). Analgesic drugs belong to two main classes: the **narcotic analgesic drugs** of which **morphine** is the traditional example, and the non-narcotic (anti-inflammatory, antipyretic) analgesics of which aspirin is the traditional example.

analgesic nephropathy   Acute or chronic renal failure arising from chronic interstitial nephritis, renal papillary necrosis and chronic pyelo-nephritis. The syndrome is associated with long-term compulsive taking of large doses of anti-inflammatory, antipyretic analgesics such as phenacetin and aspirin. Phenacetin was first suspected of being the cause in 1953 when a large number of cases of nephropathy was reported in a Swedish town in which the taking of powders containing phenacetin had almost become a social grace.

anaphrodisiac   A drug that diminishes sexual desire (*see* **aphrodisiac**).

anaphylactic shock   *See* **anaphylaxis**.

anaphylactoid reaction   An acute shock syndrome resembling generalized **anaphylaxis**, but not caused by an immunological reaction. Substances that produce an anaphylactoid reaction do so by causing the release of large amounts of **histamine** and other vasoactive substances.

anaphylaxis   An acute **immediate** or **type I hypersensitivity reaction** following administration of **antigen** to a subject who has previously received the same antigen (i.e. a primed subject). The reaction is caused by the release of **histamine**, **SRS-A** and other substances when antigen combines with **antibody** on the surfaces of cells. Anaphylaxis may be generalized (anaphylactic shock—hypotension, bronchoconstriction, urti-caria) or may be localized to the site of **injection**.

Richet first drew attention to the phenomenon in 1902. Having on one occasion injected a protein into the vein of a dog, in a dose too small to produce more than evanescent symptoms, he gave another injection to the same animal some weeks later, expecting to find some degree of immunity. Contrary to his expectations, the second injection caused an immediate and violent reaction from which the dog died. The phenomenon was subsequently found to be the usual response when proteins were administered in this way with a sufficiently long interval between injections. It appeared to Richet to be the direct opposite of immunity or phylaxis (Greek: protection) and he initially coined the term aphylaxis (no protection) to describe it. However, Richet and Poitier did not like the sound of this word so they changed it to anaphylaxis. Anaphylaxis is difficult to defend on the grounds of etymology (*ana*, up or back), but usage and convenience have given it sanction.

Richet & Poitier (1952) *Acta Allergologica* **5**, 178

androgens Steroidal compounds that stimulate maturation of the male genital organs and the development of the secondary sexual characteristics. Testosterone is the principal endogenous androgen. Fluoxymesterone is an example of a synthetic androgen.

angel dust A name given to the **drug** phencyclidine hydrochloride by American drug abusers. Chemically it is 1-(1-phenycyclohexyl)piperidine, and 'PCP' is one of its alternative names. Its official use is in veterinary medicine, in which it is employed to produce a trance-like anaesthetic state and analgesia in animals. In the USA it has become second only to marihuana as a 'street drug' of abuse. Legal manufacture ceased in the USA in April 1979, and the drug is classified as a class 2 controlled substance. Alternative 'street' names include 'angel's mist', 'peace pills', 'goon', 'hog' and 'T'. (*See* Editorial (1980) *Brit. med. J.* **281**, 1511.)

In pharmacological experiments phencyclidine has been found to bind to, and block, cation channels associated with **nicotinic cholinoceptors**, voltage-dependent K^+ channels and some Ca^{2+} channels (*see* **voltage-dependent ion channels**).

angiogenin One of a family of endogenous protein factors that induce and regulate the growth of new blood vessels. Purified angiogenin has a relative molecular mass of 14 000. The control of angiogenesis by drugs could lead to important therapies for diseases such as cancer (angiogenesis inhibitors) and ischaemic heart disease and stroke (angiogenesis stimulators).

angiotensin There are two forms, denoted I and II, but when the numeral is not included it is usually taken to mean angiotensin II. Angiotensin I is a decapeptide formed by the action of the enzyme renin (from the kidneys) on an α_2-globulin precursor called angiotensinogen in the plasma. Angiotensin I is converted to the biologically active angiotensin II (an octapeptide) under the influence of converting enzymes in the tissues, especially the lungs.

Asp–Arg–Val–Tyr–Ile–His–Pro–Phe Angiotensin II

Angiotensin II produces vasoconstriction by a direct action on the vessels. It also causes **noradrenaline** release and blocks its re-uptake, stimulates ganglion cells, and enhances the activity of tyrosine hydroxylase. It is the most potent pressor agent known, and it probably has a role in the aetiology of certain types of hypertension. Angiotensin II also causes contraction of certain other smooth muscles, and it plays a physiological role in causing the release of aldosterone from the zona glomerulosa of the adrenal cortex.

Angiotensin receptors may be blocked by saralasin (Sar–Arg–Val–Tyr–Val–His–Pro–Ala). Saralasin is a weak **partial agonist** and mainly for this reason is not successful as an **antihypertensive drug**.

Angiotensin was discovered in 1940 by two groups working independently. Braun-Menendez' group in the Argentine called it hypertensin, whereas Page's group in the USA called it angiotonin. In 1958, the compromise name angiotensin was adopted.

angiotonin   *See* **angiotensin.**

anococcygeus muscle of the rat   A small smooth muscle attached by a tendon to the coccygeal vertebrae and ending partly by merging with the longitudinal muscle of the colon and partly on the perineum or, in the male, by forming the retractor penis muscle. The muscle is innervated by motor noradrenergic sympathetic fibres and by inhibitory **NANC nerve fibres** whose transmitter remains unknown. J. S. Gillespie, in 1972, first devised an isolated innervated preparation of this muscle suitable for pharmacological studies. The same muscle in other species (cat, dog, rabbit, ox) has also been studied.

Gillespie (1980) *Trends pharmacol. Sci.* **1**, 453

anodyne   A soothing medicine that relieves pain. There is little, if any, difference between the meanings of anodyne and the more common analgesic (Greek: *an*, absence of; *odyne*, pain).

anorectic drug   A drug that reduces the desire to eat by an action exerted in the central nervous system (Greek: *anorexis*, without appetite). Examples of such drugs include amphetamine (now obsolete for this purpose) and fenfluramine.

Anorexigenic drug and anorexiant drug are alternative names.

anorexiant drug   *See* **anorectic drug.**

anorexigenic drug   *See* **anorectic drug.**

antacid drug   A drug that neutralizes gastric acid. Systemic antacids (e.g. sodium bicarbonate) are absorbed after passing through the stomach and alter the acid–base balance; non-systemic antacids (e.g. magnesium trisilicate and aluminium hydroxide) are not absorbed.

antagonist drug   A drug that counteracts or prevents the action of another drug or endogenous body chemical.

In the broadest sense of the term there are generally considered to be three kinds of antagonist action:

1   *Chemical.* The antagonist drug interacts chemically with the other drug and inactivates it. An example is the antagonism, by sodium sulphite or

cysteine, of the bisquaternary diphenyl disulphide **neuromuscular blocking drug** shown below.

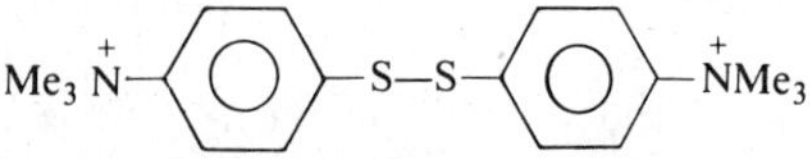

$$Me_3 \overset{+}{N} - \langle\!\!\langle\,\bigcirc\,\rangle\!\!\rangle - S\!-\!S - \langle\!\!\langle\,\bigcirc\,\rangle\!\!\rangle - \overset{+}{N}Me_3$$

This compound is inactivated chemically by sodium sulphite or cysteine. On injection of one of these inactivators, neuromuscular transmission is quickly restored. (Khromov-Borisov *et al.* (1969) *Dokl. Akad. Nauk SSSR* **186**, 236.)

2 *Physiological.* The antagonist drug produces the opposite physiological response. For example, bronchoconstriction produced by **histamine** may be counteracted by bronchodilatation produced by **adrenaline**.

3 *Pharmacological.* The antagonist drug acts on the same excitation–response coupling chain of events as the drug whose action is being opposed. A pharmacological antagonist may be specific, in that it blocks the same **receptors** as those activated by the **agonist** (e.g. naloxone blocks **morphine** at **opiate receptors**, phenoxybenzamine blocks adrenaline at α-**adrenoceptors**, tubocurarine blocks acetylcholine at **nicotinic cholinoceptors**—*see also* **competitive antagonist**, **irreversible receptor antagonist** and **non-competitive antagonist**), or it may be non-specific because it acts at a later stage in the excitation–response coupling sequence (e.g. dantrolene sodium may act as an antagonist to acetylcholine in skeletal muscle, not because it blocks nicotinic cholinoceptors, but because it impairs the contractile mechanism of the muscle; consequently, it would non-specifically antagonize a range of substances that cause contraction by different mechanisms).

Some workers prefer to restrict the term antagonist to drugs that produce specific pharmacological antagonism, because the word contains the term agonist (anti-agonist) which is defined in terms of specific receptors. In this case, the remaining types of 'antagonist' referred to above are simply covered by the broader term antidote. However, it is not certain that antagonist has the same etymological origin as agonist. Antagonist is probably derived from the Greek (*anti*, against; *agonistes*, a competitor).

anthelmintic drug   Pronounced ant-helmintic. A drug with the property of paralysing or killing parasitic helminths (worms). Paralysis or death of the worm allows it to be expelled by the normal defaecation reflex.

anthracenediones   A group of **antineoplastic drugs** of which mitozantrone is the first and best known.

anthracycline derivatives   A group of **antineoplastic drugs** of which doxorubicin (formerly called adriamycin) from *Streptomyces peucetius* var. *caesius* is the most important.

antiallergic drug   A drug with the property of suppressing some of the symptoms of allergy. Examples include **antihistamine drugs**, sodium **cromoglycate** and **glucocorticoids**.

Mitozantrone

antiandrogen drug A drug that blocks the **receptor** sites of action of **androgens**. Such drugs include the steroids, progesterone and some synthetic progestogens (e.g. chlormadinone and cyproterone), and danazol. It is possible that antiandrogens may be developed as male **oral contraceptives**, and for the therapy of disorders due to excessive action or production of testosterone.

antianginal drug A drug used to relieve the pain and reduce the frequency and severity of attacks of angina pectoris. Glyceryl trinitrate (nitroglycerin), β-**adrenoceptor** blocking drugs and nifedipine are examples of drugs used in this way.

antianxiety agent A drug with the property of reducing pathological anxiety, agitation and tension, without impairing consciousness to a great extent. Also known as anxiolytic agents. Examples include members of the group of **benzodiazepine drugs**, such as chlordiazepoxide and diazepam.

anti-arrhythmic drug *See* antidysrhythmic drug.

antiautistic activity Activity of a drug that reduces schizophrenic emotional withdrawal (Greek: *autos*, self). Trifluperidol is an example of a drug with this type of activity.

antibacterial drug A drug used to combat infection by bacteria. Sulphonamides, **penicillins** and metronidazole are examples.

antibiotic The term is usually restricted to substances that are produced by the growth of one species of micro-organism and that in high dilution inhibit the growth of, or kill, others. Some consider that this precise definition has outlived its usefulness, since some antibiotics originally obtained by extraction from the medium in which organisms were grown are now prepared synthetically or are partially synthetic modifications of naturally occurring substances, and in any case it is usually irrelevant to know whether the substance had its origin in a micro-organism. The outstanding property of all therapeutically useful antibiotics (indeed of all antimicrobial drugs) is their selective toxicity to the infecting organisms but not to the host. **Penicillin** (1941) was the first therapeutically useful antibiotic. Since its discovery, large programmes for screening fungi and bacteria for new antibiotics have been put into effect, and many successful ones have been discovered. (Greek: *anti*, against; *bios*, life.)

The word was originally used in the middle of the 19th century to describe a curious philosophy that denied the existence of life—the antibiotic hypothesis (OED).

antibiotic resistance *See* **antimicrobial drug resistance.**

antibody A protein with the molecular properties of an immunoglobulin and capable of specific combination with antigen. Antibodies are produced in the body by the lymphoid cells, especially plasma cells, in response to stimulation by **antigen.**

anticancer drug *See* **antineoplastic drug.**

anticholinesterase drug A drug that inhibits one or more of the cholinesterase enzymes. Such drugs are of two main types: **organophosphorus anticholinesterases** (e.g. dyflos) and **reversible anticholinesterase drugs** (e.g. neostigmine).

anticoagulant drug A drug with the property of delaying or preventing the process of blood coagulation. Examples include **heparin** and **warfarin.**

anticonvulsant drug A drug that prevents epileptic and related types of convulsion. Phenobarbitone, phenytoin, sodium valproate and clonazepam are examples.

antidelusional activity Activity of a drug that suppresses hallucinations and delusions. Haloperidol is an example of a drug with this type of activity.

antidepressant drugs Drugs used to elevate the mood of depressed patients. They are of two main types: **thymoleptic** and **thymerectic drugs.**

antidysrhythmic drug A drug that restores a disordered cardiac rhythm to normal sinus rhythm. Quinidine (from cinchona bark) was the first drug for which this type of activity was noted. M. Vaughan Williams has classified antidysrhythmic drugs into a number of classes.

Class I	Na$^+$ channel blocking drugs	e.g. quinidine and disopyramide
Class II	Drugs that inhibit adrenergic influences	e.g. β-**adrenoceptor** blocking drugs
Class III	Drugs that prolong the cardiac action potential and refractory period	e.g. amiodarone
Class IV	**Calcium slow-channel blocking drugs**	e.g. verapamil
Class V	Drugs that restrict anionic current	e.g. possibly alinidine (*see Lancet* 1981 **i**, 1291)

To these may be added **cardiac glycosides** and a number of miscellaneous drugs used in supraventricular tachycardia, such as methoxamine and edrophonium.

The choice of drug class depends on the type of dysrhythmia.

antiemetic drug   A drug with the property of suppressing vomiting (emesis). Examples include thioperazine and metoclopramide.

antienuretic drug   A drug used to control urinary incontinence. The **tricyclic antidepressant drug** nortriptyline is an example of a drug with this type of activity. It probably acts by virtue of its atropine-like activity.

antiepileptic drug   A drug with the property of suppressing the signs and symptoms of epilepsy. Ideally such drugs should suppress epileptic convulsions without producing sedation. *See also* **anticonvulsant drug**.

antigen   A substance that elicits a specific immune response when introduced into the body. Unless there is immunological tolerance to this effect, **antibody** production is stimulated and cell-mediated immunity develops. Antigens are usually foreign to the body (except in autoimmune diseases), and of protein or polysaccharide nature with a molecular weight greater than 1000 (**haptens** are a special case).

antiglaucoma drug   A drug used to lower intraocular pressure in glaucoma. Pilocarpine (a parasympathomimetic **miotic drug**), acetazolamide (a **carbonic anhydrase inhibitor** that inhibits the formation of aqueous humour), and **adrenaline** (a sympathomimetic vasoconstrictor that impairs secretion of aqueous humour) are antiglaucoma drugs.

antigout drugs   Drugs used to relieve the pain of gout which is a consequence of abnormally high biosynthesis of uric acid (from purine metabolism) and its deposition in the joints. The main drugs used are **uricosuric drugs** and **uric acid synthesis inhibitors**. Additionally, colchicine (an **alkaloid** from the autumn crocus) is used for acute attacks. It probably acts, through its ability to disrupt microtubules, by depressing the movement of leucocytes (which take in urate crystals by phagocytosis) and by impairing the release of enzymes from **lysosomes**.

antihistamine drug   A drug with the property of antagonizing **histamine** by blocking **histamine receptors**. Examples include mepyramine (an H_1-receptor antagonist) and cimetidine (an H_2-receptor antagonist). *See* **histamine receptors** for H_1 and H_2 subtypes of histamine receptors.

antihistaminic   *See* **antihistamine drug**.

21

antihyperlipidaemic drug A drug that lowers abnormally high plasma concentrations of cholesterol or triglycerides or both. Examples include clofibrate, which acts, at least partly, by reducing hepatic secretion of lipoprotein, cholestyramine, which is a resin that binds bile salts thereby decreasing the reabsorption of cholesterol from the gut, and probucol, which increases the catabolism of cholesterol to bile acids. The use of these drugs is largely restricted to young patients with familial hyperlipidaemias. The aim is to reduce the progression of premature atherosclerosis.

antihypertensive drug A drug used to lower abnormally high blood pressure. Examples include **ganglion blocking drugs** such as trimetaphan camsylate, **adrenergic neurone blocking drugs** such as guanethidine, β-**adrenoceptor antagonists** such as propranolol, α_1-**adrenoceptor** antagonists such as prazosin, α_2-adrenoceptor **agonists** such as clonidine, **vasodilator drugs** such as hydralazine, angiotensin **converting enzyme inhibitors** such as captopril, drugs incorporated into a false transmitter such as methyldopa, and **diuretic drugs**, especially **thiazide drugs** such as bendrofluazide. (Clonidine and methyldopa probably exert most of their action in the central nervous system.)

anti-inflammatory drug A drug used to suppress signs and symptoms of inflammation. There are two main classes: the **glucocorticoid** anti-inflammatory drugs such as prednisolone, and the **non-steroidal anti-inflammatory drugs** (NSAID) such as aspirin and indomethacin.

antileprotic agent The general name for a drug used in the therapy of leprosy (causative organism *Mycobacterium leprae*). Examples of such drugs include dapsone and rifampicin.

antimalarial drug A drug used to prevent the occurrence of, or to treat, malaria. Drugs used in the prophylaxis of malaria include proguanil, pyrimethamine, chloroquine, amodiaquine. Drugs used to treat the disease include chloroquine, primaquine, mefloquine and occasionally quinine.

antimanic activity Activity of a drug that reduces euphoria. Fluphenazine is an example of a drug with this type of activity.

antimetabolite A drug that is a structural analogue of an endogenous metabolite of an infecting organism or a cancer cell, and which competes with that metabolite for an enzyme that takes part in an essential metabolic process. The consequence is that the essential metabolic process is impaired and multiplication of the cell is halted. Examples of antimetabolites include the following:
1 The antibacterial **sulphonamides**, which compete with para-aminobenzoic acid in the synthesis of folic acid in certain bacteria; inhibition of folate synthesis impairs the synthesis of DNA and RNA by the bacteria.

2   2,4-Diaminopyrimidines, such as trimethoprim, which compete with dihydrofolic acid in the synthesis of tetrahydrofolic acid in certain bacteria and in species of *Plasmodium.*

3   Purine and pyrimidine antagonists, such as azathioprine and cytaribine respectively, which inhibit nucleic acid synthesis and are employed in the control of certain neoplasms.

antimicrobial drug resistance   Some species of organisms are naturally insensitive to certain drugs and sensitive to others. This is a reflection of the **selective toxicity** of these agents and in itself presents few therapeutic problems, because it is forecastable and because of the large number of different types of drug available. A serious therapeutic problem, however, arises from the acquisition of resistance to antimicrobial agents by species of organisms that were formerly sensitive. The problem applies to viruses and protozoa, as well as to bacteria. (A similar drug resistance may occur with cancer cells, insects and rodents.)

The biochemical mechanisms underlying resistance are of four main types.

1   *Modification of receptor sites.* Resistance may be a consequence of the production of an **isoenzyme** by the micro-organism in cases where enzyme inhibition is the toxic mechanism, or a modified protein binding site may be produced. For example, resistance to **sulphonamides** may arise from mutations in the gene specifying dihydropterate synthetase, giving rise to a sulphonamide-insensitive enzyme, and one type of streptomycin resistance is the result of a mutation that gives rise to a change in the binding site on the 30S ribosome.

2   *By-passing target enzyme.* Blockade of one biosynthetic pathway may lead to an increase in prominence of an alternative pathway. For example, some organisms may cease to be dependent on *p*-aminobenzoic acid for folate synthesis, and hence resistance to sulphonamides develops.

3   *Inhibited access to site of action.* Organisms may develop in which a relatively impermeable barrier to the site of action is acquired, so that the drug fails to reach an effective concentration at the site of action. For example, some strains of *Shigella* acquire a plasma membrane that restricts penetration of sulphonamides. Some organisms that acquire resistance to **tetracyclines**, on the other hand, do so because the drug passes easily out of the cells, instead of being held there.

4   *Production of inactivating enzymes.* Some **antibiotics** act as enzyme inducers causing the organism to produce enzymes that destroy the antibiotic. **Penicillinase** and cyclosporinase are examples of such enzymes.

Once a bacterium has acquired resistance through a gene mutation it may transfer the resistance to other organisms. The genetic resistance determinants are contained within plasmids called R-factors, and these can be transferred rapidly between Gram-negative bacteria, even between different species, through sex pili.

antimonials Organic molecules containing trivalent or pentavalent arsenic that are, or have been, used in the therapy of leishmaniasis and schistosomiasis for which they are injected parenterally. Antimonials include antimony potassium tartrate and sodium stiboglyconate, which contain trivalent arsenic, and ethylstibamine and urea stibamine, which contain pentavalent arsenic.

Antimony potassium tartrate is also known as tartar emetic. It produces vomiting when taken orally, and has been used in the past for this purpose.

antineoplastic drug A drug used to control the growth and spread of neoplasms (cancer). Antineoplastic drugs belong to four main classes:
1 **Cytotoxic drugs**.
2 Anti-invasive or antimetastasic drugs. The drug razoxane is an example, although the development of this type of drug is at an early stage.
3 **Immunostimulants** such as levamisole.
4 Specific **hormones** or their synthetic analogues where appropriate, for example primary carcinoma of the prostate may be controlled with **oestrogens**.

antineurotic drug An alternative name for **tranquillizer**.

antinociceptive action An action of a drug that prevents the overt response of an animal to an evoked nociceptive reflex without producing unconsciousness or paralysis. A nociceptive reflex is a reflex that protects the body from injury (Latin: *nocere*, to injure). The flexor reflex of the hind limb is an example.

The **hot-plate test** on mice, and the tail flick test in rats or mice, in which the normal response, for example to placing an artery clip on the tail, is a vigorous tail flick, are examples of nociceptive reflexes. Drugs that abolish these responses without simply paralysing the animals (e.g. by a neuromuscular blocking action) or anaesthetizing them are said to possess antinociceptive activity, which is probably indicative of an analgesic action, although further tests are required to confirm this.

antioestrogens Drugs that antagonize the actions of **oestrogens**. Examples include clomiphene, tamoxifen, nafoxidine, cyclofenil. Clomiphene is used to stimulate ovulation in the treatment of infertility.

antiparkinson drugs Drugs used to control the signs and symptoms of parkinsonism. Examples include **atropine-like drugs** (such as benzhexol) and levo**dopa** (with or without a peripherally acting **dopa decarboxylase inhibitor** such as carbidopa or benserazide), **dopaminomimetic drugs** (such as bromocryptine), **monoamine oxidase B inhibitors** (such as selegiline hydrochloride or deprenyl), and amantadine.

antiperspirant drug Also called antisudorific. A drug that diminishes excessive sweating (hyperhidrosis). Such drugs are of two main types:

1   **Astringents** such as aluminium chlorhydrate.
2   **Atropine-like drugs** such as propantheline bromide.

antipruritic drug   A drug used to relieve itching (pruritus). Such drugs may be applied topically; potassium permanganate may be used in this way, and **counter-irritants** such as menthol and camphor in liniments and ointments have antipruritic action. Drugs that are administered systemically to relieve pruritus include drugs with antihistamine, antiserotonin and antibradykinin actions (e.g. cyproheptadine). Neuroleptic **phenothiazines** may be used to control so-called psychogenic pruritus.

antipsoriatic drugs   Drugs used to control the skin disorder psoriasis. The main drugs for topical application are tars and **glucocorticoids**. Additional drugs that are sometimes beneficial include allantoin dithranol and benoxaprofen (formerly used as an **antirheumatoid drug**). Drugs that impair purine synthesis (e.g. azathioprine) or pyrimidine synthesis (e.g. triacetylazauridine) are occasionally used, but their efficacy has to be weighed against their considerable toxicity.

antipsychotic drug   An alternative name for **neuroleptic drug**.

antipurines   Drugs that inhibit purine synthesis, and hence the synthesis of nucleic acids. Such drugs include 6-mercaptopurine and 6-thioguanine.

antipyretic drug   A drug with the property of lowering a raised body temperature (pyrexia). Aspirin is a well-known example.

antipyrimidines   Drugs that inhibit pyrimidine synthesis and hence the synthesis of nucleic acids. 5-Fluorouracil is the main example of this class of drugs.

antirachitic action   An action to prevent the development of, and to cure, rickets in children ('rickets' comes from an Anglo-Saxon word meaning to twist). **Vitamins** of the D group (calciferol, cholecalciferol) and their active metabolite 1,25-dihydrocholecalciferol are the main compounds with antirachitic action.

antirheumatoid drugs   Usually refers to drugs with a hoped-for beneficial effect on the disease process, rather than simply drugs (i.e. the **anti-inflammatory drugs**) that relieve some of the symptoms. The antirheumatoid drugs include gold, penicillamine and levamisole. They exert toxic side-effects, and require careful and prolonged supervision by the rheumatologist.

antiriot agents   *See* **incapacitating agents**.

antischizophrenic drug   An alternative name for **neuroleptic drug**.

antiseptic   An agent that counters sepsis (Greek: *sepein*, to make rotten) by killing or inhibiting multiplication of micro-organisms. By convention, the term is usually applied to agents that are applied for this purpose to living skin or mucous membranes but not to inanimate objects such as surgical instruments, for which the term disinfectant is used. The distinction is often one of application rather than chemical structure, since the same substance (e.g. phenol) can be used in low concentrations as an antiseptic, and in higher concentrations as a disinfectant. A stronger convention is that the term antiseptic does not apply to substances taken systemically. Compounds used as antiseptics and disinfectants include various substituted phenols, biphenols, cresols, xylenols, cationic surface active agents, halogens, oxidizing agents such as hydrogen peroxide and permanganates, aniline dyes, acridine dyes, salts of heavy metals, alcohols and aldehydes.

antisudorific drug   *See* **antiperspirant drug**.

antithrombins   Substances that antagonize thrombin in the blood clotting cascade. An endogenous proteinase inhibitor (an α_2-globulin) known as antithrombin III acts as part of an intrinsic defence mechanism against thrombosis. One of the actions of **heparin** is to bind to antithrombin III and accelerate its combination with thrombin to form an inactive complex.

antithyroid drugs   Drugs that inhibit the synthesis of thyroid **hormones** and which are used to counteract excessive production of thyroid hormones. Antithyroid drugs may be classified into four main groups:
1   Drugs that inhibit the organic binding of iodine (i.e. thiocarbamide compounds such as carbimazole and iodothiouracil).
2   Ionic inhibitors that reduce the uptake of iodine (e.g. thiocyanate and perchlorate).
3   Iodine itself, which suppresses the thyroid by an unknown mechanism.
4   Radioactive iodine, which damages the gland through ionizing radiations.

antitubercular drug   A **drug** used in the **chemotherapy** of tuberculosis, i.e. infection by *Mycobacterium tuberculosis*. The main antitubercular drugs are streptomycin, rifampicin, aminosalicylic acid and its derivatives, isoniazid and its derivatives, ethambutol, thiacetazone, pyrazinamide, morinamide hydrochloride, ethionamide, prothionamide, thiocarlide, cycloserine, viomycin, kanamycin and capreomycin.

antitussive drug   A **drug** used to suppress coughing (Latin: *tussis*, cough). Cough suppressant is an alternative name. Examples of antitussive drugs include codeine and dextromethorphan.

antiviral drug A drug used to kill infecting viruses. They may act outside the host cell, on the cell surface, or inside the cell. Examples include certain isoquinoline derivatives that inactivate myxoviruses and picornaviruses outside the cell, amantadine which prevents the penetration of influenza virus through cell membranes, and methisazone, idoxuridine, cytarabine and **interferon** and its inducers which act on the virus within the cell. Because viruses are obligate intracellular parasites that make use of the host cell's metabolic processes, many drugs that inactivate viruses are likely to damage the host cells.

anxiolytic agent *See* **anti-anxiety agent**.

apamin An octadecapeptide (mol. wt. 2039) from bee venom. Its gross effects are severe unco-ordinated movements and hyperexcitability. At membrane level it blocks certain of those potassium channels that are opened by a rise in cytosol calcium ion concentration, and thereby it prevents the hyperpolarization produced in some smooth muscles and certain other tissues by some inhibitory agents. For example, it blocks hyperpolarization of the guinea-pig taenia coli and of liver cells produced by ATP or **noradrenaline**.

Habermann (1984) *Pharmacology and Therapeutics* **25**, 255

$$Cys–Asn–Cys–Lys–Ala–Pro–Glu–Thr–Ala–Leu–$$
$$Cys–Ala–Arg–Arg–Cys–Gln–Gln–His–NH_2$$
Apamin

aperient A drug that produces emptying of the bowels (Latin: *aperire*, to open). Alternative terms, perhaps denoting increasing severity of action, are lenitive, laxative, evacuative, purgative and cathartic. *See* **purgative** for the etymology of all these terms.

aperitif A substance, often in the form of an alcoholic drink, taken before a meal to enhance appetite (Latin: *aperire*, to open). They work by reflexly increasing the flow of saliva and gastric juice, and include such substances as simple **bitters** (e.g. strychnine, quinine, quassia, gentian, calumba) and aromatic bitters (e.g. tincture of orange or lemon).

aphrodisiac A drug that stimulates sexual desire (from Aphrodite, the goddess of love, Greek equivalent of Venus). Drugs reputed to have aphrodisiac action include levo**dopa**, yohimbine and **cannabis**.

appetitite-suppressant drug *See* **anorectic drug**.

apud cell An acronym derived from amine precursor uptake and decarboxylation cell. Apud cells include argentaffin cells, islet cells, parafollicular cells, and others.

area under the curve (AUC)   Usually refers to the area under the curve relating plasma concentration of a drug to time after its administration.

$$\text{Mathematically, AUC}_{0-\infty} = \int_0^\infty C_P\, dt$$

The AUC is related both to the dose administered and to the clearance of the drug. For intravenous injection, the **clearance** (Cl_P) is given by:

$$Cl_P = \frac{\text{Dose}}{\text{AUC}}$$

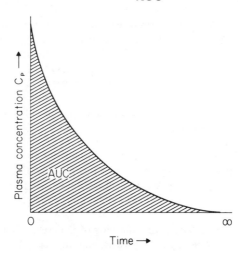

For any other route of administration the same relationship holds, except that it is the fraction (F) of the dose absorbed that is relevant, i.e.

$$Cl_P = \frac{F \times \text{Dose}}{\text{AUC}}$$

The units of AUC can be seen from the relationship

$$\text{AUC} = \frac{\text{Dose}}{Cl_P}$$

For example, if the dose is in mg and the clearance in ml/min, then:

$$\text{AUC} = \frac{\text{mg}}{\text{ml/min}} = \frac{\text{min} \times \text{mg}}{\text{ml}}$$

i.e. min × mg/ml.

Areas under the curves can be used to determine the fraction of a drug absorbed (F) from a non-vascular route of administration (e.g. orally), by

comparing the non-vascular AUC with the intravenous AUC, thus:
The rate of elimination is the clearance multiplied by the plasma concentration, i.e. $Cl_P \times C_P$.

The amount eliminated $= Cl_P \int_0^\infty C_P \, dt = Cl_P \times AUC$.

The amount eliminated = amount absorbed

$$\therefore \qquad Cl_P AUC = F \times dose$$

On intravenous injection, $F = 1$

$$\therefore \qquad F = \frac{\text{Extravascular AUC} \times \text{i.v. dose}}{\text{Intravenous AUC} \times \text{extravascular dose}}$$

If the dose given by both routes is the same, then:

$$F = \frac{\text{Extravascular AUC}}{\text{Intravenous AUC}}$$

F is thus a measure of the **bioavailability** of an extravascular dose of a drug.

aroclor 1254 A mixture of polychlorinated biphenyls used as a broad-spectrum inducer of mixed function oxygenases (**cytochromes** P_{448} and P_{450}) in laboratory rodents prior to the preparation of the hepatic microsome system for use in tests for mutagenicity, such as the **Ames test**.

aromatic amino acid decarboxylase *See* **dopa decarboxylase**.

aromatic L-amino acid decarboxylase inhibitors *See* **dopa decarboxylase inhibitors**.

arsenical drugs Organic compounds containing trivalent or pentavalent arsenic atoms in their molecules. Early in the 20th century, Paul Ehrlich discovered the effectiveness of arsphenamine (salvarsan 606) against trypanosomes and spirochaetes, and arsphenamine and related compounds formed the main treatments for syphilis until 1945 when they were replaced by **penicillin**.

Arsenicals also formed the main basis for the treatment of African sleeping sickness (trypanosomiasis) until less toxic drugs took their place. They are now obsolete except in the case of meningoencephalic stages of the disease where arsenicals that penetrate the **blood–brain barrier** may be of use.

Arsphenamine and melarsoprol are examples of trivalent arsenicals, and tryparamide and orsanine are examples of pentavalent arsenicals. Pentavalent arsenicals are **prodrugs**, having first to be reduced in the body of the host to the trivalent form before becoming active.

astringent   A substance that causes the denaturation of proteins so that they form a protective coagulated layer on mucous membranes or inflamed skin. Examples include alum $(K\ Al(SO_4)_2)$, zinc sulphate and tannic acid.

ataractic drug   An alternative name for a **tranquillizer** (Greek: *ataraktos*, undisturbed). Examples include chlordiazepoxide, diazepam and benactyzine.

atraxotoxin   A toxic principle from the venom of the Sydney funnel web spider (*Atrax robustus*). It causes initial excessive release, followed by depletion, of **acetylcholine** from motor nerve endings.

atriopeptins   Polypeptides released in the form of a precursor (atriopeptigen) from atrial myocytes in response to atrial stretch, to plasma volume expansion or to high sodium states. They act on the kidney to produce renal vasodilatation, **natriuresis** and diuresis (*see* **diuretic drug**). The atria thus function as endocrine organs. Atriopeptins may also serve as central neurotransmitters.

Needleman *et al.* (1984) *Trends pharmacol. Sci.* **5**, 506

Standaert *et al.* (1985) *Trends Neurosci.* **8**, 509

Atropa belladonna   A solanaceous plant commonly called deadly nightshade. Atropos was one of the three Greek godesses, the Fates (Atropos, Clotho and Lachesis), who were supposed to determine the course of human life. Belladonna (Latin: fair lady) is so called because Italian ladies used to make a cosmetic liquid extract from the plant. When dropped in the eye the pupils became dilated and this was regarded as attractive in appearance. *Atropa belladonna* contains the alkaloids hyoscine and hyoscyamine, racemic hyoscyamine being atropine.

atropine-like drugs   Atropine (racemic hyoscyamine) is the main active **alkaloid** present in *Atropa belladonna*. It is the prototype of drugs that block **muscarinic cholinoceptors**. Atropine-like drugs are drugs that block muscarinic receptors in a similar way. They include, among many others, tertiary amines such as hyoscine, homatropine, eucatropine, benztropine and benzhexol, and quaternary ammonium compounds such as atropine methonitrate, ipratropium, glypyrronium (glycopyrrolate) and poldine.

autacoids   Substances with pronounced pharmacological activity that occur in (or at least are extractable from) tissues, and which do not appear to possess a neurotransmitter or endocrine **hormone** function in that tissue, have been described as autacoids (Greek: *autos*, self; *akos*, remedy). Substances classed as autacoids include **histamine**, **serotonin**, **eicosanoids**, kinins (*see* **bradykinin**), **PAF-acether** and purine nucleotides. Their classification as autacoids in some tissues does not exclude a more specific role (e.g. as a neurotransmitter) at another site, perhaps in the brain. Local hormone is a term that is often used synonymously with autacoid. The term 'autacoid' was originally coined by Schafter in 1916 to replace the term hormone. However, 'hormone' has remained in use to denote the secretions of endocrine glands. It is generally believed that most autacoids probably exert a physiological function, although total proof is often lacking. There is more certainty about their role in pathological processes.

autoindicator tissues A tissue in an effector organ that responds to a specific chemical released, under appropriate experimental conditions, from a remote site in the body. For example, the chronically denervated smooth muscle of the **nictitating membrane** (the autoindicator) of an anaesthetized cat contracts in response to **noradrenaline** carried to it in the bloodstream when the sympathetic splenic nerve is stimulated. In the 1930s, the American physiologist W. B. Cannon made extensive use of techniques involving autoindicators in his studies of the nature of the sympathetic transmitter.

autoinduction *See* **enzyme induction**.

auto-oxidation reactions Oxidative chain reactions undergone by polyunsaturated fatty acids. **Free radicals** such as superoxide and hydroxyl radical or **singlet oxygen** produced *in vivo* can act as initiators, as can free radicals from certain environmental pollutants, from **paraquat** ingestion, or formed by some types of radiation, including sunlight. The reaction starts by removal of hydrogen from the methylene carbon between any pair of double bonds in the fatty acid. Many of the reactive breakdown products contribute to further oxidation, and free radicals, which attack other molecules, are formed. Lipid hydroperoxides are formed and these break up, forming dialdehydes such as malondialdehyde. Malondialdehyde causes cross-linking between various types of molecules, which may lead to cytotoxicity, mutagenicity and enzyme modification. (*See also* **lipofuscin**.) The enzymes catalase, peroxidase and **superoxide dismutase** act to protect the body against overproduction of free radicals, and α-tocopherol may act as an endogenous **free radical quencher**.

autopharmacology A term sometimes used to describe studies of **autacoids**.

autoreceptors Receptors on nerve endings that respond to the transmitter by modulating the release of the transmitter. For example, noradrenergic varicosities possess both α_2-**adrenoceptors** and β-adrenoceptors. The α_2-adrenoceptors mediate suppression of **noradrenaline** release, whereas the β-adrenoceptors mediate enhanced noradrenaline release. Overstimulation of the prejunctional β-adrenoceptor by adrenal medullary **adrenaline** may play a role in the aetiology of some kinds of hypertension (*see*, for example, Majewski & Rand (1984) *Trends pharmacol. Sci.* **5**, 500).

Postganglionic parasympathetic nerve endings possess **muscarinic cholinoceptors** that negatively modulate **acetylcholine** release, and possibly **nicotinic cholinoceptors** that enhance its release; somatic motor nerve endings in skeletal muscle may likewise possess both types of **cholinoceptor**. Probably similar kinds of modulating presynaptic autoreceptors are present in central synapses. The physiological roles of such receptors in controlling transmitter release are obviously complex and are a subject of some controversy.

Nerve endings may possess a number of other receptor types (**adenosine receptors, prostaglandin** receptors, **angiotensin** receptors, **GABA receptors** and so on) which may act to modulate transmitter release. These are not necessarily classed as 'autoreceptors', because the term refers only to receptors that are sensitive to the transmitter, or **co-transmitter**, from the same nerve ending. It is possible that in some instances such receptors respond to a co-transmitter released from the nerve ending, in which case the term autoreceptor is acceptable.

Nerve terminals may be impinged upon by endings from a different type of axon, and may possess receptors for the transmitter released from those endings. For example, many postganglionic parasympathetic nerve terminals possess α_2-adrenoceptors, and noradrenaline released from a sympathetic ending, at an axo-axonal synapse, inhibits the release of acetylcholine. Likewise, many sympathetic nerve terminals are innervated by parasympathetic branches, and acetylcholine released therefrom acts, via muscarinic receptors, to reduce noradrenaline release from the sympathetic endings. These prejunctional adrenoceptors and cholinoceptors, and other kinds of receptors that participate in similar kinds of presynaptic reciprocal inhibition, are not classed as autoreceptors.

auxotonic lever   A lightly spring-loaded lever for recording the contractions of isolated organs *in vitro*. Because of the spring, the load on the muscle increases as the muscle shortens. The term 'auxotonic' was first used in this way by von Frey in 1908 (in *Handbuch der Physiologisches Methodik*, Vol. II, No. 3 (Ed. Tigerstedt), p. 87. Hirzel, Leipzig).

avermectins   A group of broad-spectrum antiparasitic **macrolide antibiotics** which are derivatives of pentacyclic 16-membered lactones related to the **milbemycins**. They are derived from *Streptomyces avermectilis* and have activity against worms, insects and mites. The various avermectins are denoted by letters and numbers, i.e. A_{1a}, A_{2a}, A_{1b}, A_{2b}, B_{1a}, B_{2a}, B_{1b}, B_{2b}.

Avermectin B_{1a}, for example, rapidly and irreversibly paralyses **nematodes** at low concentrations by an action on the central nervous system of the worm. Neurophysiological studies of the lobster neuromuscular junction show that the compound selectively and irreversibly activates chloride conductance at **GABA receptors**. A similar effect may underlie its depressant effects on the nervous systems of worms, insects and mites.

Ivermectin is a chemical modification of an avermectin which has proved effective in eliminating microfilariae from patients infected with *Onchocerca volvulus* (river blindness).

BAAM N^1 - [3(o-allylphenoxy) - 2 - hydroxypropyl] - N^8 - bromoacetyl - (Z) - 1,8-diamino-p-methane). An alkylating β-**adrenoceptor antagonist** that forms a stable bond with β-**adrenoceptors**, and which is used as an affinity label for such **receptors**. It was synthesized by J. Pitha and colleagues of the National Institute of Health, Baltimore.

BACON An acronym for a particular drug combination sometimes used in cancer **chemotherapy**: bleomycin, adriamycin, CCNU, oncovin, nitrogen mustard.

balanced anaesthesia A term introduced by Lundy in 1926 to describe the production of unconsciousness and pain relief for **surgical anaesthesia** by the use of a number of different agents rather than of a single agent. The aim was to use doses of each agent well below the toxic dose. The later introduction of **neuromuscular blocking drugs** into anaesthetic practice extended the possibilities, and the balanced anaesthetic state was eventually defined by Gray, Rees and Woodbridge as unconsciousness, analgesia, muscle relaxation and abolition of autonomic reflexes. The usual techniques for producing this state are along the lines of sodium thiopentone for induction, nitrous oxide plus oxygen with sodium thiopentone supplements to maintain anaesthesia, a **neuromuscular blocking drug** to cause muscle relaxation and an **opioid** analgesic (e.g. pethidine or fentanyl) to abolish pain.

barbiturates A group of **drugs** that are derivatives of barbituric acid (malonyl urea), so called because it was first prepared on St Barbara's day in 1863. Barbituric acid itself is inactive. The thiobarbiturates are prepared from thiourea and have sulphur in place of oxygen as the substituent on carbon 2.

General structure of barbiturate drugs.

Those barbiturates that are, or have been, therapeutically useful exert a depressant action on the central nervous system (e.g. phenobarbitone, amylobarbitone, thiopentone, methohexitone), but stimulant barbiturates have been synthesized. Depressant barbiturates exert sedative, hypnotic, antiepileptic and anaesthetic activity. Their uses as sedatives or hypnotics are now largely obsolete, but the long-acting ones (e.g. phenobarbitone) remain in use as **anticonvulsant drugs** in epilepsy, and the short-acting ones (e.g. sodium thiopentone and sodium methohexitone) are used as **intravenous anaesthetics**. Their main mechanism of action is probably exerted at **GABA receptors**, where they act to potentiate **GABA**. The problems with barbiturates that have led to a substantial reduction in their use as sedatives and hypnotics include serious **tolerance** and **drug dependence**, and **enzyme induction**.

basal anaesthetic *See* induction agent.

batrachotoxin
The steroidal toxic principle obtained from the Colombian arrow poison frog, *Phyllobates aurotaenia*. It produces a large and irreversible depolarization of excitable membranes by causing the opening of sodium channels.

Albuquerque *et al.* (1971) *Science* **172**, 995–1002

Batrachotoxin

belladonna alkaloids
The **alkaloids** of *Atropa belladonna* (deadly nightshade), family Solanaceae. The main alkaloids are hyoscine and hyoscyamine, the (−)-isomers being the more potent. Atropine is racemic hyoscyamine. See also **solanaceous alkaloids**.

benzilylcholine mustard
A 2-halo-alkylamine that cyclizes in solution to form an ethyleniminium derivative which is a potent, specific and persistent antagonist of the muscarinic actions of **acetylcholine** and other **cholinomimetic drugs**. It is thus a powerful **ligand** at **muscarinic cholinoceptors**, its persistence of action being attributed to the alkylating activity of the ethyleniminium ion. The propyl variant of the compound has also been prepared in order to make it easier to incorporate a tritium label.

Gill & Rang (1966) *Molec. Pharmacol.* **2**, 248

HO—C—C—O—CH$_2$—CH$_2$—N $\langle$ CH$_2$CH$_2$Cl / CH$_3$

Benzilylcholine mustard (*N*-2-chloroethyl-*N*-methyl 2-aminoethyl benzilate)

benzo[a]pyrene The major coal tar carcinogen. It is also present in tobacco smoke and diesel fumes, and may be formed by heating cooking fat.

Benzo[*a*]pyrene (3,4-benzpyrene)

benzodiazepine receptor antagonists *See* benzodiazepine receptors.

benzodiazepine receptor ligands *See* benzodiazepine receptors.

benzodiazepine receptors High-affinity benzodiazepine binding sites that when bound to a clinically used benzodiazepine (e.g. diazepam) give rise to the characteristic pharmacological actions of such drugs. Benzodiazepine receptors are protein in nature and are mainly localized in **GABA** synapses. They are functionally linked to **GABA$_A$ receptors** and their associated chloride channels. The anxiolytic benzodiazepines (*see* **anxiolytic agent**) potentiate GABA by altering the kinetics of the GABA-dependent chloride channel in such a way that the frequency of channel opening is increased. Two classes of benzodiazepine receptors have been described. These are either distinct proteins or two conformational states of one receptor. In binding studies with the triazolopyridazine compound CL 218.872, type 1 (Bz$_1$) receptors bind with higher affinity than type 2 (Bz$_2$). The cerebellum contains mainly Bz$_1$ receptors, whereas hippocampus and cerebral cortex contain both Bz$_1$ and Bz$_2$ receptors. It is not known whether these two receptors serve distinct functions.

The benzodiazepine receptor is considered to be part of a large molecular complex which consists of the GABA receptor, its chloride channel, the benzodiazepine receptor, and other proteins. Guidotti and his co-workers proposed that benzodiazepines modulate GABA receptor function partly through an additional protein called **GABA modulin**, but not all authorities accept a role for such a protein.

There is as yet no impelling evidence for an endogenous **ligand** for the benzodiazepine receptor, although one proposal is that GABA is released from nerve endings along with a polypeptide **co-transmitter**, the function of which is to interact with the benzodiazepine receptor and thereby impair the efficiency of GABA, perhaps by hindering the coupling of the GABA recognition sites to the Cl^- gates. That is to say, the co-transmitter, although it combines with the benzodiazepine receptor, exerts the opposite action to the benzodiazepines. As described below, such compounds are said to have negative **efficacy** and are described as **inverse agonists**.

The benzodiazepine receptor is unusual in that occupation by different types of specific ligands produces opposite effects on GABA activity. Occupation by one type of specific ligand results in facilitation of **GABA** activity. This has been termed positive efficacy and is the mechanism of action of the therapeutically useful anxiolytic–sedative–anticonvulsant benzodiazepines, such as diazepam. The compounds may be described as positive **agonists**. Another type of specific ligand apparently binds to the same receptors (since it is blocked by the same antagonists), yet it reduces GABA activity. This has been termed negative efficacy, and compounds that exert this effect are described as negative agonists or inverse agonists. Their behavioural effect is anxiety and convulsions. A third type of specific ligand binds to the benzodiazepine receptor, yet exerts neither positive nor negative efficacy; that is, it has nil efficacy. Such compounds act as antagonists both of agonists and of inverse agonists. Between these extremes lie compounds that act as **partial** (positive) **agonists** and others that act as partial inverse agonists. The table below (adapted from Braestrap *et al.* (1984) *Biochem. Pharmacol.* **33**, 859) gives typical examples of the various types of benzodiazepine receptor ligands.

Type	Efficacy	Examples		Effects
Agonist	+ +	Diazepam Zopiclone CL 218.872 ZK 93423		Anxiolytic, anticon- vulsant, sedative, muscle relaxant
Partial agonist	+	ZK 91296 CGS 9896		Anticonvulsant
Receptor antagonist	0	Ro 15.1788 β-CCE ZK 93426	(but some + and − efficacy at high doses)	Antagonize agonists and inverse agonists
Partial inverse agonist	−	FG 7142		Anxiogenic and proconvulsant
Inverse agonist	− −	DMCM β-CCM		Convulsant and anxiogenic

CL 218.872: 3-Methyl-6-[(3-trifluoromethyl)phenyl]-1,2,4-triazolo[4,3-b]pyridazine
ZK 91296: 4-Ethyl 5-benzyloxy-4-methoxymethyl-β-carboline-3 carboxylate
ZK 93423: 4-Ethyl 6-benzyloxy-4-methoxymethyl-β-carboline-3 carboxylate
ZK 93426: 5-Ethyl 5-isopropyloxy-4-methyl-β-carboline-3 carboxylate
CGS 9896: 2-(4-Chlorophenyl)-2,5-dihydropyrazolo[4,3-c]quinoline-3[3H]-one
Ro 15.1788: Ethyl 8-fluoro-5,6-dihydro-5-methyl-6-oxo-4H-imidazo[1,5-a][1,4]benzodiazepine-3-carboxylate
β-CCE: Ethyl-β-carboline-3-carboxylate
β-CCM: Methyl-β-carboline-3-carboxylate
FG 7142: β-Carboline-3-carboxylate methyl amide
DMCM: 6,7-Dimethyl-4-ethyl-β-carboline-3-carboxylate

A note of caution. The terminology serves a useful purpose for the cognoscenti in this field, but it is not certain that the term agonist as applied to benzodiazepines is completely appropriate in comparison with substances that activate other receptors, and this then has consequences for the term inverse agonist. In any case, this latter term depends upon the absolute certainty that receptor antagonists, such as ZK 93426, are blocking the same receptor when they antagonize, for example, diazepam on the one hand, and β-CCM on the other, and this is not proven beyond doubt.

benzodiazepines The group name for a class of drugs whose chemical structures are based on 1,4-benzodiazepine or on 1,2-imidazo-benzodiazepine.

1,4-Benzodiazepine nucleus

Therapeutically useful benzodiazepines all exert the same five pharmacological effects (antianxiety, hypnotic, anticonvulsant, central muscle relaxant and anaesthetic activity), but to relatively different degrees. They also differ widely in their rates of inactivation and whether their metabolites are pharmacologically active, and these factors influence the therapeutic uses to which they are put.

Chlordiazepoxide (Librium) was the first benzodiazepine to be developed, and this was followed by diazepam (Valium) and then by numerous other compounds. Midazolam is an example of an imidazobenzodiazepine. The imidazole ring confers high basicity which allows water-soluble salts to be formed. Midazolam is the hydrochloride.

benzothiadiazines *See* thiazide drugs.

benzothiazepines A class of vasodilator **calcium slow-channel blocking drugs** of which diltiazem is the best known example.

Diltiazem

Diltiazem is 3-(acetyloxy)-5-[2-(dimethylamino)-ethyl]-2,3-dihydro-2-(4-methoxphenyl)-1,5-benzothiazepin-4(5H)-one.

3,4-benzpyrene *See* benzo[*a*]pyrene.

Bernoulli distribution *See* binomial distribution.

beta-adrenoceptors *See* adrenoceptors.

beta-lactam antibiotics *See* β-lactam antibiotics.

betel The dried, lime-treated seed (betel nut, areca, pinang) of the palm *Areca catechu* wrapped in the leaf (betel leaf or pan) of a species of pepper, *Piper betle*. The plug so formed is habitually chewed by many of the inhabitants of the Indian subcontinent and South-East Asia. It is estimated that there are about 200 million habitual users. The best known of the betel **alkaloids** is the **parasympathomimetic drug** arecoline, but it is unlikely that arecoline itself plays much part in the psychoactive properties of betel, since it is rapidly converted to arecaidine (a **GABA** uptake inhibitor) by lime treatment and by gut enzymes. The psychoactive principles of betel have not been clearly identified, but it seems likely that the effect is due to a synergistic interaction (*see* **synergistic action**) between certain tetrahydro-nicotinic acid derivatives and arecolidine present in the areca nut, and the compound piperine present in the pepper leaf.

bhang A form of **cannabis** in India. The dried leaves and flowering shoots of *Cannabis sativa*.

bicuculline A convulsant **alkaloid**, extracted from *Cordyalis* species. Bicuculline blocks **GABA$_A$ receptors**.

biguanides Compounds derived from two molecules of guanidine with elimination of ammonia. Biguanides possess one of two main pharmacological actions. Some are oral hypoglycaemic agents (e.g. phenformin, buformin, metformin) used in the control of diabetes mellitus. They lower blood glucose by reducing glucose absorption, increasing glycolysis and inhibiting gluconeogenesis. Others are **antimalarial drugs** (e.g. proguanil

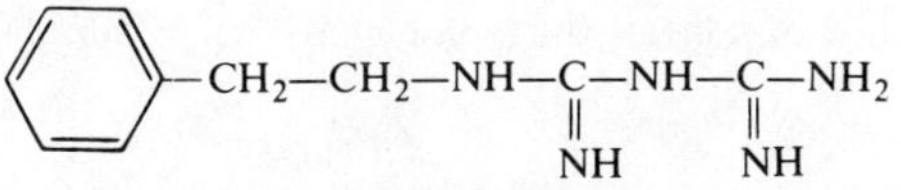

Phenformin

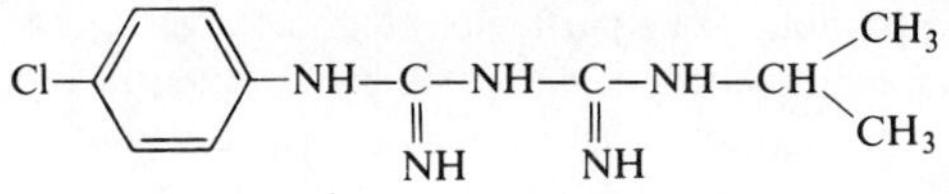

Proguanil

and chlorproguanil). They are schizonticidal for both the erythrocytic and liver forms of *Plasmodium falciparum*, and for the erythrocytic forms of *P. vivax*. The active metabolites of the drugs inhibit the enzyme dihydrofolate reductase in the parasite, thereby blocking purine synthesis.

binomial distribution The kind of distribution in which an event may occur or not occur; also known as the Bernoulli distribution. For example, in a test for lethality of a drug in a group of animals, the result in each animal is dead or not dead. If the probability of the occurrence of the event is denoted by p, then the probability of its non-occurrence (q) is $1 - p$; i.e. $q = 1 - p$, and $p + q = 1$. When the number of times that the event is tested is N (e.g. the number of animals used), the distributions of p and q are described by the successive terms in the expansion of the binomial $(p + q)^N$ which has the form:

$$q^N + \left(\frac{N!}{1!(N-1)!}\right)pq^{N-1} + \left(\frac{N!}{2!(N-2)!}\right)p^2q^{N-2}$$

$$+ \left(\frac{N!}{3!(N-3)!}\right)p^3q^{N-3} + \cdots + p^N$$

The coefficients of successive terms of the factors in the above equation form the series:

$$\frac{N!}{0!(N-0)!}, \frac{N!}{1!(N-1)!}, \frac{N!}{2!(N-2)!}, \frac{N!}{3!(N-3)!} \cdots$$

in which the first term $= 1$, since $0! = 1$. Using the symbol k to stand for a term in the series $0, 1, 2, 3, \ldots, N$, any term in the binomial expansion can be written as:

$$\left(\frac{N!}{k!(N-k)!}\right) p^k q^{(N-k)}$$

or, substituting $(1 - p)$ for q:

$$\left(\frac{N!}{k!(N-k)!}\right) p^k (1 - p)^{N-k}$$

When the value of p is 0·5, the factor $p^k(1 - p)^{N-k}$ simplifies to $0·5^N$, thus:

$$\left(\frac{N!}{k!(N-k)!}\right) 0·5^N$$

When p is 0·5 and N is very large, a smooth, symetrical bell-shaped curve relates the probability of a particular outcome (P) in any one group of N to the particular outcome (i.e. the number of events) in each group. This is known as a normal distribution or Gaussian distribution.

bioassays (biological assays) Assay techniques for determining the concentrations of pharmacologically active substances; the techniques depend on measuring the responses of living tissues or cells to the active substance in question. Comparison is made with a standard solution of known strength. Bioassay is used when chemical or physical methods are unavailable or are unsuitable (e.g. if the substance to be assayed is impure). Bioassays are usually more sensitive than are conventional chemical or physical methods, but the main disadvantages are that they have less precision than chemical or physical assays, and they are more laborious to perform.

    Radioimmunoassays may be regarded as a special type of bioassay.

bioavailability The proportion of the active drug in a formulation that is absorbed and therefore available to exert its pharmacological effect. Bioavailability is usually estimated from comparison of the concentrations of drug in plasma after intravenous injection to that after administration of the dosage form (e.g. tablet, capsule, suppository) from which the drug must be absorbed. The comparison requires a pharmacokinetic analysis (*see* **pharmacokinetics**) of the time-course of the concentration of the drug in plasma. Problems may arise when different manufacturers' preparations of the same drug have different bioavailabilities, and a patient unwittingly changes from one to the other.

bioequivalence Equivalence of **bioavailability** and hence of biological activity of two products with the same active principle but different formulations.

biogenic amines The term in German (*die biogenen Amine*) was introduced by Guggenheim in 1951 in referring to 'organic bases of low molecular weight which arise through metabolic processes in animals, plants and micro-organisms. They comprise aliphatic, alicyclic and simple heterocyclic compounds that are produced during cellular metabolism as basic substances of different degrees of physiological importance.' The term is meant to mean amines generated by living processes (and not amines that generate life). The main biogenic amines are decarboxylated products of amino acids or their derivatives (e.g. tyramine, **adrenaline, noradrenaline, dopamine, serotonin, histamine**).

biological half-life The time taken for the concentration of drug in a peripheral biophase **compartment** to decline to half of its original value ($T_{1/2}\beta$). A hybrid rate constant (β), which is a complex value related to several individual constants, can be determined from the slope of the secondary log-linear phase of the two-compartment curve. In an analogous way to that for calculating $T_{1/2}$ from the **elimination rate constant**, the biological half-life is given by $0.693/\beta$.

biological response modifier A term coined to include a number of endogenously released soluble factors, other than immunoglobulins, that serve to modulate the immune system. Biological response modifiers include **lymphokines, monokines, cytokines, thymic hormones, transfer factor, lymphotoxins, interleukins, interferons** and **chalones**.

biological standardization The determination of the potency of a pharmacologically active preparation by a **bioassay** in which an international **biological standard** is used for comparison.

biological standards Therapeutic substances that cannot be assayed by chemical or physical methods are assayed biologically by comparing their potencies against international biological standards. Their potencies are then expressed in terms of units. The first biological standard was set up by Ehrlich in 1897. It consisted of a certain weight of a dried preparation of diphtheria antitoxin. Other preparations of diphtheria antitoxin were compared with the designated standard in their ability to protect guinea-pigs against the effects of diphtheria toxin. As methods of purification and of chemical and physical assay improve, the need for biological standards diminishes, but it remains necessary to assay a few substances in this way (e.g. chorionic gonadotrophin, **insulin, heparin, vitamin** D and certain sera and **vaccines**). International biological standards are under the control of WHO. The Danish State Serum Institute is responsible for the custody and issue of immunological standards, and the British National Institute for Medical Research is similarly responsible for all other biological standards.

biopharmaceutics Wagner has defined the term as '... the study of the relationship between the nature and intensity of the biological effects observed in animals and man and the following factors: (1) the nature of the form of the drug (ester, salt, complex etc); (2) the physical state, including particle size and surface area; (3) the presence or absence of adjuncts with the active drug; (4) the type of dosage form in which the drug is administered; (5) the pharmaceutical process(es) used to prepare the dosage form.'

Some authorities include **pharmacokinetics** as a division of bio-pharmaceutics; others regard it as a separate kind of study.

biophase An abbreviation, first coined by Ferguson, of 'biologically active phase' with reference to the phase in which **general anaesthetic drugs** exert their effects. The term is now used in a more general way to designate the environment in which a drug is in the position to interact with its target site (e.g. its **receptors**) without diffusional barriers intervening (Greek: *bios*, life; *phasis*, appearance).

bitters Non-toxic amounts of substances with a bitter taste. When taken before meals they reflexly stimulate the flow of saliva and gastric juice, thereby promoting appetite. Common examples include extracts of quassia, gentian or calumba.

biventer cervicis muscle of the chick A skeletal muscle running along either side of the midline of the dorsal surface of the neck. It contains both focally and multiply innervated fibres. The motor nerve to the twitch fibres is located within the tendon and may be stimulated by passing the tendon through an electrode assembly. The muscle is isolated and mounted in an organ bath. Both twitches and drug-induced **contractures** may be recorded.

Ginsborg & Warriner (1960) *Brit. J. Pharmacol.* **15**, 410

black widow spider venom The venom of black widow spiders (*Latrodectus* species, e.g. *L. tredecimguttatus, L. mactans, L. geometricus*). *See* **alpha-latrotoxin**.

block by depolarization *See* **depolarization block**.

blood–brain barrier One or more diffusion barriers that impede the access of certain substances present in the blood (particularly substances, including drugs, that are insoluble in lipids or that bind strongly to proteins) from reaching the nervous tissue of the brain. Part of the barrier, or the barrier in relation to some drugs, may arise from the fact that the junctions between the endothelial cells of the brain capillaries are of the tight junction type. The idea of a blood–brain barrier has been realized ever since 1885 when Paul Ehrlich showed that certain acidic dyes (e.g. trypan blue) injected into the bloodstream of animals stained almost all the tissues of the body other than most of the brain and spinal cord and the cerebrospinal fluid.

Bobon clinical profile of neuroleptic drugs A classification of neuroleptic drugs in which six clinical effects, ataractic, antimanic, anti-autistic, antidelusional, extrapyramidal and adrenolytic (*see* **ataractic drugs, antimanic, anti-autistic** and **antidelusional activity, extrapyramidal side-effects, adrenolytic drugs**), are rated on a six-point scale (0–5). The classification was devised by J. Bobon and co-workers (Bobon *et al.* (1972) *Acta psychiat. Belg.* **72**, 542).

bolus injection Injection of a single dose over a short period as distinct from an infusion (Greek: *bolos*, clod).

bone seekers Metal ions, such as those of barium, strontium, lead, radium, thorium and plutonium, that may exchange for calcium ions in bone. If radioactive (e.g. Sr^{90}) they are likely to damage blood-forming cells in the bone marrow.

botulinum toxin A protein exotoxin produced by the anaerobic spore-forming bacterium *Clostridium botulinum*. The toxin is produced in at least eight immunologically distinct types (A, B, C_1, C_2, D, E, F, G), of which type A is the most toxic. The toxin produces two distinct actions: (1) it prevents transmission at all peripheral cholinergic junctions by an action on the nerve endings through which the release of **acetylcholine** by nerve impulses is inhibited, and (2) it causes agglutination of red blood cells.

One type of food poisoning (botulism) is a consequence of poisoning by botulinum toxin. Contaminated sausages (Latin: *botulus*) have a reputation for causing botulism, although inadequately sterilized home-bottled fruit is a more common cause. The toxin was once known as 'corpse acid'.

Botulinum toxin may have therapeutic value. It is presently undergoing clinical trials for the relief of blepharospasm and selected types of strabismus.

Bowditch staircase phenomenon The increase in contraction tension of ventricular preparations of the heart that occurs with increased driving frequency. Also called 'Treppe' (German: staircase) (Bowditch (1871) *Arb. Physiol.* **6**, 139). Six years earlier, Ranke (1865) had described a similar phenomenon in skeletal muscle (*Tetanus, eine physiologische Studie*, p. 380. Engelmann, Leipzig). *See also* **Woodworth staircase phenomenon**.

Changes in contractility in relation to the frequency of contractions are usually ascribed to changes in the availability of Ca^{2+} ions to the contractile apparatus (troponin C, actin, myosin). These staircase phenomena were later embodied in the concepts of positive and negative inotropic effects of activation put forward by Koch Weser and Blinks (1963, *Pharmacol. Rev.* **16**, 602).

bradykinin A nonapeptide that causes contraction of most smooth muscles but dilatation of arterioles and veins. It increases capillary permeability and it stimulates certain nervous structures (autonomic ganglia and sensory nerve endings). Its name was coined by Rocha e Silva in Brazil and is derived from the observation that it causes a slowly developing (Greek: *bradus*, slow) contraction (Greek: *kinema*, movement) of guinea-pig isolated ileum. Bradykinin is formed from precursors (**kininogens**) in the plasma, the reaction being catalysed by **kallikreins**.

[N]Arg–Pro–Pro–Gly–Phe–Ser–Pro–Phe–Arg[C]
Bradykinin (kallidin-9; kinin 9; kallidin 1)

bronchoconstrictor agent   An agent that produces constriction of the bronchi. Examples include **histamine**, **bradykinin**, **leukotrienes**, certain **prostaglandins** (e.g. $PGF_{2\alpha}$) and **acetylcholine**.

bronchodilator agent   An agent that produces dilatation of the bronchi. Examples include, **adrenaline**, isoprenaline, salbutamol, other **β-adrenoceptor** agonists, **atropine-like drugs** and theophylline.

brown fat   A form of adipose tissue first studied in rodents, in which it constitutes about 1% of the total body fat. Brown fat is the major source of non-shivering thermogenesis (i.e. thermogenesis not involving skeletal muscles) in cold-adapted rodents, and it plays a major role in diet-induced thermogenesis. Brown fat contains many mitochondria which have the unusual property of oxidizing fatty acids through an influx of protons without the production of ATP, that is, oxidative phosphorylation is uncoupled and the energy produced is generated as heat. Both non-shivering and diet-induced thermogenesis are driven by **noradrenaline** acting via **β-adrenoceptors** on the **adenylate cyclase–cyclic AMP** system. Diet-induced thermogenesis also requires **insulin**. As the fat stores decrease inside the brown fat cell, lipolysis in white fat is enhanced, so that fatty acids can be transferred to brown fat and be resynthesized ready for oxidation. Thus, non-shivering thermogenesis reduces the white fat stores and counteracts obesity. The genetically obese (ob/ob) mouse is deficient in brown fat and is incapable of non-shivering thermogenesis.

Brown fat is also present in human beings, including adults, where it is present in the para-aortic and perirenal fat depots. In all species, the amount of brown fat present diminishes with age, and this is one of the main reasons underlying the increased obesity characteristic of age. The amount of brown fat is under hormonal control, prolactin being one of the hormones responsible for its diminution with age.

Future pharmacological approaches to the control of obesity may revolve around methods of stimulating the uncoupled oxidative phosphorylation specifically in brown fat, or of increasing the amount of brown fat present. There is evidence that the β-adrenoceptors on brown fat cells differ to some extent from other β-adrenoceptors so that it may be possible to devise **agonists** that selectively lead to the oxidation of brown fat. This would have the secondary effect of mobilizing white fat stores.

Bruce effect The failure of a recently mated female mouse to produce young if housed near a strange male. The mated female is not upset by her own stud mate or by strange males if they have been castrated, nor does she fail to reproduce, despite a strange male, if her olfactory bulbs are destroyed. The phenomenon was first reported by Hilda Bruce in 1959. It has subsequently been shown that the urine of the strange male contains a **pheromone** which, when detected by the olfactory sense of the female, inhibits prolactin secretion and thereby prevents implantation of the fertilized ovum.

bulk laxative An agent that produces emptying of the bowels by causing an increase in the contents of the colon, thereby stimulating the peristaltic reflex of defaecation. Examples of bulk laxatives include agar and cellulose derivatives. **Saline purgatives** are generally not included under this heading, although they act by virtue of the increase in bulk that they cause.

bungarotoxins Polypeptide toxins derived from the venom of the elapid snake, the Taiwan (Formosan) banded krait (*Bungarus multicinctus*). There are two main toxins, α-bungarotoxin which binds irreversibly to **nicotinic cholinoceptors** at the neuromuscular junction in skeletal muscle and in the electric organs of certain fishes and eels, and β-bungarotoxin which acts on somatic motor nerve endings initially to increase the release, and subsequently to deplete and therefore decrease the release, of **acetylcholine**. Much has been learned about the number, site and structure of endplate nicotinic cholinoceptors from experiments in which α-bungarotoxin has been used as a tool.

A polypeptide impurity in some samples of α-bungarotoxin combines with and blocks the ganglionic type of nicotinic cholinoceptor. This impurity has been termed P-4 bungarotoxin. Also a toxin termed κ-bungarotoxin which also blocks neuronal nicotinic receptors has been isolated.

Saiani *et al.* (1984) *Molec. Biol.* **25**, 327
Chiappinelli (1984) *Trends pharmacol. Sci.* **5**, 425

butyrophenones A group of **neuroleptic drugs** with potent **dopamine antagonist** action, and having a butyrophenone moiety in their molecular structures. Examples include haloperidol, droperidol, trifluperidol, moperone, and spiperone.

Haloperidol (all butyrophenones possess the part of the molecule that is thickened).

butyrylcholinesterase A cholinesterase enzyme (acetylcholine acyl-hydrolase, EC 3.1.1.8) that shows its highest activity against butyryl-choline. It is the main pseudocholinesterase present in mammals, being located in plasma, intestine, skin and other tissues.

cadaverine The amine (1,5-pentanediamine, $NH_2(CH_2)_5NH_2$) derived from the decarboxylation of lysine. It is present in ribosomes. Cadaverine and **putrescine** were once erroneously thought to be responsible for the symptoms of food poisoning (hence their horrifying names). Together they were called the ptomaine (Greek: *ptoma*, a corpse) poisons.

Calabar bean The seed of *Physostigma venenosum* (Leguminosae) and the botanical source of the prototype **anticholinesterase drug**, physostigmine. It is conventional to give synthetic reversible anticholinesterase drugs the same ending, i.e. '-stigmine'. Hence, neostigmine, pyridostigmine and distigmine, but not all drugs of this type have been so named (e.g. ambenonium, edrophonium, benzpyrinium).

calcitonin gene-related peptide (CGRP) A 37-amino acid poly-peptide which is not calcitonin but which is specified by the calcitonin gene via an alternative processing of the primary RNA transcript. CGRP is present in thyroid tissue and in nervous tissue, being especially abundant in the spinal cord alongside **substance P**. It is also present in the heart, lung, gastrointestinal tract, blood vessel walls and plasma. It stimulates sympathetic activity when injected into the cerebral ventricles, and it is a powerful vasodilator when injected peripherally.

calcium antagonist *See* calcium channel blocking drug.

calcium channel activators Also called calcium channel **agonists**. A group of dihydropyridines that act to facilitate the passage of Ca^{2+} through membrane calcium channels. (These drugs are not calcium **ionophores**, which have a different mechanism of action.) The group of dihydropyridines as a whole includes calcium channel agonists, **calcium channel blocking drugs** or antagonists (e.g. nifedipine), and drugs that may be described as **partial agonists** at the calcium channel.

Calcium channel activators produce vasoconstriction, increased smooth muscle tone generally, and have a positive **inotropic action** on the heart. They have no obvious clinical use at present except perhaps as antidotes to poisoning by nifedipine and related drugs. The structures of two examples of calcium channel activators are shown below.

Calcium channel activators appear to act by modulating gating function in the calcium channel in such a way that mode 2 gating (long-lasting channel opening with only brief closures) is promoted. *See* **calcium channel blocking drugs** for an explanation of gating modes.

BAY K 8644   CGP 28 392

calcium channel blocking drugs Drugs that appear to act by inhibiting the entry of Ca^{2+} into cardiac and smooth muscle cells, through specific **voltage-dependent** or **receptor-operated** calcium **ion channels**. Examples of such drugs include verapamil, nifedipine and diltiazam. These three drugs are examples of three chemically distinct groups of compounds, and the evidence suggests that each type binds at a distinct, though interrelated, binding site or **receptor** in the channel.

The actions of blocking drugs of the dihydropyridine type (nifedipine, nitrendipine, nimodipine) on heart cells have been studied by Tsien and coworkers with the aid of a **patch clamp** electrode. Single cardiac Ca^{2+} channels normally exhibit three modes of gating. *Mode 1 gating* is the most usual when the membrane is clamped at a depolarized potential; the current records indicate brief channel openings occurring in bursts. *Mode 2 gating* appears in rare oscilloscope sweeps and is characterized by long-lasting openings with brief closings. *Mode 0 gating* occurs in occasional sweeps and is characterized by lack of opening. The dihydropyridine type of blocking drugs increase the number of mode 0 gatings and thereby reduce the Ca^{2+} current. The effects of these drugs together with the **calcium channel activators** cannot be explained in terms of a simple physical plugging of the channel, but rather they indicate a mechanism dependent on modulation of gating.

Drugs in this class are also known as calcium slow-channel blocking drugs, calcium channel antagonists or simply as calcium antagonists. Calcium antagonist is not a recommended term since it may imply that calcium ions and the drug molecules bind at the same site and this is probably not the case. *See also* **calcium channel activators**.

calcium slow-channel blocking drugs *See* **calcium channel blocking drugs**.

calmodulin A widely distributed intracellular protein that binds calcium ions with high **affinity** and specificity. It exists as a monomer of molecular weight 17 000 daltons. It resembles, but is not identical with, the troponin C of skeletal and cardiac muscle. Binding of Ca^{2+} results in a conformational change which causes the calcium ion–calmodulin complex to

47

activate a number of cellular enzymes and so modulate a range of cellular functions including secretion, motility, mitosis, cyclic nucleotide metabolism and glycogen metabolism. Some drugs are capable of binding to calmodulin and thereby interfering with its ability to bind Ca^{2+}. Examples of such drugs include bepridil, pimozide, calmidazolium (R24,571), and phenathiazines such as trifluperazine. Such drugs are often referred to as calmodulin antagonists or calmodulin inhibitors.

calmodulin inhibitors *See* **calmodulin.**

calpain 1 A protease enzyme that uniquely catalyses the degradation of **fodrin.** Calpain may play a part in memory storage. Repeated synaptic activity at certain cortical synapses facilitates the entry of large amounts of Ca^{2+} into the dendritic cytoplasm of the postsynaptic cell. The consequent activation of calpain and breakdown of fodrin cause a permanent change in the synaptic connection and expose an increased number of **glutamate receptors.** These synaptic changes are thought to underlie memory storage. The substance leupeptin blocks the action of calpain and has been found to impede certain types of memory storage in rats.

cAMP *See* **cyclic AMP.**

cannabinoids The pharmacologically active principles of **cannabis.** They include the tetrahydrocannabinols (Δ^1-*trans*-THC and Δ^6-THC) the Δ^1-tetrahydrocannabinol acids (A and B), cannabinol, cannabidiol, and cannabidiolic acid. The pharmacological actions of cannabis are due mainly to Δ^1-*trans*-THC, but there are both pharmacodynamic and pharmacokinetic interactions with other cannabinoids. (By analogy with **opioids** and **opiates,** cannabinates might have been a preferable term.)

cannabis A generic term for various preparations of the leaves, flowers and resin of *Cannabis sativa* (Indian hemp). The preparations include marihuana, bhang, ganja, charas, hashish, dagga and kabak, which are used for their euphoriant effects.

The main stems of *C. sativa* were also used as a source of hemp fibres for rope- and canvas-making. Cannabis is in fact the Latin word for hemp.

carbonic anhydrase inhibitors Drugs that inhibit the enzyme carbonic anhydrase which enhances the rate at which equilibrium is reached in the reaction:

$$CO_2 + H_2O \rightleftharpoons H_2CO_3$$

Carbonic anhydrase is present in the cortex of the kidney, the eye, the pancreas, the gastric mucosa and the brain. The role of carbonic anhydrase in the above reaction is important in the kidney, especially the proximal tubule. Hydrogen ion from dissociated H_2CO_3 exchanges with Na^+, and $NaHCO_3$ is reabsorbed. Inhibition of the enzyme results in excessive excretion of $NaHCO_3$ in the urine with accompanying water. The main carbonic anhydrase inhibitors used as **diuretic drugs** are acetazolamide, dichlorphenamide, ethoxzolamide and methazolamide.

Carbonic anhydrase is also involved in the secretion of gastric juice, pancreatic juice and aqueous humour. Inhibitors find some use in the control of glaucoma, where they lower intraocular pressure by reducing the formation of aqueous humour. The exact role of carbonic anhydrase in the brain is unclear, but inhibition of the enzyme has a sedative effect, and some carbonic anhydrase inhibitors, notably sulthiame, have found some use in the control of myoclonic epilepsy.

carcinogenicity The propensity to cause carcinoma. In fact the term is used in relation to cancer generally (Greek: *karkinos*, a crab).

cardiac glycosides Glycosides with a pronounced effect on the heart. In therapeutic doses, the main cardiac effect takes the form of a positive **inotropic action**. The main cardiac glycosides are those obtained from *Digitalis purpurea* (purple foxglove) and *D. lanata* (woolly foxglove), *Strophanthus kombé*, *S. gratus* and *Urginea maritima* (squill), but substances with similar properties are present in lily of the valley, hawthorn, oleander and certain other plants, and also in the skin of toads of the genus *Bufo*. The principal drugs in therapeutic use are digoxin, digitoxin, strophanthin-K and ouabain.

cardioselective β-adrenoceptor blocking drugs An alternative name for β_1-**adrenoceptor** blocking **drugs**. β_1-Adrenoceptors are not in fact confined to the heart, but cardiac muscle probably is the most important tissue containing such **receptors**. The drugs include atenolol, metoprolol, acebutolol and (the largely obsolete) practolol.

carminative A substance with the property of assisting the expulsion of gas from the stomach and intestines. Most carminatives contain volatile oils which possess a mild irritant action on smooth muscle. Their mechanism of action is unknown but they produce reflex stimulation of the gut and relaxation of sphincters. Oil of peppermint is a common example of a volatile oil with carminative action.

carotenoids Substances derived from carotenes which are pigments present in many fruits and vegetables, including carrots and tomatoes. Many carotenoids (e.g. retinol and retinoic acid) possess **vitamin** A activity. (Retinol is in fact vitamin A1.) Retinoic acid (vitamin A acid), and some derivatives of it, applied topically are effective in the treatment of **acne** vulgaris and infection by tinea versicolor.

catecholamines Amines containing a catechol nucleus. The three that occur in mammalian tissues are **dopamine**, **noradrenaline** and **adrenaline**.

catechol-O-methyltransferase (COMT) An enzyme that catalyses the transfer of the methyl group from adenosylmethionine to the *meta*-
(i.e. 3-) hydroxy group of **catecholamines**. The 3-methoxy products of
dopamine, noradrenaline and **adrenaline** are 3-methoxytyramine, normetanephrine and metanephrine respectively. COMT is an intracellular
cytoplasmic enzyme and is especially abundant in liver and kidneys. It
differs in importance at different sites of noradrenergic transmission. At
some, it plays a significant role in terminating transmitter action after
uptake of the transmitter into the cells containing the enzyme.

catechol-O-methyltransferase inhibitors Drugs that inhibit
catechol-O-methyltransferase. They include catechol, pyrogallol, tropolone derivatives, certain flavenoids, and the compounds 3,5-dihydroxy-4-
methoxybenzoic acid and dopacetamide.

cathartic A drug that produces emptying of the bowels (Greek: *kathartikos*, making completely clean). Alternative names and their etymological
origins are given under **aperient** and **purgative**.

cathodal block Conduction block that arises in an excitable membrane
as a consequence of prolonged cathodal current flow. The sodium
channels, which are transiently opened, become closed again (inactivated)
and the voltage-dependent potassium channels remain open (*see* **voltage-
dependent ion channels**). These changes in the ionic channels oppose
excitation. The phenomenon has some similarities to block by depolarization (*see* **depolarization block**) at the neuromuscular junction where the
depolarized endplate zone acts like a persistent cathode.

centrally acting muscle relaxants Drugs that relieve muscle spasm
by an action exerted within the brain or spinal cord. They include
mephenesin, baclofen and **benzodiazepines** such as diazepam.

cephalomycins A series of **antibiotics** similar to the **cephalosporins** but
derived from *Streptomyces* species. They have a methoxyl group at
position 7 of the beta-lactam ring.

cephalosporins A series of **antibiotics**, the first of which were obtained
from *Cephalosporium acremonium*. Three active compounds, cephalosporins P, N and C, were obtained. The isolation of the active nucleus of
cephalosporin C, 7-aminocephalosporanic acid, allowed the production of
semi-synthetic cephalosporins which are resistant to **penicillinases**. Their
mechanism of action resembles that of the **penicillins**.

General structure of cephalosporins.

cGMP *See* **cyclic GMP**.

chalones (Greek: *chalan*, to relax or to slacken.) Water-soluble substances (probably glycoproteins) that are produced by living cells. They are tissue-specific, but not species-specific, in their actions. They act, reversibly, to inhibit mitosis and thereby cell multiplication. For example, chalones from rabbit epidermis inhibit mitosis in epidermal cells of most, and perhaps all, species, but are without effect in cells of other tissues. Chalones may play a role in determining the shape and size of organs, and deficiency may be involved in the aetiology of cancer, and in wound-healing.

An obsolete meaning of chalone is a substance that inhibits the action of a **hormone**.

charybdotoxin A basic protein toxin (relative molecular mass about 7000) from the venom of the Israeli scorpion *Leiurus quinquestriatus*. Charybdo-toxin reversibly blocks large Ca^{2+}-activated K^+ channels in mammalian skeletal muscle.

Miller *et al.* (1985) *Nature* **313**, 316

cheese reaction A catch phrase that refers to potentiation by **monoamine oxidase inhibitors** of the pressor actions of indirectly acting sympathomimetic amines, notably tyramine, in certain foods, including some cheeses (but also yeast and meat extracts, pickled herrings and certain wines). A serious hypertensive crisis may arise when patients being treated with monoamine oxidase inhibitors ingest such foods, and they are strongly warned against them by both doctors and pharmacists. The antidepressant action of monoamine oxidase inhibitors is predominantly associated with inhibition of MAO-A. Selective inhibitors of MAO-A might therefore have some advantage, in that MAO-B would be left intact, especially in the gut where it represents the first line of defence against ingested tyramine. (Tyramine is a substrate for both MAO-A and MAO-B.) However, the **noradrenaline** that is released by tyramine from storage granules in sympathetic nerve varicosities would still exert an augmented pressor effect. This noradrenaline is normally largely destroyed by mitochondrial MAO-A before being released. Consequently, any advantages of selective MAO-A inhibition are likely to be limited in so far as the 'cheese reaction' is concerned.

chelating agents Compounds that sequester polyvalent metal ions by forming two or more co-ordinate bonds, or a combination of co-ordinate and ionic bonds. Their main use is in the treatment of heavy metal poisoning. Examples include edetate, pentetate, desferrioxamine and penicillamine.

Some **drugs** possess chelating activity although their therapeutic use is not as chelating agents. Such drugs include tetracyclines and 8-hydroxy-quinolines (Greek: *chele*, a claw).

chemotherapy Literally means therapy with chemicals, i.e. with drugs, but in fact the term is usually restricted to mean drug treatment of cancer and of diseases caused by infecting micro-organisms.

Chen's therapeutic index A risk-benefit ratio derived from data obtained in laboratory animals and calculated from LD_5/LD_{50}. The LD_5 is the lethal dose in 5% of animals in a group (cf. LD_{50}).

chimeric toxin A hybrid toxic protein or glycoprotein formed synthetically by combining, through disulphide bonds, the enzymatically active moiety (i.e. the A-chain) of certain naturally occurring toxins (e.g. **abrin**, **ricin**, modeccin, diphtheria toxin) to a **ligand** moiety that has a selective **affinity** for **receptor** sites on certain cells. Typical ligand moieties include **lectins**, specific sugars, **hormones** or **monoclonal antibodies** to cell-surface **antigens**. The ligand chosen to replace the original B-chain of the naturally occurring toxin depends on the proposed use of the hybrid chimeric toxin. The mechanism of action involves binding of the ligand group to the cell surface of specific cells, followed by release and penetration into the cytosol of the toxic B-chain, which acts to inhibit protein synthesis. Chimeric toxins have potential uses in experimental biology and in therapeutics, including cancer **chemotherapy**, diseases associated with hyperfunction of certain endocrine glands, some allergic conditions in which it might be beneficial to kill those lymphocytes carrying the offending antigen, and in some parasitic diseases (e.g. malaria).

In Greek mythology, a chimera was a monster with a lion's head, a goat's body and a serpent's tail. The use of the adjectival form chimeric, in the present sense, is intended to indicate that the toxin is a hybrid derived from different natural sources.

cholagogue A **drug** that stimulates bile flow from the gall bladder into the intestine. The term includes both **choleretic** and **hydrocholeretic drugs**.

cholera toxin The protein exotoxin secreted by the bacterium *Vibrio cholerae*. Its special interest to pharmacology lies in its ability to activate the enzyme **adenylate cyclase**. Cholera toxin is itself an enzyme that catalyses the transfer of ADP-ribose from intracellular NAD^+ to the GTP-binding (or N_s) protein associated with adenylate cyclase. The result is that the N_s protein can no longer hydrolyse its bound GTP and so it activates adenylate cyclase continuously once an appropriate **agonist** has combined with its **receptor**. Prolonged elevation of **cyclic AMP** in the intestinal epithelium leads to prolonged efflux of Na^+ and accompanying water into the lumen, and so to the pronounced diarrhoea characteristic of cholera.

choleretic drug A drug that stimulates bile formation. Ox bile extract has this action. It contains the sodium salts of bile acids which are absorbed and secreted in the bile, producing increased formation of other bile constituents and increasing bile flow. Ox bile is sometimes used for treating conditions in which there is a non-obstructive deficiency of natural bile. *See also* **hydrocholeretic drug**.

cholestatic effect A type of **hepatotoxicity** in which, for one reason or another, there is stoppage or suppression of the flow of bile. Several drugs may occasionally produce this unwanted effect (e.g. nitrofurantoin, **sulphonamides**, phenindione, tolbutamide, chlorpromazine).

cholinergic crisis Muscle weakness consequent upon excessive use of **anticholinesterase drugs** by patients with **myasthenia gravis**. Temporary withdrawal of the anticholinesterase drug and subsequent readjustment of dose restores the expected beneficial effect.

cholinergic nerve fibre A nerve fibre that releases a choline-like substance (in fact **acetylcholine**) as a neurotransmitter. *See* **adrenergic nerve fibre** for discussion of the restricted use of the suffix '-ergic'.

cholinoceptors Receptors specifically sensitive to **acetylcholine**. Acetylcholine receptors is an alternative term, but cholinergic receptors is not recommended. (*See* **adrenergic nerve fibre** for a discussion of the ending '-ergic'.)

Cholinoceptors are of two main subtypes: **muscarinic** and **nicotinic cholinoceptors**.

cholinomimetic drug A drug that mimics the actions of choline or **acetylcholine**. Examples include carbachol and methacholine.

chromodacryorrhoea The secretion of bloody tears. This is a characteristic response to **agonists** at **muscarinic cholinoceptors** and **anticholinesterase drugs** in the albino rat (Greek: *chroma*, colour; *dacryon*, tear; *rhoea*, to flow).

chromogranins Acidic water-soluble proteins present in the transmitter storage vesicles of **adrenergic nerve fibres** and in chromaffin cells. Some are probably concerned with the binding of **catecholamines** within the vesicles. One of the chromogranins has been identified as the enzyme **dopamine-β-hydroxylase**. Chromogranins are released from the nerve endings and from chromaffin cells along with **noradrenaline** and **adrenaline** (and ATP).

chromone-2-carboxylic acid derivatives *See* **cromoglycate**.

chromones *See* **cromoglycate**.

chromosome damage A complete break or cleavage in one or both strands of the chromosome leading to chromosome deletion, translocation, or duplication. Losses or gains in chromosome number may arise after exposure to certain chemicals.

chronobiology The study of the mechanisms underlying biological rhythms including **circadian rhythms**. Such rhythms can profoundly influence the effects of drugs and other stimuli upon the organism.

chronopharmacology The study of the effects of drugs upon biological rhythms, and the influence of biological rhythms on responses to drugs.

chronotropic response A change in frequency, often applied to the heart. Thus, **adrenaline** produces a positive chronotropic response of the heart (i.e. an increase in beat frequency). **Acetylcholine** produces a negative chronotropic response of the heart (i.e. a decrease in beat frequency). (Greek: *chronos*, time; *trepein*, to turn. Thus, a change in time, e.g. in beat interval.)

chrysotherapy Therapy with gold-containing compounds (Greek: *kriso*, gold) such as sodium aurothiomalate or sodium aurothioglucose. Such treatment is sometimes given to patients with rheumatoid arthritis or lupus erythematosus.

cinchonism A syndrome (tinnitus, impaired hearing, blurred vision, nausea, headache) arising from toxicity of cinchona **alkaloids** (e.g. quinine).

circadian rhythm A biological rhythm that corresponds to the 24-hour rotation of the earth (Latin: *circa*, about; *dies*, day). An example is the more than fourfold variation in serum **corticosteroid** concentration that occurs over 24 hours in man, the peak concentration occurring shortly after rising, at the onset of the active period of the day.

circamensual (adj.) Applies to a biological rhythm with a period of about (*circa*) a lunar month (*mensis*).
> Brady (1979) *Biological Clocks*. Institute of Biology, Studies in Biology No. 104. Edward Arnold, London.

circannual (adj.) Applies to a biological rhythm with a period of about (*circa*) a year (*annus*).
> Brady (1979) *Biological Clocks*. Institute of Biology, Studies in Biology No. 104. Edward Arnold, London.

clearance Refers to the volume of blood or plasma cleared of a drug in unit time (i.e. Cl_B or Cl_P respectively). It is defined as the product of the volume of distribution and the elimination rate constant, i.e.

$$Cl_P = V_D k_{elim}$$

The rate of elimination is given by $Cl_P \times C_P$. If the volume of distribution is in ml, and k_{elim} is in units of min^{-1}, then Cl_P has the dimensions ml/min.

clinical (Greek: *klinicos*, relating to a bed.) Pertaining to a clinic or to patients in bed; pertaining to observation or treatment of patients as distinct from theoretical or basic science. In this latter sense, the word is not restricted to patients in bed despite the etymology of the term.

clyster An injection into the rectum; an **enema** (Greek: *klyster*, a syringe).

coca leaves *See* cocaine.

cocaine An **alkaloid** from the leaves of the shrubs *Erythroxylon coca* and *E. truxillense* which are indigenous to Bolivia and Peru, and cultivated in Java. Cocaine is the prototype **local anaesthetic drug**, although it is now virtually obsolete for this purpose because of its **dependence**-producing liability and other unwanted effects. Cocaine also blocks the re-uptake of **noradrenaline** (uptake 1, *see* **neuronal uptake of noradrenaline**) and may be used in pharmacological experiments for this purpose. The names of synthetic local anaesthetic drugs are usually given the same ending, i.e. '-aine'; thus, procaine, lignocaine, benzocaine, cinchocaine (dibucaine), etc.

co-carcinogen *See* tumour-promoter.

coenzyme Q *See* ubiquinone.

coleonol *See* forskolin.

colistin Polymyxin E. *See* polymyxins.

collyria Solutions intended for application to the conjuctiva: eye lotions. Singular, collyrium.

comedo *See* comedone.

comedolytic action An action to reduce the occurrence of **comedones**. Tretinoin (**vitamin** A acid) is an example of a **drug** with a comedolytic action.

comedone A plug of sebum (usually blackened by the action of light) at the mouth of the follicle of a sebaceous gland, i.e. a 'blackhead' (Latin: *comedo*, a glutton; the term is derived from the fact that the gland and its follicle become engorged with sebum to form a characteristic **acne** papule).

compartments Usually refers to a **pharmacokinetic** concept relating to drug distribution. A compartment refers to those organs and tissues for which the rates of uptake and **clearance** of a **drug** are similar.

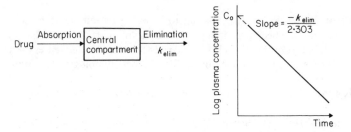

The simplest case is a single-compartment model into which the drug is absorbed and from which it is eliminated. The graph of log plasma concentration against time is a straight line.

This simple one-compartment model for pharmacokinetic analysis is not valid when the rate of passage of a drug between the plasma and some other compartment(s) of the body is rate-limiting in the attainment of equilibrium. The plot of log plasma concentration against time is then a curve rather than a straight line. The simplest multi-compartment model is with two compartments. Elimination usually occurs from the central compartment. An example of an exception to this would be the **neuro-muscular blocking drug** atracurium, which is partly destroyed at its site of action by **Hofmann elimination**.

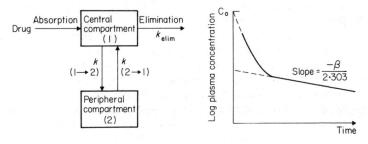

Three-compartment models have been invoked to account for the pharmacokinetics of a few drugs, e.g. dicoumarol and the neuromuscular blocking drug, vecuronium.

competitive antagonist A drug that interacts reversibly with a set of **receptors** to form a complex that excludes the **agonist**; the antagonist–receptor complex does not elicit a response because the **intrinsic activity** of the **antagonist drug** is zero. The quantitative analysis of competitive antagonism was described by Gaddum (1937, *J. Physiol.* **89**, 7), Schild (1947, *Brit. J. Pharmacol.* **2**, 189) and Arunlakshana and Schild (1959, *Brit. J. Pharmacol.* **14**, 48). The log concentration–effect curve for the agonist should, in the presence of the competitive antagonist, simply be shifted to the right without any change in its slope or amplitude, and the extent of this shift (the dose ratio, r) should be linearly related to [A] according to the equation:

$$r - 1 = [A]/K_A$$

where A is the antagonist and K_A is the equilibrium constant for the antagonist–receptor complex. A competitive antagonist is traditionally defined as one that is surmountable by excess agonist. Some antagonists do, however, combine irreversibly with the receptors and these are defined in this volume under **irreversible receptor antagonist**. *See also* **noncompetitive antagonist** for a different kind of antagonism, and for a comparison with competitive antagonism.

competitive inhibitor   A drug that inhibits an enzyme-catalysed reaction in a competitive manner. The inhibitor and the substrate combine reversibly with the same site on the enzyme, so that the one excludes the other. The maximum rate of reaction obtainable in the presence of the inhibitor is the same as in its absence, given a sufficiently high concentration of substrate.

For a competitive inhibitor it can be shown that:

$$\frac{1}{v} = \frac{1}{V} + \frac{(1 + i/K_i)K_m}{V} \times \frac{1}{s}$$

where v = the reaction rate for the decomposition of the enzyme–substrate complex, V = the maximal rate of reaction (i.e. V_{max}), i = concentration of inhibitor, K_i = the dissociation constant for the inhibitor–enzyme complex, K_m = the dissociation constant for the enzyme–substrate complex (i.e. the Michaelis–Menten constant, *see* **Michaelis–Menten equation**), and s = the original concentration of substrate. The graph of $1/v$ against $1/s$ (**Lineweaver–Burk plot**) is a straight line for the reaction in the presence of the inhibitor (Fig. a), just as it is in the absence of inhibitor. The slope of the line of the inhibited reaction is steeper, the difference in slope being proportional to the inhibitor concentration. The intercept on the abscissa ($1/v = 0$) is $-1/K_m$ in the absence of inhibitor and $-1/(K_m[1 + i/K_i])$ in its presence. The inhibitor has increased the apparent K_m for the substrate.

A plot of $1/v$ against i is also a straight line with the following equation:

$$\frac{1}{v} = \frac{1}{V}(1 + K_m/s) + (iK_m/sK_i)$$

If the substrate concentration is changed, the slope changes and the intercept on the $1/v$ axis ($i = 0$) changes, but if the lines are extrapolated they intersect at a point whose co-ordinates correspond to the value of $-K_i$ on the abscissa (i axis) and $1/V$ on the ordinate ($1/v$ axis).

confidence level

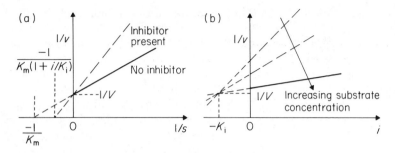

Competitive enzyme inhibition. (a) Lineweaver–Burk plot. The maximum obtainable rate, $1/V$, is the same whether the inhibitor is present or not. (b) Plots of $1/v$ against inhibitor concentration, i, using three different concentrations of substrate. In the case of competitive inhibition, the extrapolated portions of the lines intersect at the same point, corresponding to $-K_i$ on the abscissa and $1/V$ on the ordinate.

confidence level Given by 1 minus the probability, or 100 minus the percentage probability. The rejection of a **null hypothesis** may be given with the confidence level at which the hypothesis is rejected. The confidence level is $1 - P$ (or $100 - P\%$), where P is the probability of the null hypothesis. For example, a difference which is regarded as statistically significant with $P = 0.05$ (or $P\% = 5$) could be expressed as a difference at the 0.95 (or 95%) confidence level.

contracture Gasser (1930) defined a contracture as a muscle contraction 'in which tension, heat and lactic acid are produced and the active portion of the muscle becomes negative. Only conduction of the mechanical response and a wave-like action potential are missing.' Thus, the muscle shortening or tension increase produced by, for example, **acetylcholine** in a chronically denervated skeletal muscle, or in certain muscles composed of multiply innervated fibres, fulfils Gasser's definition of a contracture, in that the contraction is accompanied by an overall membrane depolarization which is not propagated. However, the term is commonly used merely to denote a slowly developing and prolonged contraction of whatever cause, including a pathological change in the contractile mechanism. In the latter case, it is defined as a condition of fixed high resistance to passive stretch.

Gasser (1930) *Physiol. Rev.* **10**, 35

converting enzyme inhibitors Drugs that inhibit the converting enzyme (dipeptidyl carboxypeptidase) that catalyses the cleavage of **angiotensin** I to form angiotensin II. The same enzyme also degrades **bradykinin**. Examples of converting enzyme inhibitors include captopril and enalapril. They are useful **antihypertensive drugs**.

$$\text{HS—CH}_2\text{—CH—CO—N}$$

with CH$_3$ group on the CH and COOH on the pyrrolidine ring

Captopril

Captopril was tailor-made to fit the known active site of the enzyme. It is ironic therefore that the mechanism of its antihypertensive action depends only partly on inhibition of converting enzyme and consequent reduced production of angiotensin II. Additional mechanisms probably include a reduction in sympathetic tone.

convulsant drug   A drug that produces convulsions (Latin: *convellere*, to pull together), i.e. a violent contraction or series of contractions of the voluntary muscles, evoked by an action within the central nervous system. If the convulsions arise predominantly from an action within the brain they are usually of the alternating contraction and relaxation type, i.e. clonic convulsions. Picrotoxin, **bicuculline**, bemegride and leptazole are examples of convulsant drugs that produce clonic convulsions. If the convulsions arise predominantly from an action in the spinal cord, they are usually of the sustained tetanic or tonic type. Strychnine is an example of a convulsant drug that produces tonic convulsions.

co-operativity   Facilitation of binding of a second and/or subsequent small molecule to a macromolecule as a consequence of the binding of the first molecule. For example, the binding of the first O$_2$ to deoxyhaemo-globin is characterized by a relatively low affinity constant (*see* **affinity**), and significant energy is required for O$_2$ association. However, when an O$_2$ association does occur it induces a conformational change in the haemoglobin molecule that facilitates the binding (i.e. lower energy is required) of the other three O$_2$ molecules to the other haem sites. There is evidence that some agonist–receptor binding (*see* **agonist–receptor interaction**) is also co-operative. For example, the binding of one **acetylcholine** molecule to a **nicotinic cholinoceptor** may co-operatively facilitate the binding of a second acetylcholine molecule.

Negative co-operativity also occurs. For example, the binding of **insulin** to its **receptors** inhibits further binding and hastens dissociation from the receptors. This mechanism ensures greater responses at lower concentrations of insulin with decreasing reactivity as concentration increases.

cordial   Literally a heart tonic—obsolete use. Now used simply to mean a non-alcoholic drink with a fruit base.

coronary vasodilator drugs   Drugs that dilate the coronary arteries and arterioles of the heart. Examples include nifedipine, perhexilene, and organic nitrates. The question as to whether such drugs are able to dilate diseased atheromatous coronary vessels in angina pectoris is a matter of some controversy. Their value in angina pectoris may be due to a different action.

corticosteroid blocking drugs   Drugs that block the actions of **corticosteroids**. The compound RU34486 [17β-hydroxy-11β-(4-dimethylaminophenyl)-17α-(prop-l-ynyl)-estra-4,9-dien-3-one] is an example. It also blocks progesterone.

> Philibert *et al.* (1982) RU34486—a new lead for steroidal anti-hormones. 64th Annual Meeting Endocrine Society, San Francisco. Abst. 668.

RU34486

corticosteroids   The steroid **hormones** synthesized and secreted by the adrenal cortex. The main ones are hydrocortisone, corticosterone, aldosterone and dehydroepiandrosterone. Some authors use the term more loosely to include synthetic analogues of the naturally occurring compounds in addition to the endogenous ones. Synthetic analogues include cortisone, fludrocortisone, prednisolone and dexamethasone among several others.

co-transmitter   A substance that is released from a nerve ending by nerve impulses along with the main transmitter, and that serves to modulate the efficiency of the main transmitter. Conclusive evidence for the existence of co-transmitters that function in this way is lacking, but there is suggestive evidence at some sites. Many central axons, in addition to the main transmitter, contain one or more polypeptides that may function in this way, and it has been proposed that ATP or **neuropeptide Y** may serve a co-transmitter function in some **noradrenergic nerve fibres**. *See also* **benzodiazepine receptors**.

cough suppressant   *See* **antitussive drug**.

counter-irritants   Substances that relieve a troublesome irritation by producing a more pronounced but less unpleasant sensation. The effect of the counter-irritant is thought to take precedence and partly divert the attention of the brain away from the original painful stimuli. It is common experience that scratching the skin with the finger nails (a counter-irritant) relieves itching. The concept of counter-irritation has long been made use of in **rubifacient** liniments and ointments for application to the skin to relieve pain in underlying muscles. They contain irritant substances that stimulate sensory nerve endings and they cause cutaneous vasodilatation and a feeling of warmth. Counter-irritants include methyl salicylate, capsaicin, camphor, menthol and oil of turpentine.

cromoglycate   An **antiallergic drug** of the chromone-2-carboxylic acid series. It was discovered by Cox and co-workers as a result of attempts to develop the smooth muscle relaxant action of the related naturally occurring substance khellin (from the seeds of *Ammi visnaga*). In fact, cromoglycate is not a smooth muscle relaxant, but during the screening programme it was found to have a unique action in that it prevented subsequent **antigen**-induced bronchospasm in a volunteer with atopic asthma. Subsequent experiments showed that cromoglycate prevents the release of mediators from mast cells, and this has been assumed to be its mechanism of action. However, some doubt has been cast on the idea that this is the sole or even the main mechanism of action in man. Cromoglycate has been shown to reduce the discharge in afferent C fibres from the lung subjected to a sensory stimulus. Since bronchospasm is usually provoked by stimulation of lung sensory receptors, attenuation of this effect of cromoglycate may be an important component of its action.

Many antiallergic compounds related to cromoglycate have been synthesized and tested, but none has proved successful in the long-term prophylaxis of asthma or allergic rhinitis. Hence cromoglycate holds a unique place, which is the reason for its inclusion here as an item in its own right.

Sodium cromoglycate

crotamine   A basic polypeptide toxin isolated from the venom of the rattlesnake *Crotalus durissus terrificus* var. *crotaminicus*. It appears to act by activating sodium channels in muscle fibre membranes, thereby producing depolarization and **contracture**. Its action is prevented by **tetrodotoxin**.

crotoxin   The major toxic component of the venom of the Brazilian rattlesnake, *Crotalus durissus terrificus*. It both prevents the release of **acetylcholine** from **cholinergic nerve fibre** endings and prevents the response to acetylcholine at the neuromuscular junction.

Bon & Jeng (1979) In *Advances in Cytopharmacology*, Vol. 3 (Eds. Ceccarelli & Clementi). Raven Press, New York.

curare An extract made from the South American plants *Chondrodendron tomentosum* or *Strychnos toxifera* and used as an arrow poison for hunting game by South American Indians (e.g. in Peru). The word 'curare' is said to be derived from local words meaning 'bird' and 'to kill', and is supposed to have been first used in Europe by one of Sir Walter Raleigh's officers on their return from South America. Curare made from *C. tomentosum* was often packed in bamboo tubes (tube curare) and its principal **alkaloid** is tubocurarine. Curare made from *S. toxifera* was often packed in gourds or pots (pot curare) and its principal alkaloid is toxiferine I. Claude Bernard published the first convincing experiments to determine the site of action of curare in the early 1850s. **Neuromuscular blocking drugs** are often called curare-like drugs.

curare-like drugs *See* **neuromuscular blocking drug.**

curariform drug An alternative name for **curarimimetic drug.**

curarimimetic drug A drug with the properties of **curare**; that is, a **neuromuscular blocking drug.** Gallamine and pancuronium are examples.

cyanogens Substances that generate cyanide (HCN) in the body. Several foods may contain cyanogens and are toxic if incorrectly prepared for consumption. Such foods include cassava, bitter almonds, immature bamboo shoot tips and some varieties of Lima beans.

Laetrile is a substance consisting largely of amygdalin obtained from apricot stones. It is a cyanogen and is claimed to be broken down selectively in cancer cells by β-glucuronidase to yield benzaldehyde and HCN, the latter in sufficient quantities to kill malignant cells. However, there is no convincing evidence of efficacy of laetrile in cancer therapy, and its sale is banned in many countries, both because of its toxicity and because it may deter patients from seeking proper treatment.

cyclic adenosine 3′,5′-monophosphate *See* **cyclic AMP.**

cyclic AMP A cyclic nucleotide formed by an intramolecular condensation of ATP under the influence of the enzyme **adenylate cyclase** which is present in the plasma membranes of most cells. Cyclic AMP has the property of phosphorylating **protein kinase**, which in turn phosphorylates other proteins, thereby either activating or inactivating their enzymatic functions. Membrane **receptors** for several **hormones** (the first messengers) are coupled to adenylate cyclase. The hormone–receptor interaction activates adenylate cyclase so that cyclic AMP (the **second messenger**) is formed, and brings about the appropriate cellular response. Although cyclic AMP plays a wide role as a second messenger, control is exerted at two points in the system: (1) whether the cell membrane possesses specific receptors for the particular hormone, and (2) whether the cytosol possesses particular enzymes that are activated by phosphorylated protein kinase.

Hormones that act through an adenylate cyclase–cyclic AMP system include **adrenaline** and **noradrenaline** acting on β-**adrenoceptors**, glucagon, vasopressin, parathyroid hormone, thyrotrophin, corticotrophin, leutenizing hormone and melanocyte stimulating hormone.

cyclic GMP Cyclic guanosine 3',5'-monophosphate. The cyclic nucleotide formed from guanosine triphosphate (GTP) under the influence of the enzyme guanylate cyclase. For further details regarding its second messenger role, see **guanylate cyclase** (and cf. **adenylate cyclase**).

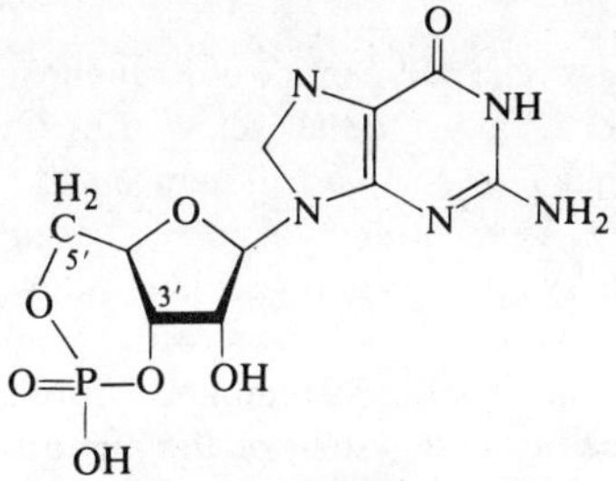

Cyclic GMP

cyclic guaninosine 3',5'-monophosphate *See* cyclic GMP.

cyclic nucleotide phosphodiesterases *See* **phosphodiesterases**.

cyclo-oxygenase The **prostaglandin** synthase complex of enzymes which catalyses the biosynthesis of prostaglandins from polyunsaturated fatty acids. The major pathway is from arachidonic acid derived from cell membrane phospholipids. The step catalysed by cyclo-oxygenase, a microsomal enzyme, is the cyclization of carbon atoms 8–12 of arachidonic acid to form the cyclic endoperoxide 15-hydroperoxide (PGG$_2$); the reaction requires two moles of molecular oxygen.

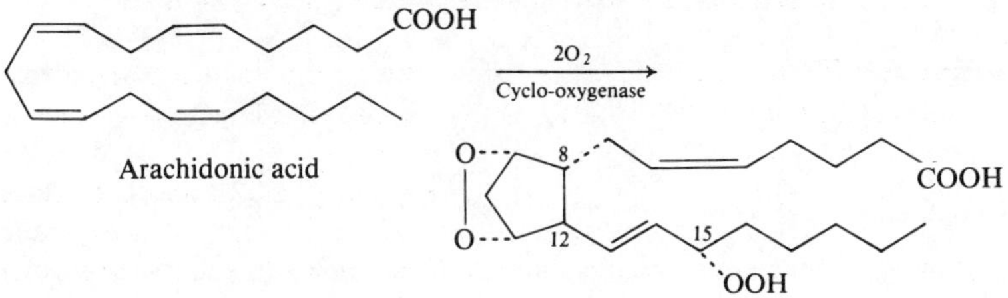

Arachidonic acid

PGG$_2$

cyclo-oxygenase inhibitors **Drugs** that inhibit **cyclo-oxygenases** directly and irreversibly include aspirin, indomethacin and other **nonsteroidal anti-inflammatory drugs**.

Steroidal anti-inflammatory drugs (**glucocorticoids**), including hydrocortisone, prednisolone, and betamethasone, reduce the availability of the substrate (arachidonic acid) for cyclo-oxygenase by inhibiting **phospholipase** A_2 (*see* **phospholipase** A_2 **inhibitors**). Phospholipase A_2 catalyses the release of arachidonic acid from membrane phospholipids.

cyclopyrrolones   A class of central nervous system depressant drugs with pharmacological actions similar to those of the **benzodiazepines**. Like the benzodiazepines they act at sites related to the **$GABA_A$ receptors**, although these sites are not the **benzodiazepine receptors**. Examples of this class of drugs include zopiclone (**hypnotic drug**) and suriclone (**antianxiety agent**).

cyclosporin A   A cyclic polypeptide of 11 amino acids, one of which (given the name C9-ene) is unique to the cyclosporins. Cyclosporins are obtained from the soil fungi *Trichoderma polysporum* and *Cylindrocarpon lucidium*. Cyclosporin A was first found to possess weak antifungal activity (by inhibiting chitin synthesis), but was later shown to exert marked immunomodulatory action. It acts by selectively inhibiting that part of the immune system that relies on T-lymphocyte proliferation, but it does not interfere with the myeloid system or the humoral system. Consequently, previously acquired immunity and immunity involving the myeloid and humoral systems are unimpaired.

Cyclosporin A has an important clinical role in immunosuppression to prevent rejection of transplants (kidney, pancreas, liver, heart, heart and lung, bone marrow) and in the control of autoimmune diseases.

Cyclosporins C and G also possess **immunosuppressant** activity.

White (1982) *Drugs* **24**, 322

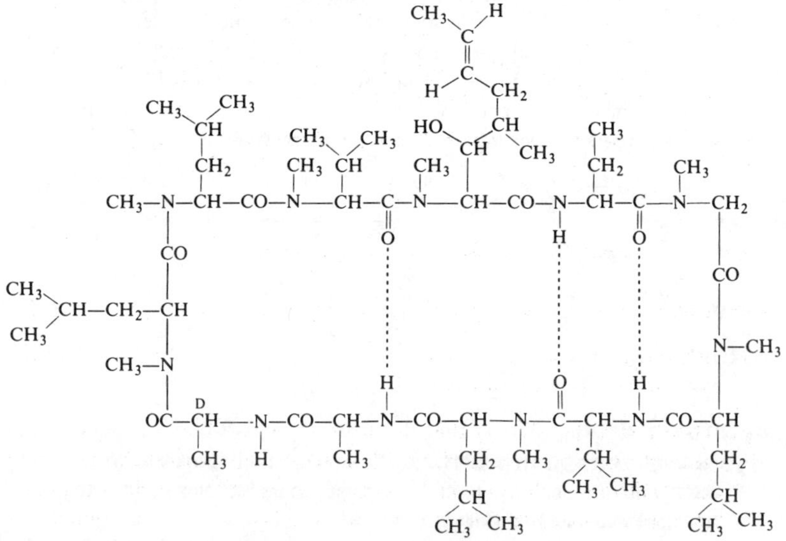

Cyclosporin A. All amino acids have L-configuration except for the alanine labelled D

cytochalasins   A class of more than 20 metabolites obtained from various moulds. The most widely studied is cytochalasin B, which was formerly called phomin because it was isolated from moulds of *Phoma* species. The main actions of cytochalasin B depend upon its ability to disorganize contractile actin microfilaments in cells. The actions include blockage of cytoplasmic cleavage in telophase so that multinucleate cells are formed, inhibition of cell movement, induction of nuclear extrusion, inhibition of Na^+-independent glucose transport, inhibition of thyroid secretion and of growth hormone release, and inhibition of phagocytosis, of platelet aggregation and of clot retraction. In general, cytochalasins are used as tools in cytological research.

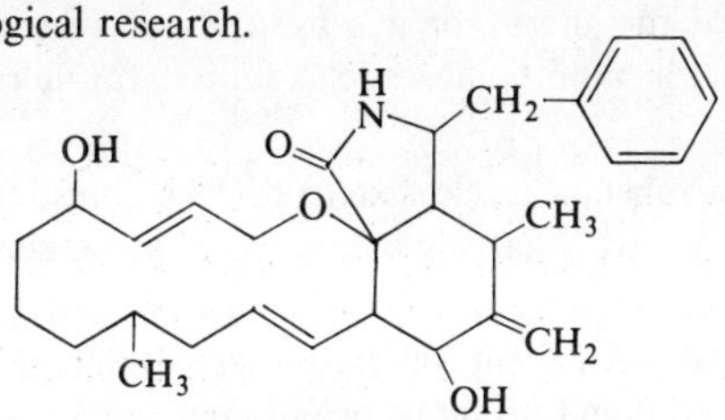

Cytochalasin B

cytochrome P$_{450}$ The cytochrome component of an electron transport chain that is present in the endoplasmic reticulum of liver and some other cells. It is unique to the endoplasmic reticulum, being absent from the mitochondrial electron transport chain. The 450 denotes the fact that the reduced form of the cytochrome has an absorption band at 450 nm. ATP is not synthesized by this endoplasmic reticulum system. Its primary function is in the hydroxylation of various metabolites, and it plays an important part in the metabolism of certain drugs (e.g. phenobarbitone, steroids, sterols, fatty acids, polycyclic hydrocarbons and some amino acids). The place of cytochrome P$_{450}$ in the chain is illustrated below.

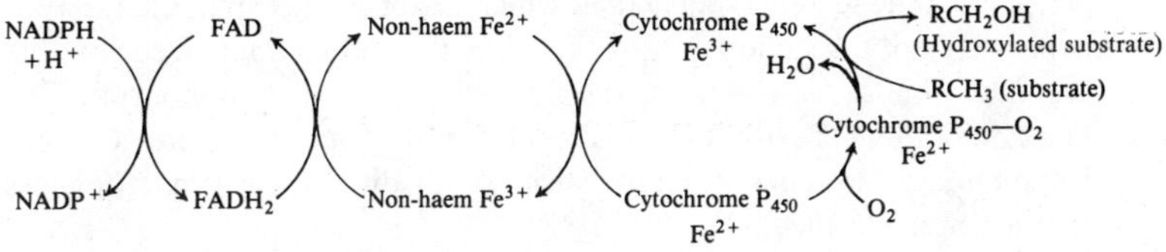

cytokine   A **biological response modifier** produced by a range of cell types.

cytopharmacology   The study of drug action on cells (Greek: *cytos*, a receptacle or a cell; *pharmakon*, drug).

cytotoxic drugs   Drugs that are toxic to cells. Many are used in the **chemotherapy** of neoplastic disease (e.g. **alkylating agents** such as mustine, **antimetabolites** such as methotrexate, certain **antibiotics** such as daunorubicin, some plant **alkaloids** such as vinblastine, and a number of miscellaneous compounds including procarbazine, cisplatin, and milotane). Some cytotoxic drugs are also used as **immunosuppressants.**

Dale–Schultz reaction   An anaphylactic reaction (*see* **anaphylaxis**) in an isolated smooth muscle. An isolated smooth muscle, taken from an animal which has been sensitized with **antigen**, contracts when the antigen is applied to it in an isolated organ bath. Dale and Schultz did not work together on this phenomenon but each did much to elucidate the mechanism (*see*, for example, Dale (1913) *J. Pharmacol. exp. Ther.* **4**, 167). The Dale–Schultz reaction has historical importance in that it demonstrated that **antibody** can become fixed to tissue cells, since the reaction occurs equally in tissues that have been thoroughly washed free of blood. It also demonstrated that **histamine** can not be the sole mediator of the response, since the uterus of a sensitized rat responds to antigen by contraction, yet histamine causes relaxation of rat uterine smooth muscle.

Darmstoff   A substance released from frog intestine (German: *Darm*, intestine), known to be largely composed of **prostaglandins** E_1 and $F_{1\alpha}$.

debriding agent   An agent (often an enzyme) that assists in the removal of foreign material and fibrinous or purulent exudate from a wound until surrounding healthy tissue is exposed. The word probably comes from the French word meaning to unbridle (*débridement*), although it may have been confused with débris which has a different origin (French: *briser*, to break).

delayed hypersensitivity reactions   These belong to the group of T-cell mediated immunological reactions which include transplantation and cancer immunity as well as defence mechanisms against many viruses, protozoa and certain bacteria (e.g. tubercle and leprosy). **Antigen**, presented by macrophages, causes proliferation of T-lymphocytes with specific antigen-reactive sites. When these cells react with antigen in the periphery, they secrete **lymphokines** which activate macrophages. Delayed hypersensitivity reactions in the periphery are characterized by the accumulation of activated macrophages as well as lymphocytes. The function of these effector T-cells is regulated by means of suppressor T- or B-lymphocytes that may react specifically with antigen, or by macrophages that act non-specifically.

Consequently, delayed hypersensitivity reactions can be enhanced by substances that either increase effector T-cell function (e.g. bacterial **endotoxin**, thymic hormones, **transfer factor**, lymphokines, levamisole, adriamycin) or reduce suppressor cell function (e.g. cyclophosphamide, **cyclosporin-A**).

Turk & Parker (1984) *Trends pharmacol. Sci.* **5**, 472

deliriants   A general term for substances such as aerosol propellants, fuels, glue solvents, etc. with the common pharmacological property of producing general anaesthesia to at least stage 2, excitement or delirium.

delta sleep-inducing peptide A nonapeptide (Trp–Ala–Gly–Gly–Asp–Ala–Ser–Gly–Glu) extracted from the venous blood of rabbits in which sleep had been induced by electrical stimulation of the thalamus. The substance has been reported to produce slow-wave sleep, with EEG activity predominantly in the delta band, when injected into other rabbits. Similar sleep-promoting effects are produced in man, and in addition the substance is reported to improve alertness and stress tolerance during the subsequent awake period.

demulcent A substance used to coat mucous membranes. Demulcents are colloidal solutions of a gum or protein and are effective to some extent in protecting mucous membranes from irritation. For example, milk has a demulcent action in protecting the stomach from the irritant action of alcoholic beverages.

dendrotoxin A polypeptide toxin from the venom of the Eastern green mamba, *Dendroaspis angusticeps*. It increases the evoked, but not the spontaneous, release of **acetylcholine** from somatic motor nerve endings and hence facilitates neuromuscular transmission. It is highly potent and does not damage the nerve terminals. It appears to bind tightly to an important site involved in the transmitter release mechanism. Dendrotoxin is not selective for the neuromuscular junction. It also facilitates transmitter release at autonomic noradrenergic junctions and at central synapses. The molecule of dendrotoxin contains 59 amino acid residues held together by three disulphide bridges.

denervation supersensitivity Supersensitivity of a tissue to the transmitter and related **agonists** arising after severence and degeneration of the efferent nerve supply. The phenomenon has been studied most intensively in skeletal muscle, which exhibits increased sensitivity to **acetylcholine** and other nicotinic agonists, in the ciliary muscle and salivary glands, which show an increased sensitivity to acetylcholine and other muscarinic agonists, and in the nictitating membrane of the cat which exhibits increased sensitivity to **noradrenaline**. The phenomenon is largely explained by **up-regulation of receptors**. In skeletal muscle there is also a spread of **receptors** to involve the whole muscle fibre membrane instead of just the motor endplate region. This effect arises because some as yet unidentified trophic influence of the nerve normally limits the synthesis of acetylcholine receptors to the endplate region.

An additional factor involved in the increased sensitivity to acetylcholine in skeletal muscle is that the spreading new **cholinoceptors** are not associated with **acetylcholinesterase**. In a sympathetically innervated tissue degeneration of the **noradrenergic nerve fibres** removes the neuronal uptake (*see* **neuronal uptake of noradrenaline**) process and this contributes to the increased sensitivity to noradrenaline.

deodorants Preparations intended to reduce body odour. Body odour is usually the result of bacterial decomposition of sweat. Deodorants usually contain a skin disinfectant, such as hexachlorophane, to restrict bacterial activity, and a perfume to mask other odours. Some also contain an **antiperspirant drug.**

dependence *See* **drug dependence.**

depilation *See* **depilatory agents.**

depilatory agents Agents that facilitate the removal of hair (Latin: *de*, away; *pilus*, hair). The softening action of reducing agents on keratin allows unwanted hair to be gently scraped away (depilation). Agents used for this purpose include barium sulphide and thioglycolic acid and its calcium salt, which are usually applied in a paste.

depolarization block Conduction block arising from a persistent fall in membrane potential. In excitable membranes, such as those of nerve and skeletal muscle, a prolonged fall in membrane potential (produced by cathodal current or by a **drug**) causes the voltage-sensitive sodium channels, which initially have been opened, to close again (inactivation). At the same time, the voltage-sensitive potassium channels remain open. These delayed effects of prolonged depolarization oppose excitation, and so conduction block occurs. (It should be recalled that a brief depolarization is an excitatory stimulus, but prolonged depolarization has the opposite effect.) **Batrachotoxin** and KCl are examples of substances that depolarize excitable membranes and thereby produce initial excitation followed by conduction block.

The term is most commonly used to describe a particular type of neuromuscular block that occurs in focally innervated skeletal muscle fibres. Prolonged action of an **agonist** at the **nicotinic cholinoceptors** of the motor endplate produces a long-lasting endplate potential. This standing depolarization in the middle of a surrounding expanse of normal muscle fibre membrane causes persistent local circuit currents to flow into the endplate region from the surrounding membrane. Inactivation of the Na^+ channels in the immediately surrounding membrane, and therefore a zone of conduction block, is set up. Consequently, nerve impulses can no longer excite the muscle fibre to contract, and flaccid paralysis ensues. Drugs (agonists) that produce endplate depolarization leading to neuromuscular block include **acetylcholine** itself under appropriate circumstances (i.e. large doses and previously inhibited **acetylcholinesterase**), nicotine, decamethonium, succinylcholine (suxamethonium), carbolonium (hexacarbacholine) and dioxonium. Of these, only succinylcholine is extensively used in anaesthetic practice. Although these drugs are capable of producing true depolarization block under appropriate conditions, their action is often more complex than this, in that initially there is block by depolarization but subsequently the action may change to an indeterminate type of block (called **phase 2 neuromuscular block**) which to some extent resembles block produced by a **curare**-like drug. *See also* **dual block**.

depolarizing neuromuscular blocking drugs Drugs that produce **depolarization block** at the neuromuscular junction in skeletal muscle. The main drug of this type used in anaesthetic practice is succinylcholine (suxamethonium).

dermorphin A heptapeptide (Tyr–D-Ala–Phe–Gly–Tyr–Pro–Ser–NH$_2$) isolated from the skin of South American frogs of the *Phylomedusae* family. It possesses powerful **opioid** activity, being many times more potent than met-enkephalin.

desensitization *See* **receptor desensitization**.

detoxification *See* **drug metabolism**.

diabetogenic drugs Drugs that produce diabetes mellitus by damaging the B-cells of the islets of Langerhans. Such drugs include **alloxan**, the **antineoplastic drugs** streptozotocin and hexamethylmelamine, the **antihistamine**–antiserotonin **drug** cyproheptadine, the antitrypanosome drug pentamidine, and the rodenticide Vacor (*N*-3-pyridylmethyl *N'*-*p*-nitrophenyl urea). Alloxan and its metabolites probably produce damage by giving rise to **free radicals**. Streptozotocin also has this effect, but mainly acts through its alkylating properties, the end effect being depletion of NAD$^+$. Cyproheptadine and hexamethylmelamine inhibit the synthesis of proinsulin. Vacor depletes NAD$^+$ by an unknown mechanism. The mechanisms through which the toxic actions of these drugs are particularly directed towards the islets of Langerhans is not known.

diacylglycerol A **second messenger** that activates **protein kinase C**. *See* **PI response**.

diaphoretic drug A drug that promotes excessive sweating whether or not body temperature is raised. Sudorific is an alternative name. The **parasympathomimetic drug** pilocarpine has this action. Its use for this purpose is now obsolete, but it was formerly used to remove excess water and urea, via the sweat, in nephritis. It may still be used as a diagnostic agent to determine whether anhidrosis (absence of sweating) is the result of failure of the sweat glands, in which case pilocarpine is inactive, or to loss of their innervation, in which case pilocarpine is active (Greek: *dia*, idea of motion through; *phorein*, carry).

dibenzazepines Drugs having a dibenzazepine nucleus in their chemical structures. Such drugs include azapetine, which is an α-**adrenoceptor**

antagonist with vasodilator action, **tricyclic antidepressant drugs** such as imipramine and desipramine, and the **anticonvulsant drug** carbamazepine.

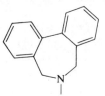

Dibenz[*b*,*f*]azepine (as in imipramine and carbamazepine)

Dibenz[*c*,*e*]azepine (as in azapetine)

dibucaine number Dibucaine has the property of inhibiting plasma cholinesterase. Normal plasma cholinesterase is inhibited by more than 71% by 10^{-5} mol/l dibucaine. Atypical plasma cholinesterase in atypical homozygotes is inhibited by less than 30%. The percentage inhibition of the enzyme by 10^{-5} mol/l of dibucaine when the substrate is 10^{-3} mol/l benzoylcholine chloride is called the dibucaine number. Anaesthetists make use of the dibucaine number as an indication of a patient's ability to metabolize succinylcholine. The value is determined if the anaesthetist suspects any abnormality of plasma cholinesterase in the patient.

Dibucaine is the United States Pharmacopoeia name for the drug called cinchocaine in the UK. It was originally synthesized for use as a **local anaesthetic drug** and it continues to be used for this purpose.

digitalization *See* **loading dose.**

dioxin *See* **2,4,5-T.**

disabling agents *See* **incapacitating agents.**

dissociation constant of an agonist *See* **agonist–receptor interaction.**

dissociative anaesthesia *See* **general anaesthetic drug.**

diuretic drug A **drug** that increases the rate of production of urine, in particular (for therapeutic purposes) by increasing the excretion of sodium ions (Greek: *diourein*, to urinate). Examples of diuretic drugs include **mercurial diuretic drugs, thiazide diuretic drugs, loop diuretics, carbonic anhydrase inhibitors, aldosterone antagonist drugs** and **potassium-sparing diuretic drugs.**

Dixon plot A method of testing for competitive antagonism (*see* **competitive antagonist**) in which $1/y$ (y is the response as a fraction of the maximal response) is plotted against antagonist concentration [A]. The equation is:

$$\frac{1}{y} = [A]\left(\frac{K_D}{K_A[D]}\right) + \frac{K_D}{[D]} + 1$$

where K_A is the dissociation constant of the antagonist, K_D is the dissociation constant of the **agonist**, and [D] is the concentration of agonist. For competitive antagonism, the equation predicts that the plot will be a straight line with a slope that is inversely proportional to the agonist concentration, and that the lines for different concentrations of the agonist will intersect at a point with co-ordinates corresponding to $-K_A$ on the [A] axis and the maximal response (i.e. 1) on the $1/y$ axis.

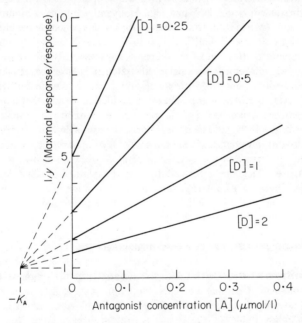

Dixon plots: reciprocal of response against antagonist concentration for various concentrations of agonist ([D]), taking $K_D = 1$, $K_A = 0.1$, and other parameters as shown on the plots.

dominant lethal test A test for the production of a mutation in a germ cell that may result in the immediate death of the fertilized egg, or in the later death and abortion of the young embryo. Dominant lethal tests are applied to new chemicals to which man and animals may be exposed.

Bateman (1977) In *Handbook of Mutagenicity Test Procedures* (Ed. Kilbey), p. 325. Elsevier North Holland, Amsterdam.

dopa An acronym of *d*ihydr*o*xyphenyl*a*lanine, the L-isomer being the biological amino acid precursor of the **catecholamines**. The L-isomer (levodopa) is also used as a **drug** in the therapy of parkinsonism.

dopa decarboxylase A cytoplasmic enzyme (EC 4.1.1.26) present in kidney and liver cells and in **adrenergic nerve fibres** and chromaffin cells. It catalyses the decarboxylation of **dopa** with the formation of **dopamine**. It requires pyridoxal phosphate as a coenzyme. The enzyme also catalyses the decarboxylation of other aromatic amino acids including *meta*-tyrosine and 5-hydroxytryptophan. For this reason it is also called aromatic amino acid decarboxylase.

dopa decarboxylase inhibitors Drugs that inhibit the enzyme **dopa decarboxylase**. Such drugs include carbidopa, benserazide, α-methyl-5-hydroxytryptophan, 3-hydroxybenzyloxyamine and DL-α-monofluoromethyldopa (MFMD). Carbidopa and benserazide penetrate the blood–brain barrier only poorly and are used in Parkinson's disease to prevent the peripheral conversion of levodopa to **dopamine**. MFMD is an enzyme-activated inhibitor (i.e. a **suicide substrate**). It is decarboxylated to yield a highly reactive intermediate which alkylates the enzyme and irreversibly inhibits it. MFMD is an example of a series of irreversible inhibitors of this type. The enzyme dopa decarboxylase (or aromatic amino acid decarboxylase, EC 4.1.1.26) catalyses the conversion of **dopa** to dopamine, of 5-hydroxytryptophan to **serotonin**, and of tryptophan to tryptamine.

dopamine The amine formed by decarboxylation of **dopa** (dihydroxyphenylalanine). An alternative name for dopamine is 3-hydroxytyramine. Dopamine is the immediate precursor of **noradrenaline** and is also the transmitter of **dopaminergic nerve fibres**.

dopamine agonists *See* **dopaminomimetic drugs**.

dopamine antagonists Drugs that antagonize the actions of **dopamine** by blocking **dopamine receptors**. Dopamine antagonists include many of the **neuroleptic** antipsychotic **drugs** such as chlorpromazine, haloperidol and pimozide.

dopamine-β-hydroxylase The enzyme that catalyses the conversion of **dopamine** to **noradrenaline**. It requires ascorbic acid as a cofactor. Dopamine-β-hydroxylase is present in the **catecholamine** storage particles. It acts on a range of substrates that are derivatives of phenylethylamine (e.g. tyramine → octopamine; epinine → **adrenaline**). An alternative name is phenylethylamine-β-hydroxylase.

   The enzyme is inhibited by various hydrazine and oxyamine derivatives, including 3-hydroxy-4-bromobenzyl oxyamine, diethyldithiocarbamic acid, 1-phenyl-3-(2-thiazoyl)-2-thiourea.

dopamine receptors Receptors specifically sensitive to **dopamine**. Most authorities believe that a number of (at least two) subtypes exist, but there is some confusion regarding their classification. Other workers consider that a single dopamine receptor type is in accordance with the evidence.

Dopamine receptors have been subclassified according to location: thus, (1) postsynaptic receptors on the innervated cell, (2) **autoreceptors** on the cell body and dendrites of the **dopaminergic nerve fibre** which determine the frequency of the impulses passed down the axon, and (3) presynaptic receptors on dopaminergic and other types of nerve terminals that control transmitter release. Another classification refers to class I receptors for which both **agonists** and antagonists have a high **affinity**, class II receptors for which agonists have high, and antagonists low, affinity, and class III receptors for which antagonists have high, and agonists low, affinity. A third classification depends on behavioural effects after intracerebral injection of various agonists and antagonists in rats and cats. According to this classification, DA_e receptors mediate excitatory effects, and DA_i receptors mediate inhibitory effects, on behaviour. Perhaps the most widely accepted subclassification is that of Kebabian and Calne who define two types, D-1 and D-2, according to the criteria given in the table below.

	D-1	D-2
Coupled to adenylate cyclase	Yes	No
Dopamine	Agonist in μmol	Agonist in nmol
Apomorphine	Partial agonist or antagonist	Agonist
Dopamine-like ergot derivatives	Potent antagonists	Agonists
Selective antagonist	SCH 23390	Metoclopramide Sulpiride Molindone
Radiolabelled ligand	Cis-flupenthixol	Dihydroergocryptine
Location of prototype receptor	Bovine parathyroid	Mammotroph of anterior pituitary

Receptors are traditionally classified according to the rank orders of potency of agonists and the affinity constants of antagonists, and the D-1/D-2 classification comes closest to this.

Horn et al. (1981) Pharmac. Weekbl. Sci. Ed. **3**, 145

Stoof & Kebabian (1984) Life Sci. **35**, 2281

dopaminergic nerve fibre A nerve fibre that releases **dopamine** as a neurotransmitter. See **adrenergic nerve fibre** for discussion of the restricted use of the suffix '-ergic'.

Dopaminergic nerve fibres are present mainly, although not exclusively, in the brain (nigrostriatal pathway, mesolimbic system, vomiting centre, hypothalamus–pituitary axis).

dopaminomimetic drug   A **drug** that reproduces some or all of the actions of **dopamine** by a direct agonistic action on **dopamine receptors**. Examples include apomorphine, bromocriptine, lergotrile, lisuride and pergolide, piribedil and the compound N 0437 (5-hydroxy-2(*N-n*-propyl-*N*-2-thienylethyl)-aminotetraline).

double-blind trial   A clinical trial in which neither the subject (patient or volunteer) nor the observer (physician, nurse, or pharmacologist) knows what is being given. For example, neither knows which is **placebo** and which is the **drug** under test. The aim is to avoid bias resulting from preconceived ideas.

down-regulation of receptors   The capacity of a cell to reduce the number of functional **receptors** in its membrane in response to increased activity of specific **agonists**. The protein **fodrin** appears to be responsible, at least in some neurones, for down-regulating the number of receptor binding sites. Receptors may be internalized by endocytosis and destroyed in the lysosomes.

Down-regulation of receptors is also involved in the homeostatic control of cholesterol uptake by liver cells. Cholesterol is taken up into the cells in combination with low density lipoprotein (LDL). Specific LDL receptors are present in cell membranes. Once the LDL-cholesterol binds to a LDL receptor it is taken up by endocytosis and the cholesterol is released into the cytoplasm, and some is esterified. The accumulation of cholesterol esters acts to inhibit (i.e. down-regulate) the replenishment of LDL receptors, thereby blocking further uptake of cholesterol. *See also* **up-regulation of receptors**.

Draize test   A test for irritancy devised by J. H. Draize and applied to substances intended for topical application (drugs for skin diseases, cosmetics, shampoos). The test involves the application of the substance to the skin and eyes of rabbits.

dromotropic action   An action that modifies conduction, usually of a nerve fibre (Greek: *dromos*, a course; *trope*, turning). Thus a positive dromotropic action results in increased conduction (velocity), and a negative dromotropic action results in decreased conduction (velocity).

drug   In a pharmacological sense the word is generally used to describe any substance that modifies the activity of any living tissue (animal or plant) in any way (toxic, beneficial or otherwise). In lay circles, the term may be restricted to mean only the active ingredient(s) (presumably beneficial) of a medicine, or even to drugs of dependence.

drug addiction   This was defined by a WHO expert committee in 1957 as:

'a state of periodic or chronic intoxication produced by repeated consumption of a drug (natural or synthetic). Its characteristics include: (1) an overwhelming desire or need (compulsion) to continue taking the drug and to obtain it by any means; (2) a tendency to increase the dose; (3) a psychic and generally a physical dependence on the effects of the drug; (4) detrimental effect on the individual and on society.'

The definition was meant to include addiction to opium, coca and **cannabis** and their products and derivatives, but not alcohol, tobacco and other drugs which were regarded as habit-forming rather than addictive. In fact, further study showed that such clear-cut distinctions cannot be made, and the terms addiction and habituation began to lead to confusion. For this reason these terms have become obsolete in the scientific–medical literature, and the term **drug dependence** is used instead.

drug delivery system   A device or a formulation designed to control the release of a **drug** and, as far as possible, to restrict its action to the diseased target tissue or organ. Drug delivery systems include, amongst many others, mini-osmotic pumps, incorporation of drugs into **liposomes**, and even into erythrocytes which are then injected. If the surface layer of the liposome or erythrocyte incorporates a specific marker (e.g. a **monoclonal antibody**), the selectivity of action can be greatly improved.

drug dependence

'A state, psychic and sometimes also physical, resulting from the interaction between a person and a drug, characterized by behavioural and other responses that always include a compulsion to take the drug on a continuous basis in order to experience its psychic effects, and sometimes to avoid the discomfort of its absence. Tolerance may or may not be present. A person may be dependent on more than one drug.'

(Report of the 16th Expert Committee on Drug Dependence, *WHO Technical Report Series*, No. 407, 1969)

For a discussion of the difficulty in defining the condition *see* Bowman & Rand (1980) *Textbook of Pharmacology*, 2nd Edition, p. 42.94. Blackwell Scientific Publications, Oxford.

The concept of drug dependence should be distinguished from therapeutic dependence, although there is no apparent difference in principle. Thus, an **insulin**-dependent diabetic person will certainly wish to avoid the discomfort of its absence and may have a compulsion to take the drug. There are problems in adding phrases such as 'for non-therapeutic purposes' or 'when there is no underlying disorder warranting recourse to the drug'. Many people regarded as drug dependent continue to take the drug for what they perceive as a therapeutic purpose, and it could be argued that the very fact that a person becomes drug dependent is an indication of an underlying disorder.

Drug dependence is now classified into types denoted by the drug concerned. There were formerly eight types (20th Expert Committee on Drug Dependence, *WHO Technical Report Series*, No. 551, 1974):

1 Alcohol–**barbiturate** type.
2 Amphetamine type.
3 **Cannabis** type.
4 **Cocaine** type.
5 **Hallucinogen** type.
6 Khat type (preparations of *Catha edulis* Forssk).
7 **Opiate** type.
8 Volatile solvent type.

To these, there are arguments in favour of adding tobacco type, caffeine type and **betel** type.

drug disposition The fate of drugs after absorption. The term includes the distribution (**pharmacokinetics**) and metabolism (**drug metabolism**).

drug metabolism The chemical transformation of **drugs**, usually in the liver, but also, in some cases, in the lungs, the kidneys, the intestinal mucosa and other tissues. Many of the enzymes involved in drug metabolism, after occurring during evolution, may have persisted as means of ridding the body of lipid-soluble substances, by catalysing their conversion to water-soluble products that are eliminated in the urine. Drug metabolism usually results in attenuation or loss of pharmacological activity, in which case it may be described as detoxification. In some cases, however, an active metabolite may be formed from an inactive precursor or **prodrug**, or the metabolite may have a different kind of pharmacological activity from the parent drug.

Drug metabolism may be divided into two main phases: phase I in which oxidation, reduction or hydrolysis may occur, and phase II in which a conjugate of the drug or a metabolite with, for example, glucuronic acid or sulphate groups is formed.

drug resistance *See* **antimicrobial drug resistance**.

dual block A term coined by the late E. Zaimis to describe the biphasic type of block produced in some muscles by some **neuromuscular blocking drugs** of the depolarizing type. The block is characterized by an initial phase of depolarization followed by a phase resembling that produced by a non-depolarizing (or **curare-like**) **drug**.

Zaimis (1959) In *Curare and Curare-like Agents* (Eds. Bovet, Bovet-Nitti & Marinibettolo), p. 191. Elsevier, Amsterdam.

dualist A term introduced by Ariëns and colleagues (1954–60) to designate an **agonist** that is incapable of producing a maximal response and that reduces the response to more active agonists. The term has now largely been replaced by **partial agonist**.

dynein   A collective name for high molecular weight Ca^{2+}- or Mg^{2+}-requiring ATPases associated with microtubules and which are involved in the energy supply for microtubular function. Dynein is inhibited by vanadate in concentrations much lower than those necessary to inhibit other ATPases (e.g. myosin ATPase).

dynorphin   A heptadecapeptide which stimulates **opiate receptors** and may act as an endogenous **ligand** of such **receptors**. It is found in the pituitary and in the duodenum.
Tachibana *et al.* (1982) *Nature* **295**, 339

dysrhythmogenic drug   A **drug** that causes a disorder of the heart's rhythm. Such drugs include aconitine (from aconite root), delphinine (from delphinium seeds), certain barium and calcium salts, and **cardiac glycosides**. In some instances, the cardiac dysrhythmia is an unwanted toxic effect of a therapeutically useful drug (e.g. cardiac glycosides such as digitalis). In other cases, certain drugs (e.g. aconitine) may be used experimentally to produce a dysrhythmia of heart tissue against which potential new **antidysrhythmic drugs** may be tested.

EA compounds   A series of synthetic cannabinoids based on the structure of Δ^3-tetrahydrocannabinol. They were synthesized by H. F. Hardman and colleagues and given code numbers with the prefix EA (e.g. EA 1507, EA 1542, EA 1544).

Eaton–Lambert myasthenic syndrome   Muscle weakness often accompanied by malignant disease, particularly bronchogenic carcinoma. As in **myasthenia gravis**, the site of the lesion is at the neuromuscular junction, but it differs from myasthenia gravis in that exercise improves performance and the defect is prejunctional. The endplate potential is smaller than normal because its quantal content is reduced. There is evidence that the Eaton–Lambert syndrome is an autoimmune disease in which there are circulating **antibodies** to a nerve terminal protein concerned with **acetylcholine** release, possibly to the Ca^{2+} channels in the nerve endings.

Drugs that facilitate evoked acetylcholine release (tetraethylammonium, guanidine, 4-aminopyridine) produce some beneficial effect.

ED$_{50}$ The effective dose of a **drug** in 50% of animals in a group, or the median effective dose. The expression is analogous to and is derived in the same way as LD_{50}, except that the response noted is not death, but some other quantal response. For example, in a now obsolete assay of **insulin** the response noted was hypoglycaemic convulsions in mice. In this instance, the ED_{50} was the dose producing convulsions in 50% of mice in a group. In the determination of **therapeutic index**, the ED_{50} value used is the dose that produces the desired therapeutic effect in 50% of animals.

The term ED_{50} relates to a quantal response produced in 50% of animals. It should not be used to denote the concentration or dose of a drug that produces 50% of the maximal response in a particular tissue; for example, 50% of the maximal contraction of a length of isolated guinea-pig ileum. The term $E_{max\,50}$ concentration or $E_{max\,50}$ dose is a more correct expression in this instance.

EDRF Endothelium-derived relaxing factor. A vasodilator factor released from the endothelium of arteries in response to activation of certain receptors. R. Furchgott first detected the release of the factor in response to **acetylcholine** acting upon the endothelial cells of isolated artery segments, and much of the subsequent work has been carried out by Furchgott and his colleagues. In the absence of endothelium, acetylcholine loses its dilator capacity and in fact may cause a weak constriction through its direct action on the smooth muscle. The chain of events with acetylcholine and endothelium present may be summarized thus:

Acetylcholine → Muscarinic → Influx → EDRF → Guanylate cyclase
         receptors   of Ca^{2+} released of smooth muscle
        on endothelial   ↓
           cells   Cyclic GMP
                                      ↓
                                Vasodilatation

The identity of EDRF has not yet been ascertained, although there is evidence that it is an unstable compound with a carbonyl group at or near its active site.

More recent work has shown that vasodilatation produced by a number of other agents (ATP, ADP, **substance P**, **histamine**, **serotonin**, **bradykinin**, thrombin, hydralazine) also depends upon the release of EDRF, at least in some arteries. **Muscarinic cholinoceptors** are not of course involved. Some vasoconstrictor agents, such as serotonin on coronary arteries and noradrenaline acting on α_2-**adrenoceptors**, may also cause the release of EDRF, which then exerts a negative modulating role. These agents produce a more powerful vasoconstriction in the absence of the endothelium.

efficacy The capacity of an **agonist** to initiate a response once it occupies **receptor** sites was termed efficacy by R. P. Stephenson. The value of this parameter can range from zero, for a pure antagonist, to a large positive number for a highly active agonist. The activity of an agonist depends on the product of efficacy and **affinity**.

Efficacy may be related to the ratio β/α in the equation:

$$D + R \underset{k_2}{\overset{k_1}{\rightleftharpoons}} DR \underset{\alpha}{\overset{\beta}{\rightleftharpoons}} DR^*$$

where D = agonist, R = **receptor**, DR = agonist–receptor combination in the inactive form, DR^* = agonist–receptor combination in the activated form (e.g. a conformational change induced in the receptor protein complex), and k_1, k_2, α and β are rate constants. Efficacy has also been viewed as a measure of the *probability* that an agonist occupying a receptor will induce the change or stimulus (e.g. a conformation change) that leads to the response.

If the stimulus is denoted as S, then the relationship between S, efficacy (e), receptor occupation, and the mass action equation that is given under **agonist–receptor interaction** is given by:

$$S = \frac{e[DR]}{[R_T]} = \frac{e[D]}{[D] + K_D}$$

which can be rearranged:

$$S = \frac{e[D]/K_D}{[D]/K_D + 1}$$

With highly active agonists, for which e has a high value:

$$S \rightarrow e[D]/K_D$$

As far as receptor occupation is concerned, Stephenson's efficacy factor (e) is the same as Ariens' **intrinsic activity** factor (α). However, the factors are seen to differ when the relationship between receptor occupancy ($[DR]/[R]$) and fractional response (E/E_{max}) is considered. (*See* **occupation theory** for the meaning of these terms.)

Thus, for intrinsic activity:

$$\frac{E}{E_{max}} = \frac{\alpha[DR]}{[R]}$$

but for efficacy:

$$\frac{E}{E_{max}} = f(S) = f\frac{e[DR]}{[R]}$$

where f denotes a function. The relationship between response and S is arbitrarily defined such that $S = 1$ when the response is half the maximal response produced by a highly active agonist.

eicosanoids Substances derived from 20-carbon polyunsaturated fatty acids such as arachidonic acid. The name eicosanoids is a generic term embracing the **prostaglandins**, the **thromboxanes** and the **leukotrienes**.

eidetics   *See* **psychotomimetic drugs.**

electron affinity sensitizer   A type of **radiosensitizing drug** which appears to depend for its activity on the electron affinity or reduction potential of its molecules. The mechanism of action is not fully understood. It has been suggested that these drugs intercept and interact with short-lived bioradicals formed by the action of ionizing irradiation on critical cellular components. Another suggestion is that the molecules are electron carriers with the facility to delocalize the attached electrons and so damage critical cellular structures.

   An example of an electron affinity sensitizer is the compound misonidazole (chemically related to the antitrichomonal and antianaerobe drug metronidazole).

electron transfer inhibitors   Agents that inhibit electron transfer in the mitochondrial electron transfer chain, thereby impairing the synthesis of ATP. The electron-transferring proteins and other carriers of the chain are arranged sequentially in the inner mitochondrial membrane. Metabolites from the tricarboxylic acid cycle, the fatty acid β-oxidation sequence and from glycolysis pass sequentially along the chain, finally to react with molecular oxygen. Thus:

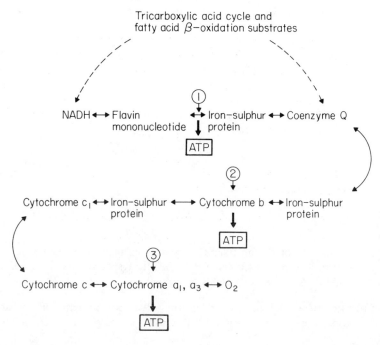

The sites of action of a number of electron transfer inhibitors are indicated by 1, 2 and 3 above.

1   Rotenone (from derris root) and the **barbiturate** drug amylobarbitone (amytal) inhibit at the level of the flavoprotein, NADH dehydrogenase. (This is not related to the clinical use of amylobarbitone.)

2   The **antibiotic** antimycin A inhibits at the level of cytochrome b.

3   Cyanide, azide and carbon monoxide inhibit the terminal step, catalysed by cytchrome oxidase, by combining with the oxidized haem iron (Fe^{3+}) in cytochromes a_1 and a_3 so as to prevent the reduction of this haem iron by electrons derived from cytochrome c.

electrophoretic administration of drugs

The administration of a highly ionized **drug** through the skin by means of passing an electric current. One electrode is placed in contact with a pad soaked with drug solution and placed on the affected area. The indifferent electrode is placed elsewhere on the skin. The applied current drives the appropriate ion through the skin. Methacholine has been administered in this way to produce vasodilatation in peripheral vascular spasm.

elimination rate constant (K_{elim})

The elimination rate constant is a constant that describes the rate of removal of **drug** from the body.

The equation describing the curve relating plasma concentration of drug to time is:

$$C_P = C_0 e^{-K_{elim}t}$$

where C_P = concentration of drug in plasma at time t, C_0 = concentration of drug in body at start, and K_{elim} = the elimination rate constant. Rewriting:

$$\ln C_P = \ln C_0 - K_{elim}t$$

Or, in logs to the base 10:

$$\log C_P = \log C_0 - \frac{K_{elim}t}{2 \cdot 303}$$

Therefore a plot of log C_P against time is linear with a slope of $-K_{elim}/2\cdot303$. *See* **compartments**.

The elimination rate constant can be obtained from a linear log C_P against time plot (i.e. single compartment, *see* **compartments**). Thus:

$$\ln C_P = \ln C_0 - K_{elim}t \text{ (as above)}$$

i.e.

$$\ln \frac{C_P}{C_0} = -K_{elim}t$$

When t = the half-time $T_{1/2}$ then $C_P/C_0 = 0\cdot5$

elixir

$$\therefore \quad \ln 0{\cdot}5 = K_{\text{elim}} T_{1/2}$$

but

$$\ln 0{\cdot}5 = 0{\cdot}693$$

$$K_{\text{elim}} = \frac{0{\cdot}693}{T_{1/2}}$$

K_{elim} has the dimensions of s^{-1}, $\min^{-1}$ or h^{-1}, depending on whether $T_{1/2}$ is in seconds, minutes or hours. (NB Note also that $T_{1/2} = 0{\cdot}693/K_{\text{elim}}$.)

elixir   An alcoholic solution of a medicament.

$E_{\text{max}\,50}$ *See under* **ED$_{50}$**.

emetic drug   A drug that produces vomiting (emesis) (Greek: *emeticos*, provoking vomiting). Examples include apomorphine (centrally acting) and oral emetine (reflex action on intestine).

emollient   An agent (e.g. lanolin) that softens or soothes the skin (Latin: *emolliens*, softening).

endobiotic substance   A chemical produced within the biological system (Greek: *endon*, within; *biosis*, living). For example, **acetylcholine** and **insulin** may be described as a endobiotic substances (cf. **xenobiotic substance**).

endocardin   *See* **endoxin**.

endodigin   *See* **endoxin**.

endorphins   **Opioid peptides** derived from β-lipotropin, a fat-mobilizing hormone of the pituitary. The term endorphin has been used synonymously with opioid peptide, but this has led to confusion, and so the above, more restricted, definition has now been generally accepted (*see*

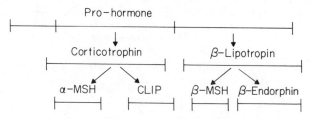

CLIP, corticotrophin-like intermediate lobe peptide.

Morley (1981) in *Perspectives in Peptide Chemistry* (Eds. Aberle *et al.*), p. 329. Karger, Basel.)

β-Endorphin is a 31-residue peptide originating from a prohormone that is the common precursor of corticotrophin, and of α- and β-melanocyte stimulating hormone (α- and β-MSH), as well as of β-endorphin. The diagram illustrates the relationship.

β-Endorphin has the structure:

1   16
Tyr–Gly–Gly–Phe–Met–Thr–Ser–Glu–Lys–Ser–Gln–Pro–Leu–Val–Thr
                                                                                    |
Glu–Gly–Lys–Lys–Tyr–Ala–Asn–Lys–Ile–Ile–Ala–Asn–Lys–Phe–Leu
31   27   17

α-Endorphin is 1–16
γ-Endorphin is 1–17
δ-Endorphin is 1–27

β-Endorphin is the most potent naturally occurring analgesic agent. It is present in pituitary and brain, and in peripheral tissues.

endothelium-derived relaxing factor *See* **EDRF**.

endoxin A circulating factor that inhibits Na^+, K^+-ATPase and which possesses a structure that is 'recognized' by **antibodies** to digoxin. Also called endodigin or endocardin. Endoxin may be identical to **natriuretic hormone**.

Gruber *et al.* (1980) *Nature* **287**, 743
LaBella (1982) *Trends pharmacol. Sci.* **3**, 354

enema A liquid medicament for injection into the rectum (plural: enemas or enemata; Greek: *enema*, to send in).

enkephalin convertase A carboxypeptidase specifically concerned with the biosynthesis of enkephalins. Enkephalin convertase is inhibited by **GEMSA**.

enkephalinergic nerve fibre A nerve fibre that releases an enkephalin as a neurotransmitter. *See* **adrenergic nerve fibre** for discussion of the restricted use of the suffix '-ergic'. **GEMSA** may be employed histochemically to trace out enkephalinergic fibres in the CNS.

enteramine A substance, subsequently shown to be **serotonin**, detected in the walls of the intestine and the salivary glands of the octopus in the early 1940s.

enteric coating A coating for a tablet or capsule that prevents disintegration in the stomach. The coating is soluble in the alkaline intestinal contents, but insoluble in the acid of the stomach.

enzyme induction   Usually applies to hepatic drug-metabolizing enzymes. An increase in enzyme activity arising from *de novo* synthesis of additional enzyme induced by chronic administration of a drug or other chemical. The effect is blocked by inhibitors of protein synthesis.

The cell's DNA contains the gene or operon for an enzyme or enzymes that metabolize a certain drug, not because the cell has evolved with the ability to modify that particular drug, but rather because the evolutionary process has selected genes and enzyme products for modifying environmental chemicals to which the drug coincidentally bears some chemical resemblance. There are many instances in which operons on DNA are blocked by regulatory proteins called repressors. Enzyme inducers combine with the repressor and induce a conformational change in it that causes it to detach from the operator site on DNA. RNA polymerase then attaches to the promotor and the sequence of events leading to enzyme synthesis takes place.

Enzyme inducers enhance drug metabolism and thereby reduce the duration and intensity of drug action. Many drugs may act in this way, but phenobarbitone and the polycyclic hydrocarbon **benzo[*a*]pyrene** are the most widely studied. Each causes a typical spectrum of increased enzyme activity, and other inducers resemble one or the other, so that they have been classified into two groups: phenobarbitone type and polycyclic hydrocarbon type. The phenobarbitone types are the more important from the point of view of drug therapy, but the polycyclic hydrocarbon types are important in the aetiology of certain cancers produced by chemical carcinogens.

Important inducing agents of the phenobarbitone type include other **barbiturates**, phenytoin, DDT, meprobamate and tolbutamide. Inducing agents may stimulate the synthesis of enzymes that metabolize the inducer as well as other drugs. Barbiturates are important examples, and this effect contributes largely to the **tolerance** that occurs to barbiturates. The induction of self-metabolizing enzymes in this way is known as **autoinduction**.

epinephrine   *See* **adrenaline**.

erabutoxin b   A protein toxin from the sea snake *Laticauda semifasciata*. The toxin resembles α-**bungarotoxin**, in that it blocks **nicotinic cholinoceptors** at the motor endplate in skeletal muscle.

ergolines   Drugs derived from or chemically related to ergot **alkaloids** (*see* **ergot of rye**). Most of them have dopaminomimetic activity (*see* **dopaminomimetic drug**). Bromocriptine and lergotrile are examples.

ergot of rye   A fungus *Claviceps purpurea* that forms small purplish black banana-shaped projections on infected ears of rye. The word ergot (Latin: *ergota*) means cock's spur, and refers to the appearance of the fungal projections. Ergot contains **alkaloids** (ergot alkaloids) which are used as **oxytocic agents** and in the therapy of migraine. It also contains **acetylcholine** and **histamine**.

ergotism Chronic poisoning from excessive use of ergot **alkaloids** (*see* **ergot of rye**) as a medicine (e.g. in migraine), or from eating grain (especially rye) that has been infected with the fungus. Ergotism is marked by cerebrospinal symptoms, spasms, cramps and a dry gangrene due to intense vasoconstriction. *See* **St Anthony's fire**.

estrogen *See* **oestrogen**.

euphoriants An alternative name for **antidepressant drugs** of the class of **thymerectic drugs**.

eutectic mixture A liquid mixture of two substances, each of which by itself is a solid (Greek: *eutexia*, to melt). A familiar example is a mixture of ice and sodium chloride, which form a liquid solution when mixed. An example in pharmacology is a mixture of the insoluble bases of the two **local anaesthetic drugs** lignocaine and prilocaine in equal quantities. This forms an oily liquid which may be formulated in an emulsifying cream for application to the skin to produce surface anaesthesia. One commercially available mixture is known as EMLA (2·5% of each local anaesthetic in an emulsifying cream).

evacuative A drug that produces emptying of the bowels (Latin: *e*, from; *vacuare*, to empty). Alternative names and their etymological origins are given under **aperient** and **purgative**.

evening primrose oil The oil extracted from the seeds of the evening primrose, *Oenothera biennis* and *O. lamarkiana*, a yellow-flowered plant related to the willow herb and not in fact a primrose. It is indigenous to North America but has been brought to Europe where it is now a common weed. Increasingly, it is being grown commercially for its oil content.

The oil is a rich source of linoleic acid and, more importantly, of gamma linolenic acid which is converted in the body, mainly into prostaglandin E_1. Evening primrose oil is a health food product which, because of its potential to increase PGE_1 production, is claimed to be beneficial in a wide range of diseases. It is said to reduce the severity and frequency of attacks in multiple sclerosis, to relieve the symptoms of premenstrual tension, and to be of value in cardiac disease, vascular disorders, obesity, diseases of the skin, hair and nails, inflammatory diseases, schizophrenia, alcoholism and cancer. A great deal of further work is required to test these claims, and a large number of clinical trials are in fact being carried out in centres around the world.

excitatory amino acid receptors Receptors, on central neurones, that are specifically sensitive to excitatory amino acids. At least three types exist, the preferred **agonists** being *N*-methylaspartate (NMA), quisqualate and kainate (*see* **kainic acid**).

   Quinolinic acid may be the endogenous excitatory **ligand** for NMA receptors and kynurenic acid may be an endogenous antagonist. Excess quinolinic acid is neurotoxic to the neurones that possess NMA receptors. Disturbance in the balance between quinolinic and kynurenic acids may be the basis of some degenerative disorders of the central nervous system.

excitotoxin concept A concept formulated by J. W. Olney that acidic amino acids that have potent neuroexcitatory effects can cause neuronal degeneration by excessively depolarizing neurones that are sensitive to them. The hypothesis may be relevant to mechanisms involved in certain neurodegenerative disorders.

expectorant A drug that is given to decrease the viscosity of tenacious mucus, or increase the secretion of mucus in a dry, unproductive cough. Examples include ipecacuanha, potassium iodide, liquorice root, oil of anise and bromhexine.

extraneuronal uptake of amines Also called non-neuronal uptake or uptake 2. An uptake process for **noradrenaline** and certain other amines into effector cells, but not into nerve. It has a higher threshold than has **neuronal uptake of noradrenaline** and is saturated only by very high concentrations of noradrenaline. All of the amines that are taken up by neuronal uptake are also taken up by extraneuronal uptake. However, **adrenaline** is a better substrate for uptake 2 than for uptake 1, and isoprenaline is taken up by uptake 2 (but not by uptake 1). Phenoxy-benzamine blocks uptake 2 as well as uptake 1, but **cocaine and tricyclic antidepressants** do not affect uptake 2. Uptake 2 is blocked by meta-nephrine and normetanephrine and by cortisol and other steroids. (Interestingly, the steroid **neuromuscular blocking drug** pancuronium blocks uptake 1 but not uptake 2.)

extrapyramidal side-effects Side-effects of a drug (muscle rigidity, tremor, akinesia) arising from actions (usually blockade of **dopamine receptors**) on the extrapyramidal nervous system. **Phenothiazine neuroleptics** (*see* **phenothiazines** and **neuroleptic drugs**) produce side-effects of these types. Similar signs and symptoms are characteristic of Parkinson's disease.

false transmitter An abnormal neurotransmitter synthesized in nervous tissue as a consequence of supplying an excess of abnormal substrate to the transmitter-synthesizing enzyme system. For example, triethyl-2 aminoethanol (triethylcholine) may be acetylated in cholinergic nerve endings in place of choline, and the product then released by nerve impulses as a false transmitter. Likewise, in **noradrenergic nerve fibres**, the L-isomer of α-methyl**dopa** (methyldopa) may be acted upon by **dopa decarboxylase** with the formation of α-methylnoradrenaline in place of **noradrenaline**.

fatty acid dioxygenases   *See* **cyclo-oxygenases**.

Fick's law   An equation that expresses the rate of flow (i.e. the flux per unit area, given the symbol J) of uncharged solute molecules by simple diffusion in the direction of their concentration gradient.

$$J = -D\frac{dC}{dx}$$

where D is a simple diffusion coefficient (the negative sign indicates that the solute moves towards the lower concentration), and dC/dx is the concentration gradient. *See also* **passive diffusion**.

Finkelman preparation   A preparation of an isolated segment of jejunum from the rabbit set up in a physiological salt solution (**Krebs**, **Tyrode** or **McEwen solution**). A portion of mesentery, which contains the sympathetic nerve supply, is left attached to the jejunum and is passed through stimulating electrodes. Stimulation of the nerves inhibits the spontaneous pendular movements and causes relaxation of the tissue. The preparation is useful for studying the effects of drugs that modify adrenergic mechanisms.

Finkelman (1930) *J. Physiol.* **70**, 145

first-order kinetics   A process (e.g. drug absorption or elimination) follows first-order kinetics when the rate of change of amount is proportional (or inversely proportional) to the amount present. It is described as first order because, in mathematical terms, the exponent of the function is 1.

For absorption by first-order kinetics the following equations are applicable:

$$D_t = fDe^{-tK_{abs}}$$

and

$$Q_t = fD(1 - e^{-tK_{abs}})$$

where D_t is the amount remaining unabsorbed after time t, Q_t is the amount that has been absorbed, D is the amount administered and f is the fraction that is bioavailable. e is the base of natural logarithms and K_{abs}

(which has the dimensions of time^{-1}) is the rate constant for absorption.

For elimination by first-order kinetics, the following equations are applicable:

$$M_t = M_0 e^{-tK_{elim}}$$

where M_t is the amount of drug remaining in the body at time t, M_0 is the amount of drug in the body at the beginning and K_{elim} is the rate constant for elimination, and:

$$C_t = C_0 e^{-(\ln 2)t/T_{1/2}}$$

where C_t = the concentration of drug in plasma after time t, C_0 is the initial concentration of drug in plasma, and $T_{1/2}$ is the half-life of the drug.

first-pass effect Refers to the proportion of absorbed **drug** that is removed before entering the general circulation. For example, a drug given orally may be largely destroyed in the liver on its first passage via the portal vein before it reaches the general circulation. This would be a large first-pass effect.

The extraction ratio (E) is the fraction of drug removed from the blood during a single passage through an organ such as the liver.

$$E = \frac{Cl_H}{Q_B}$$

where Cl_H is the clearance of drug by the liver and Q_B is the blood flow to the liver. The fraction reaching the systemic circulation is therefore $1 - E$.

fluctuation analysis Mathematical analysis of the fluctuations of current or voltage arising from the random opening and closing of many individual ion channels in a membrane. Katz and Miledi first noted, in the early 1970s, that the application of **acetylcholine** to the motor endplate of a muscle not only caused overall membrane depolarization, but in addition gave rise to an increased 'noisiness' of the membrane potential. Under **voltage clamp** conditions, similar fluctuations of the membrane current are evident. Fluctuation analysis is based on the idea that each activation of an ion channel produces a brief pulse of current of fixed amplitude, i, and of duration, t. The amplitude of the current pulse is the product of the channel conductance, γ, and the driving force on ion movements, $V_m - V_n$, where V_m is the membrane potential and V_n is the null (or reversal) potential at which no current flows when the ion channel opens. Channel open times are random variables drawn from a **Poisson** (exponential) **distribution**. The mean value of this distribution is the **mean channel open time**, τ, of the ion channels. τ is the reciprocal of the rate constant α for the closing step in the diagram given under **receptor-operated ion channels** (i.e. $\tau = 1/\alpha$).

In a membrane containing many channels that can be activated by the same .**agonist**, the independent activity of a large number of randomly activated ion channels will sum to produce an overall membrane current response which fluctuates about a mean level. This fluctuating current can be analysed by mathematical processes (Fourier analysis or autocorrelation function) to yield estimates of γ and τ for channels activated by a particular agonist.

Neher & Stevens (1977) *Ann. Rev. Biophys. Bioeng.* **6**, 345
Colquhoun (1981) *Trends pharmacol. Sci.* **2**, 212
McBurney (1983) *Trends Neurosci.* **6**, 297

fodrin A **spectrin**-like protein that lines the cortical cytoplasm of neurones and which appears to link actin filaments to the membrane. Fodrin is thought to down-regulate the number of **receptor** binding sites on neuronal membranes (*see* **down-regulation of receptors**). Its breakdown by the Ca^{2+}-dependent protease, **calpain 1**, leads to the exposure of more receptors. Studies to date have been concerned with **glutamate receptors**, but there may well be a similar fodrin-mediated mechanism underlying the down- and up-regulation of other types of neuronal receptors (*see also* **up-regulation of receptors**).

There is a suggestion that the increase in receptor number arising from fodrin breakdown plays a part in memory storage.

forskolin A diterpene, 7β-acetoxy-8,13α-epoxy-1α,6β,9α-trihydroxylabd-14-en-11-one, obtained from the roots of the plant *Coleus forskohlii* found in India. The name is derived from that of the Swedish naturalist Pehr Forskål who died in the Arabian desert in 1768. An alternative name for forskolin is coleonol.

Forskolin is a valuable experimental tool because it has a powerful and specific action to stimulate the **adenylate cyclase** of eukaryotic cells, and so elevate the concentration of **cyclic AMP**. In stimulating the enzyme it bypasses all known membrane receptors and it does not act via the guanine necleotide subunits. It therefore probably acts directly on the catalytic subunit of the enzyme.

Forskolin

free radical quenchers **Free radical** intermediates are produced during normal mitochondrial processes, but are too reactive and toxic to be

89

tolerated in living tissue. Several mechanisms have evolved to deal with them. In addition, several exogenous chemicals may act as free radical quenchers (also called free radical scavengers). Cellular protective mechanisms include the following.

Enzymes. The main enzymes are cytochrome oxidase, **superoxide dismutase**, catalase and peroxidase. The reactions they catalyse are shown in the diagram, superimposed on the univalent pathway for reduction of molecular oxygen, which results in superoxide anion radical ($\cdot O_2^-$), hydrogen peroxide (H_2O_2) and hydroxyl radical ($\cdot OH$).

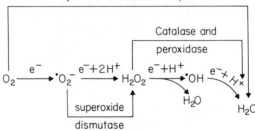

Cytochrome oxidase complex

Hydrophobic protective regions. Hydrophobic lipid membranes sequester hydrophobic non-polar groups. α-Tocopherol (**vitamin** E) intercalated in the cell membrane provides hydrogen atoms and prevents chain-propagating actions in lipid membranes. (α-Tocopherol and β-carotenes may also interact with **singlet oxygen** and thereby prevent lipid hydroperoxide formation.)

Hydrophilic protective mechanisms. Ascorbic acid, cystein and reduced glutathione control free radical reactions in the water compartments. Caeruloplasmin and transferrin in the plasma also have scavenging capacity.

Cholesterol. The intercalated cholesterol molecules in the cell membrane may structurally protect the fatty acid double bonds from peroxidation injury.

Exogenous free radical scavengers. A number of substances are capable of 'mopping up' free radicals, and these may be used for this purpose in experiments to detect whether a free radical mechanism is involved in a particular effect. Such substances include mannitol and dimethylsulphoxide which are hydroxyl scavengers.

free radical scavengers *See* **free radical quenchers.**

free radicals Any atom, group of atoms, or molecule with one unpaired electron occupying an outer orbital is described as a free radical. The lone electron present in the outer orbital endows the free radical with unusual chemical reactivity and physical characteristics. Free radical reactivity is due to the strong tendency of the unpaired electron to interact with other electrons to form an electron pair and thus a chemical bond.

A few common molecules (e.g. nitrous oxide, NO, and nitrogen dioxide, NO_2) contain an unpaired electron in an outer orbital in their normal state and are therefore free radicals.

Free radicals differ from ions as illustrated by the following, where the dots represent electrons:

$$A:B \rightarrow A^{\cdot} + .B \text{ (free radicals)}$$
$$A:B \rightarrow A:^{-} + B^{+} \text{ (ions)}$$

(Several symbols are used to denote free radicals; thus, for example, superoxide anion radical may be denoted O_2^{-}, $O_2^{\cdot}$ or $^{\cdot}O_2^{-}$).

The main free radicals produced in cells are superoxide anion ($^{\cdot}O_2^{-}$) and the more reactive, and toxic, hydroyl radical ($^{\cdot}OH$). Superoxide anion is produced as a product of reactions catalysed by xanthine oxidase, aldehyde oxidase, dihydrogenase and flavin dehydrogenases. Superoxide anion leads to the production of hydroxyl radical by interacting with its dismutation product H_2O_2 (*see* **superoxide dismutase**). This is known as the Haber–Weiss reaction.

$$^{\cdot}O_2^{-} + H_2O_2 \rightarrow O_2 + OH^{-} + ^{\cdot}OH$$

Hydroxyl radical is a very reactive, and therefore unstable, oxidizing species which reacts with a large variety of organic compounds. There are endogenous protective mechanisms that prevent the overproduction of free radicals (*see* **free radical quenchers**). However, leucocytes are thought to make use of free radicals in killing bacteria.

If the production of free radicals becomes excessive, a number of deleterious consequences arise. Cell membrane damage leading to cell death can occur, due to the production of a chain reaction of free radical production in the polyunsaturated membrane lipids. Intracellular enzymes escape into the extracellular fluid. This type of effect is characteristic of ageing (*see* **lipofuscin**). There may also be cross-linking between reactive molecules, leading to mutagenicity and cancer. Superoxide anion radical and its sequelae are produced by xanthine oxidase in the heart, not during an ischaemic episode, but rather in the post-ischaemic or reperfusion phase when oxygen is re-introduced to the ischaemic region. This effect may underlie reperfusion damage and dysrhythmias.

The hydroxyl radical is thought to contribute to the neuronal damage produced by 6-hydroxydopamine, and may also be a factor in the rapid brain ageing seen in Down's syndrome, **Alzheimer's disease** and Parkinson's disease.

Freund's complete adjuvant

An emulsified preparation of heat-killed tubercle bacilli in mineral oil. It is used in experimental immunology to promote the formation of **antibodies** against weakly antigenic substances, and in pharmacology to produce an animal model of arthritis (**adjuvant arthritis**).

functional antagonist   A drug that produces the opposite pharmacological effect to the substance antagonized. For example, **adrenaline** (bronchodilator) is a functional antagonist of **histamine** (bronchoconstrictor). Also called a physiological antagonist.

GABA   An amino acid (gamma-aminobutyric acid or 4-aminobutanoic acid) that functions as an inhibitory neurotransmitter in certain parts of the mammalian central nervous system, and at the neuromuscular junction of crustaceans such as the lobster. *See* **GABA receptors**. GABA also plays a role in intermediary metabolism.

GABA modulin   A polypeptide associated with **GABA receptors**. It is probably located in the postsynaptic membrane, and it is thought to down-regulate the **GABA** recognition site allosterically (*see* **down-regulation of receptors**). GABA modulin inhibits the facilitation of **benzodiazepine** binding to GABA receptors that is elicited by GABA itself. *See also* **benzodiazepine receptors**.

GABA receptors   Receptors for which gamma-aminobutyric acid is a specific **agonist**. GABA receptors are not homogeneous. Two subtypes have so far been described—$GABA_I$ or $GABA_A$ receptors for which muscimol is a relatively selective agonist and **bicuculline** an antagonist, and $GABA_{II}$ or $GABA_B$ receptors for which baclofen is a relatively selective agonist.

$GABA_A$ receptors are coupled to chloride channels. At postsynaptic $GABA_A$ receptors, the concentration gradient and equilibrium potential cause an influx of Cl^- when the ion channels are opened by GABA, and hence the membrane is hyperpolarized. GABA is also the transmitter responsible for presynaptic inhibition in the spinal cord. Here the concentration gradient and equilibrium potential are such that there is an efflux of Cl^-, so that the nerve endings are depolarized.

$GABA_B$ receptors are coupled to **adenylate cyclase** via the GTP-binding (Ni) protein. Their activation leads to enhanced **cyclic AMP** production through inactivation of the inhibitory protein. The consequence is an increased K^+ permeability and a reduced Ca^{2+} permeability.

Bowery *et al.* (1984) *Proc. IUPHAR Cong.*, Vol. **3**, p. 159. Macmillan, London.

GABAergic nerve fibre   A nerve fibre that releases gamma-aminobutyric acid (**GABA**) as a neurotransmitter. *See* **adrenergic nerve fibre** for discussion of the restricted use of the suffix '-ergic'.

GABAmimetic drug   A drug that mimics the actions of **GABA** (gamma-aminobutyric acid) by acting as an **agonist** on **GABA receptors**. Muscimol, baclofen, isoguvacine, (+)*trans*-3-aminocyclopentane carboxylic acid, and

THIP are examples of GABAmimetic drugs. Baclofen also acts to increase GABA release at some sites.

GABA   Muscimol   Isoguvacine

THIP   (+) *Trans*-3-amino   Baclofen
cyclopentane carboxylic acid

Gaddum's chemotherapeutic ratio A risk-benefit ratio derived from data obtained in laboratory animals and calculated from LD_{50}/ED_{50}. *See* **therapeutic index**.

gamma adrenoceptors *See* **adrenoceptors**.

gamma-aminobutyric acid *See* **GABA**.

galanin A 29 amino acid neuropeptide isolated from porcine upper small intestine. It is present in nerve fibres in the mucosa, smooth muscle, intramural ganglia and around blood vessels of the gastrointestinal tract. (*See* Ekblad *et al.* (1985) *Brit. J. Pharmacol.* **86**, 241.)

ganglion blocking drugs Drugs that block transmission through autonomic ganglia by interacting with **acetylcholine** receptor complexes. Examples include tetraethylammonium, hexamethonium and trimetaphan. Recent electrophysiological analysis by Rang has shown that trimetaphan acts in what might be regarded as the traditional way, by blocking the recognition sites of the **cholinoceptors**, whereas hexamethonium acts by occluding the ion channels that are part of the receptor complex (*see* **ion channel block**).

Ganglion blocking drugs were formerly important for the control of hypertension, but are now largely obsolete for this purpose, except when rapid emergency lowering of blood pressure is required, or when blood flow to an organ is required to be reduced during **surgical anaesthesia**.

ganglion stimulating drugs Drugs that stimulate autonomic ganglia. Most drugs in this class act by virtue of being **agonists** at the **nicotinic cholinoceptors** on the ganglion cells. Such drugs include **acetylcholine** itself, nicotine, and dimethylphenylpiperazinium (DMPP).

Sympathetic ganglion cells also possess **muscarinic cholinoceptors** and certain drugs exert a selective stimulant action on these. Such drugs include **McN-A-343** and AH 6405.

Transmission through sympathetic ganglia is negatively modulated through small dopaminergic interneurone-like cells (SIF cells) that are activated through muscarinic receptors. Indirect stimulation of the ganglion may be induced by inhibiting the small intensely fluorescent (SIF) cells, for example by **dopamine antagonists** or by atropine.

Gaussian distribution *See* **binomial distribution**.

GEMSA Guanidinoethylmercaptosuccinic acid. A selective and potent inhibitor of **enkephalin convertase**.

gene mutation An alteration in the DNA molecule that results in the replacement, addition or loss of nucleotide bases.

general anaesthetic drug A drug that produces reversible general **anaesthesia** to a depth sufficient to permit surgery. General anaesthetics may be inhaled (inhalational anaesthetics), or may be injected intravenously (intravenous anaesthetics).

Inhalational anaesthetics include the volatile liquids halothane, enflurane, isoflurane and methoxyflurane, and the gases cyclopropane and nitrous oxide. Rapid blood flow to the brain causes rapid transport of the blood-borne agent to the brain. The agents are lipid-soluble as well as water-soluble, and rapid equilibration between blood and brain is quickly reached. The mechanism of action of inhalational anaesthetics has not been proved convincingly. However, the uptake of the agents into the lipid membranes of nerve cells and their processes must alter the environment of ion channels and is therefore likely to modify their function. It seems likely that the mechanism of action depends on this effect to some extent. In addition, it seems that anaesthetic agents may interact with membrane proteins, and in particular the **glycine receptor** has been implicated. Possibly the anaesthetic agents modify the receptor binding site in such a way that glycine binding is enhanced. The potency of inhalational anaesthetics is expressed in terms of the **MAC value**.

Intravenous anaesthetics include sodium thiopentone, sodium methohexitone, ketamine, etomidate and alphaxalone (Althesin). Ketamine is used to produce what is called dissociative anaesthesia, which is a state of sedation, immobility, amnesia, analgesia and a feeling of dissociation from the environment. Of the other intravenous anaesthetics, sodium thiopentone has largely regained its prime place because of unwanted effects produced by the other drugs.

generic equivalence Equivalence of bioavailability between various commercial preparations of the same **drug**. In fact, there are several examples of differences in bioavailability and in therapeutic response between different preparations, even though the preparations conform to pharmacopoeial specifications. Examples that have been found to lack generic equivalence include some brands of tablets of digoxin, griseofulvin, tolbutamide and oxytetracycline, among others.

genetic damage Damage to DNA. This may be of two types: **chromosome damage** and **gene mutation**. Genetic damage may be produced by exposure to certain chemicals. **Mutagenicity tests** are applied in attempts to detect compounds with this potential toxicity.

genetic engineering *See* **recombinant DNA technology**.

geometric mean The geometric mean ($\bar{G}$) is given by:
$$\bar{G}_Y = (Y_1 \times Y_2 \times \cdots \times Y_N)^{1/N}$$
or
$$\log \bar{G} = \frac{\Sigma \log Y}{N}$$

Gillespie–Muir pithed rat preparation A pithing rod (e.g. steel knitting needle) is passed down the spinal canal, via the eye socket, of an anaesthetized rat. Arterial pressure is recorded. The pithing rod is left in position and used as a stimulating electrode for stimulating the autonomic outflow. The consequences of stimulating the somatic outflow are prevented by a large dose of a **neuromuscular blocking drug** that is free from ganglion blocking action (e.g. gallamine). By insulating the pithing rod in appropriate places, particular parts of the autonomic outflow may be selectively stimulated.

Gillespie & Muir (1967) *Brit. J. Pharmacol.* **30**, 78

glucocorticoids Those steroid **hormones** of the adrenal cortex and their synthetic analogues that have a relatively more powerful action on carbohydrate metabolism than on electrolyte and water balance. (Hormones with a relatively more powerful action on electrolyte and water balance are called **mineralocorticoids**.) Glucocorticoids include the hormones hydrocortisone and corticosterone, and synthetic analogues such as prednisolone, prednisone, triamcinolone, betamethasone, dexamethasone and beclamethasone. Some of them are used in replacement therapy, and they are also used as **anti-inflammatory drugs** and **immunosuppressants**.

glutamate receptors **Receptors** specifically sensitive to and operated by **glutamic acid**. Glutamate receptors are coupled to Na^+ channels. Influx of Na^+ depolarizes the postsynaptic cells. Unusually, glutamate receptors are sensitive to both D and L isomers.

glutamic acid A dicarboxylic amino acid which probably functions as an excitatory neurotransmitter in certain regions of the spinal cord (dorsal horns), cerebellum (granule cells) and possibly other regions. Additionally, it plays a role in intermediary metabolism.

$$HOOC\!-\!CH_2\!-\!CH_2\!-\!\underset{\underset{\displaystyle COOH}{|}}{CH}\!-\!NH_2$$

glutaminergic nerve fibre A nerve fibre that releases **glutamic acid** as a neurotransmitter. *See* **adrenergic nerve fibre** for discussion of the restricted use of the suffix '-ergic'.

glycine An amino acid that probably functions as an inhibitory neurotransmitter in the lower brain stem and spinal cord of vertebrates, especially at the endings of interneurones in the spinal cord. Strychnine blocks the inhibitory action of glycine. **Tetanus toxin** inhibits its release.
Glycine also plays a role in intermediary metabolism.

$$NH_2\!-\!CH_2\!-\!COOH$$

glycine receptors Receptors specifically sensitive to **glycine**. Glycine receptors present on spinal cord neurones are coupled to Cl^- channels. Influx of Cl^- through these channels causes hyperpolarization of the postsynaptic cell. Glycine receptors are blocked by strychnine.

glycinergic nerve fibre A nerve fibre that releases **glycine** as a neurotransmitter. *See* **adrenergic nerve fibre** for discussion of the restricted use of the suffix '-ergic'.

goitrogenic agents Agents that induce goitre (goiter in USA), an enlargement of the thyroid gland. The cause is usually insufficient synthesis of thyroid hormone, so that the pituitary is stimulated to release thyrotrophin which acts on the thyroid to cause enlargement. Goitrogenic agents include goitrin (present in turnips and related plants), the antituberculous drug para-aminosalicylic acid and lithium salts (used in manic depression).

grayanotoxins The toxins contained in the leaves of plants of the family Ericaceae, such as the rhododendron. There are several active components including grayanotoxins I and III, and α-dihydrograyanotoxin II. Other

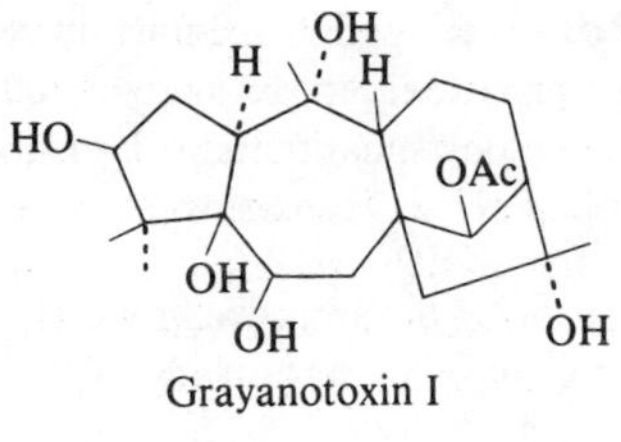

Grayanotoxin I

components are almost inactive. They produce a reversible increase in sodium permeability in excitable membranes rather like that produced by **batrachotoxin**.

Narahashi (1979) In *Advances in Cytopharmacology*, Vol. 3 (Eds. Ceccarelli & Clementi). Raven Press, New York.

growth factors   Polypeptide factors that are produced by certain cells and that exert a mitogenic action on other cells. They interact with specific cell membrane **receptors** and thereby induce DNA replication and division. They are necessary for tissue growth. Their mechanism of action is similar to, and interrelated with, that of the **oncogenes**, and they also have a pathological role in cancer. Growth factors that have been studied in some detail include **nerve growth factor** (NGF), platelet-derived growth factor (PDGF) and epidermal growth factor (EGF), which is probably identical with urogastrone. **Insulin** and somatomedin also function as growth factors. NGF is produced by salivary gland and specifically stimulates nerve growth. PDGF acts on a number of tissues, including bone, and EGF stimulates epidermal growth and keratinization, and also acts on a variety of other cells.

Cancer cells may produce and respond to their own growth factors, so-called autocrine growth factors. Oncogenes code directly for autocrine peptide growth factors or their receptors, and also amplify the signals generated by the growth factor at its receptor. Cancer cells therefore become independent of external growth factors.

Negative autocrine growth factors have also been identified, and these act to antagonize the positive autocrine growth factors.

guanethidine-like drug   *See* **adrenergic neurone blocking drug**.

guanylate cyclase   An enzyme containing a haem moiety that catalyses the production of cyclic guanosine-3′,5′-monophosphate (**cyclic GMP**) from GTP (cf. **adenylate cyclase**). Guanylate cyclase occurs in at least two forms: one is in the cytosol and another is associated with the particulate fraction of broken cells. The cellular content of cyclic GMP is about 10 times lower than that of **cyclic AMP**. Like cyclic AMP, cyclic GMP acts by activating specific **protein kinases**. Endogenous activators of guanylate cyclase include **EDRF**, unstable intermediates in **prostaglandin** synthesis (*see* **PI response**), and the inhibitory transmitter mechanism of the **NANC** innervation of the bovine retractor penis and related smooth muscles.

Cyclic GMP, like cyclic AMP, mediates smooth muscle relaxation. However, it is often produced during smooth muscle contraction elicited by a smooth muscle stimulant. In these instances it acts as a negative modulator that limits the size of the contraction. The activating stimulus to the enzyme may be EDRF released by the contraction from the endothelium of vascular tissues, or arachidonic acid peroxide or prostaglandin endoperoxide released during the PI response.

A **drug** that acts as a powerful stimulant of guanylate cyclase is the vasodilator drug sodium nitroprusside. It does not act by releasing EDRF. Substances that stimulate guanylate cyclase are antagonized by haemoglobin. It is not certain whether haemoglobin interacts with the enzyme or with the stimulating substance. It is possible that the stimulating substances preferentially combine with the haem of haemoglobin.

H_1 (or H_2) receptors *See* **histamine receptors.**

Haber–Weiss reaction *See under* **free radicals.**

Haidenhain pouch A pouch formed surgically from a segment of the stomach under anaesthesia in an experimental animal, usually the dog. It is used for studying gastric secretion and the effects of drugs upon it. A Haidenhain pouch is similar to a **Pavlov pouch**, except that it is completely separated from the main part of the stomach. Consequently, it is vagally denervated, although it retains its sympathetic innervation. Its blood supply from the splenic artery remains intact.

half-time *See* $T_{1/2}$.

hallucinogens *See* **psychotomimetic drugs.**

haloalkylamines Drugs that are derivatives of haloalkylamine. Those most relevant to pharmacology are the β-haloalkylamines which include dibenamine and phenoxybenzamine (chloroalkylamines) and the compound SY 28 (a bromoalkylamine). Only phenoxybenzamine is used therapeutically. These compounds possess α-**adrenoceptor** blocking activity. The initial antagonism is competitive (*see* **competitive antagonist**) but with time a non-surmountable **receptor** block develops. This is because the β-haloalkylamines undergo cyclization to form an ethyleniminium ion which alkylates the receptor. The β-haloalkylamines also block **histamine receptors, serotonin receptors** and **muscarinic cholinoceptors.**

Phenoxybenzamine

hapten A substance of low molecular weight (e.g. a **drug**) that by itself cannot stimulate the formation of **antibodies**, but which may do so when combined with a large carrier molecule such as plasma albumin (Greek: *haptein*, to fasten).

harassing agents *See* **incapacitating agents**.

harmonic mean The reciprocal of the arithmetic means of the reciprocals of the original measurements:

$$\bar{H} = \frac{1}{\dfrac{\Sigma(1/Y)}{N}} = \frac{N}{\Sigma(1/Y)}$$

The harmonic mean is used when quantities are expressed as reciprocals, e.g. pulse intervals or **volumes of distribution**.

HeLa cells A cultured line of human cells derived from a carcinoma of the uterine cervix from a patient named Henrietta Lacks (hence the name). The cells have been cultured and subcultured many times and are commercially available.

Henderson–Hasselbalch equation An equation developed by Henderson and Hasselbalch to relate the relative amounts of ionized and non-ionized forms of a weak base or a weak acid in solution to the pH of that solution. Many **drugs** are weak acids or weak bases. The equation states that for a weak base:

$$\log \frac{[\text{non-ionized}]}{[\text{anionic form}]} = pK_a - pH$$

and for a weak acid:

$$\log \frac{[\text{non-ionized}]}{[\text{cationic form}]} = pH - pK_a$$

where K_a is the ionization constant and pK_a is its negative logarithm.

Thus, it can be seen that when the pK_a equals the pH, the number of ionized and non-ionized molecules are equal (since $\log 1 = 0$). The higher the pH (i.e. the more alkaline), the greater is the ionization of acidic drugs and the lower the ionization of basic drugs.

heparin A heteroglycan containing alternating sulphated units of glucuronic acid and glucosamine in a straight chain of 30–70 glycose units. It is highly acidic on account of the sulphate groups, and its preparations are supplied as the sodium salt.

As the name implies, it was first found in liver, but is now obtained from lung and intestinal mucosa. It is present in the tissues stored in mast cells. Heparin prevents coagulation of blood by acting at a number of sites in the clotting process.

hepatotoxicity Toxicity manifested in the liver. The hepatotoxic effects of **drugs** and other chemicals may take the form of cholestatic jaundice (e.g. with tolbutamide), of hepatocellular damage (e.g. with chloroform), or of carcinogenesis (e.g. **nitrosamines**).

herbalism The practice that deals with herbs, parts of which are used for the benefit of man as medicines or foods, or for their scent or flavour.

herbicides Chemicals used in agriculture and gardening to destroy weeds, and sometimes in war as defoliants to expose areas of dense bush (e.g. Agent Orange in Vietnam). Their relevance to pharmacology lies in their toxicity to man and animals. They include chlorophenoxy compounds such as 2,4-D and **2,4,5-T**, substituted dinitrophenols such as dinitro-orthocresol (DNOC), bipyridyl compounds such as **paraquat**, certain carbamates (e.g. propham), substituted ureas (e.g. monuran), triazines (e.g. atrazine), aniline derivatives (e.g. alachlor) and benzoic acid derivatives (e.g. amiben).

   Paraquat and 2,4,5-T are dealt with in separate entries because of their special toxicity problems.

HETE Hydroxyeicosatetraenoic acid. The precursor of **leukotrienes** formed from **HPETE**.

high-ceiling diuretics *See* **loop diuretics**.

Hill plot The straight line graph of $\log r/(1 - r)$ against $\log[D]$, where r is the proportion of **receptors** occupied by a **drug** and $[D]$ is the concentration of the drug in the **biophase**. In practice, r is usually taken as the fraction of the maximal response obtained with the drug, on the basis that the response is linearly proportional to receptor occupancy and the maximal response is reached when the total number of receptors is occupied. However, this assumption is not always justified (*see* **occupation theory**).

   The slope of the Hill plot (n), known as the Hill coefficient, gives the number of drug molecules that combine with each receptor. There are many instances where $n = 1$, but this is not always so. When $n = 1$, the Hill plot is the same as the Langmuir adsorption isotherm (*see* **agonist–receptor interaction**).

   The Hill plot is named after the physiologist A. V. Hill who devised it when studying the relationship between the partial pressure of oxygen and the percentage saturation of haemoglobin.

histamine The decarboxylation product of the amino acid histidine. Histamine was synthesized in 1907, and its pronounced pharmacological properties were studied by Dale and Laidlaw around 1910 when they found it in an ergot extract (*see* **ergot of rye**) where it had been formed by bacterial decarboxylation of histidine. Histamine dilates terminal arterioles, but most other smooth muscles contract in response to it. It is a powerful stimulant of gastric acid secretion. Dale and his colleagues recognized that the actions of histamine resemble those of many tissue extracts, and those of injecting a protein into a previously sensitized animal. In 1927, Best, Dale and their colleagues isolated histamine from fresh liver and lung, thereby establishing that it is an endogenous constituent of the body tissues (Greek: *histos*, tissue; thus histamine is an amine of the tissues). Lewis and colleagues around 1927 provided evidence that histamine and their 'H-substance' were one and the same. H-substance was liberated from the skin by injurious stimuli, including **antigen–antibody** reactions. It is now known that histamine is involved in many physiological and pathological processes, and, as well as its **autacoid** function, it may serve as a neurotransmitter in certain nerve fibres in the brain.

$$CH_2CH_2NH_2$$

Histamine
6(2-(4-imidazolyl)ethylamine
or β-aminoethylimidazole)

Histamine in many tissues is stored in the **mast cells**, in which it is bound together with **heparin** and ATP. In human blood, histamine is contained within the basophils which closely resemble mast cells. *See also* **histamine receptors**.

histamine H$_1$ (or H$_2$) receptors   *See* **histamine receptors**.

histamine receptors   Specific **receptors** with which **histamine** interacts. Work by Folkow, Furchgott, Schildt and Black and their co-workers showed that histamine receptors are not homogeneous. They may be divided into at least two subtypes termed histamine H$_1$ receptors and histamine H$_2$ receptors. H$_1$ receptors are present, for example, in smooth muscles, and in most cases mediate contraction, whereas H$_2$ receptors are present, for example, on oxyntic cells, and mediate secretion of gastric acid. Both H$_1$ and H$_2$ receptors are present in the brain. Relatively selective synthetic **agonists** for H$_1$ receptors include 2-methylhistamine and 2-(2-thiazolyl)ethylamine. Relatively selective synthetic agonists for H$_2$ receptors include 4-methylhistamine and dimaprit. Antagonists at H$_1$ receptors include all of the 'classical **antihistamine drugs**', such as mepyramine (pyrilamine in USA), antazoline, buclizine, diphenhydramine and chlorpheniramine. Antagonists at H$_2$ receptors include newer drugs such as cimetidine and ranitidine which are mainly used to control peptic ulcer. H$_1$ receptors are often, and possibly always, coupled to membrane ion channels, whereas H_2 receptors are often, and possibly always, coupled to **adenylate cyclase**, and so stimulate the production of **cyclic AMP**.

histaminergic nerve fibre   A nerve fibre that releases **histamine** as a neurotransmitter. *See* **adrenergic nerve fibre** for discussion of the restricted use of the suffix '-ergic'.

histrionicotoxin   The major toxin from the skin of the Columbian frog *Dendrobates histrionicus*. This toxin, and **perhydrohistrionicotoxin**, are thought to have the specific action of binding to and blocking the cation channels associated with the **acetylcholine** receptors (*see* **cholinoceptors**) at the motor endplate without affecting the acetylcholine recognition sites of the receptors. (*See* **ion channel block**.)

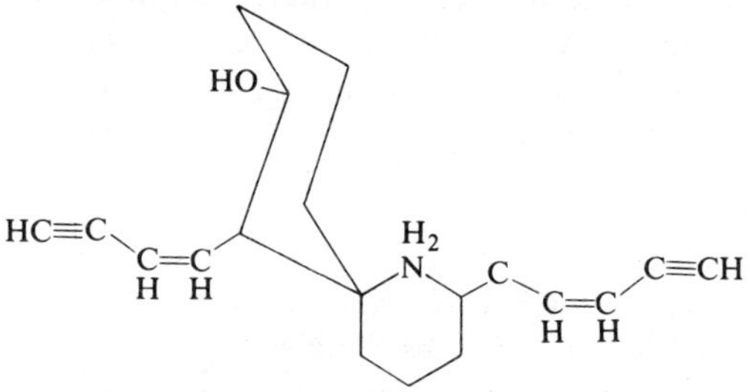

Histrionicotoxin

Albuquerque & Oliveira (1979) In *Advances in Cytopharmacology*, Vol. 3 (Eds. Ceccarelli & Clementi), p. 197. Raven Press, New York.

Hofmann elimination   A chemical reaction in which a quaternary ammonium group is converted into a tertiary amine, which is eliminated from the molecule through the breaking of a carbon–nitrogen bond. Electron withdrawal towards the quaternary nitrogen group weakens the βC–H bond with the result that a proton is lost from the C in the position β to the N, yielding an olefinic double bond with the breakage of one of the carbon–nitrogen bonds, viz:

$$HO^- \quad H{-}CH_2{-}CH_2{-}NR_3 \rightarrow H_2O + CH_2{=}CH_2 + NR_3$$
$$\beta \qquad \alpha$$

The reaction in its simple form requires treatment of the quaternary salt with NaOH and heating to 100°C. However, the presence of a second electron-withdrawing group attached to the βC causes further weakening of the βC–H bond, with the result that elimination may occur at physiological temperature and pH values. J. B. Stenlake and his colleagues made use of this concept in designing the **neuromuscular blocking drug** atracurium, which accordingly possesses a built-in 'self-destruct' mechanism. Consequently, termination of neuromuscular blocking action is independent of enzymes, redistribution or excretion (*see* Stenlake (1982) *Pharm. J.* **229**, 116). It is of interest, in view of the pharmacological use to which the concept has been put, that the German chemist, W. Hofmann, discovered the reaction that bears his name in the same year (1851) in which Claude Bernard first described the site of action of **curare** in the frog.

Incorporation into new drug molecules of features that facilitate a Hofmann elimination reaction may be useful in other fields not yet considered, perhaps including the preparation of **prodrugs**.

homeopathy (or homoeopathy) A system of therapy devised by Christian Samuel Hahnemann (1755–1843) in Germany, although it has its origins in earlier beliefs. Hahnemann was a graduate in medicine from the Universities of Leipzig and Vienna and, not surprisingly, he was disillusioned with the medicine of his day. He is said to have developed his system of homeopathic treatment (Greek: *homos*, same; *patheia*, suffering, i.e. pathology) after his observation, on himself, that cinchona (which contains quinine) in large doses produces toxic symptoms somewhat similar to those of the ague (a rather vague condition incorporating everything from malaria, through rheumatism, to a feverish chill), yet cinchona was used to treat the ague. He revived Hippocrates' suggestion that 'like cures like' (*similia similibus curantur*) with the concept that a drug which in large doses produces particular symptoms in a healthy individual may be used to treat a patient who is suffering from those symptoms. Homeopathy involves the principle that a person is not sick because his organs misfunction, but rather that his organs misfunction because he is sick; surely a sound enough idea in many instances. The aim then becomes to treat the person (i.e. his 'vital force') rather than his malfunctioning organs. Where homeopathy differs most from pharmacology, indeed is the antithesis of pharmacology, is in the method of dosing with **drugs**. In pharmacology, response is regarded as being proportional to the dose, whereas in homeopathy a laid down series of sequential dilutions of the drug is made, far beyond Avogadro's constant, so that it is unlikely that the dose actually contains even a single molecule of the drug. The drug is said to have been 'potentized' by the diluting procedure and, even though no longer present, to have left its 'energy' or 'power' in the diluent which the patient takes.

hormonagogue An agent that stimulates the secretion of a **hormone** (Greek: *agogos*, leading). For example, **nicotine** stimulates the secretion of antidiuretic hormone and therefore acts as a hormonagogue in this respect.

hormones 'Chemical messengers' (steroids, simple proteins or glycoproteins, polypeptides or derivatives of amino acids) that are synthesized, stored and secreted into the bloodstream by a diverse group of ductless glands (endocrine glands). The hormones are 'recognized' by **receptors** in the cells of specific target tissues, which respond in a characteristic fashion.

Starling first used the word 'hormone' in the joint Croonian lecture by Bayliss and Starling in 1904. The word is derived from the Greek (*hormhao*, I arouse to activity), and is said to have originated at a dinner in Caius College, Cambridge, at which Starling was a guest of W. B. Hardy and during which the inspiration was supplied by the classical scholar, W. T. Vesey.

hot-plate test A test for analgesic activity. Mice are placed on a plate which is heated to a constant temperature of 55°C. After a latent period they show signs of discomfort such as raising or licking the forepaws or jumping. **Analgesic drugs** prevent or delay the appearance of these signs. The test is made quantitative by administering different doses of the new potential analgesic drug to different groups of randomly distributed animals, and determining the percentage of animals in each group that fail to exhibit signs of discomfort in a given time. Doses of a standard drug, such as **morphine**, are administered to similar groups for comparison.

The temperature of 55°C has been shown not to cause tissue damage even when the mice, through analgesic action, fail to remove their forepaws from the plate.

HPETE Hydroperoxyeicosatetraenoic acid. A hydroperoxide intermediate formed during the initial interaction of the lipoxygenase enzyme with arachidonic acid in the formation of **leukotrienes**. HPETE and **HETE** are chemotactic substances, having the ability to attract neutrophils into an area of inflammation. They are taken up and incorporated into the cellular lipids of neutrophils, so altering their membrane characteristics. HPETE is also a potent inhibitor of prostacyclin formation.

5-HT *See* **serotonin**.

HT-receptors *See* **serotonin receptors**.

hydrocholeretic drug A drug that increases the volume of the bile and hence the amount that flows into the intestine. Examples include dehydrocholic acid, florantyrone and tocamphyl. *See also* **choleretic drug**.

8-hydroxyquinolines A series of compounds, containing a halogenated 8-hydroxyquinoline group, with antimicrobial activity. Examples include chiniofon and clioquinol. They are used for the treatment of enteric infections (including intestinal amoebiasis) that are resistant to treatment with other drugs. Some members of the series (e.g. chlorquinaldol) may be used topically for skin infections. Clioquinol was formerly commonly recommended for the treatment of so-called traveller's diarrhoea, but its efficacy is doubtful and its potential toxicity makes its use for such a relatively trivial condition unwise. The use of high doses of 8-hydroxyquinolines for periods of 14 days or more has been implicated in the incidence of subacute myelo-optic neuropathy (**SMON**).

5-hydroxytryptamine   *See* serotonin.

5-hydroxytryptamine receptors   *See* serotonin receptors.

hypersensitivity reactions   Adverse reactions to drugs that are triggered by the immune response. They range from the relatively trivial (such as rash) to incapacitating disease (such as asthma) and even to life-endangering anaphylactic shock. Probably about 10% of adverse reactions to drugs are hypersensitivity reactions. Most drugs, being of low molecular weight, must act as **haptens** in order to induce a hypersensitivity reaction. Hypersensitivity reactions to drugs have been classified into four types: type I, anaphylactic reactions; type II, cytolytic reactions; type III, toxic precipitin reactions; and type IV, cell-mediated hypersensitivity reactions.

hypnotic drug   A drug that promotes sleep (Greek: *hupnos*, sleep). Amylobarbitone, nitrazepam and chloral hydrate are examples.

hypoglycaemic drugs   Orally active drugs that produce a fall in blood glucose concentration. They include sulphonylurea derivatives such as tolbutamide, which act by stimulating the release of **insulin** from the islets of Langerhans, derivatives of pyridinyl benzene sulphonamide, such as glymidine, which act in a similar way, and **biguanides**, such as phenformin, which enhance glucose uptake by muscle in diabetic patients, reduce glucose absorption, increase glycolysis and reduce gluconeogenesis.

These drugs may be used in the control of diabetes mellitus in some maturity-onset diabetics.

iatrogenic disease   Literally physician-caused disease (Greek: *iatros*, a physician) and often applied to disease arising from side-effects of **drugs** or from inappropriate prescribing of drugs. It is unjust to ascribe cases of drug toxicity solely to the physician; the pharmaceutical industry, pharmacists, pharmacologists, and others involved should take a share of the blame.

ibotenic acid   A substance obtained from the mushrooms *Amanita pantherina* and *A. muscaria*. It has insecticidal action, and it potentiates barbiturates in mammals. In rats it produces lesions of the nucleus basalis magnocellularis which is thought to be the rodent equivalent of the nucleus of Meynert in man. The nucleus of Meynert is one of the main sources of cholinergic input to the cerebral cortex, and it is severely degenerated in

Alzheimer's disease. Ibotenic acid has therefore been used in attempts to produce an animal model of Alzheimer's disease.

Ibotenic acid

immediate hypersensitivity reaction   A rapidly occurring (within 30 min) **antibody**-mediated reaction arising from the release of **histamine** and other vasoactive substances. The antibody (an immunoglobulin, usually of IgE type) fixes to cells, especially **mast cells**. On contact with **antigen**, the cell is disrupted and vasoactive substances are released and produce **anaphylaxis**.

Type I hypersensitivity reaction is an alternative name for immediate hypersensitivity reaction.

immunopharmacology   The study of drugs in relation to immunology.

immunopotentiating agent   An agent that enhances the build-up of immune mechanisms on secondary exposure to **antigen**. Levamisole, originally synthesized as an **anthelmintic drug**, is an example. It potentiates cell-mediated immunity by an action that resembles that of thymic hormones. **Cyclic GMP** may be involved. *See also* **delayed hypersensitivity reactions**.

immunostimulants   Substances that increase the intensity of the immune response. So-called adjuvants, which are administered together with the **antigen**, come into this category. Adjuvants include pertussis vaccine (often used to enhance the antigenic activity of diphtheria vaccine), nucleic acids and **Freund's complete adjuvant**.

The drug levamisole, originally produced as an **anthelmintic drug** for ascaris infections, has the additional property of potentiating cell-mediated immunity when this is in a previously depressed state. Drugs with this type of action are usually described as **immunopotentiating agents** rather than as immunostimulants.

immunosuppressants   Agents that suppress the immune response. These include cytotoxic drugs (such as cyclophosphamide, methotrexate, azothioprine, cytaribine and actinomycin D) which inhibit proliferation of lymphocytes, anti-inflammatory steroids (*see* **glucocorticoids**) which act at the recognition phase of the immune response as well as on the proliferative stage, and **cyclosporin A**.

immunotoxins   Hybrid molecules containing an **antibody** component of defined fine specificity coupled to a cytotoxic moiety (*see* Jansen *et al.* (1982) *Immunol. Rev.* **62**, 185). The cytotoxic moiety is usually an anticancer agent (e.g. α-amanitin, methotrexate, the A chains of ricin or abrin, $^{125}I^-$ or $^{131}I^-$). The antibody component might be a **monoclonal antibody**. *See also* **chimeric toxin**.

implants of drugs   A method of placing drugs, formulated into pellets, under the skin to achieve a prolonged action. Steroid **hormones** may be administered in this way. The active drug slowly dissolves in the tissue fluid before diffusing into the capillaries. The pellet becomes surrounded by fibrous connective tissue which further slows its rate of dissolution. Implants of deoxycortisone acetate have been found to remain effective for up to six months.

incapacitating agents   Agents intended to cause a rapid-onset, but temporary, disablement of aggressive individuals or groups of individuals (sometimes used by military or police). Most act by sensory irritation of the eyes or respiratory tract leading to lachrymation (lachrymators or tear gases) or sneezing (sternutators). Such agents include CS gas, DM gas, CR gas and CN gas. A different type of agent, derivatives of glycolate esters, produces a kind of temporary psychosis in which the victim is confused, disoriented and apprehensive, and has hallucinations. The effects appear to arise from a central atropine-like action. The US army code name, BZ compounds, refers to this type of agent.

Alternative names for the group include disabling agents, harassing agents and anti-riot agents.

indirectly acting sympathomimetic   A **sympathomimetic drug** that acts by releasing **noradrenaline** from storage vesicles in adrenergic nerve varicosities, rather than by itself exerting **agonist** activity directly on **adrenoceptors**. Indirectly acting sympathomimetic drugs include tyramine, ephedrine, amphetamine and 2-aminoheptane. Tyramine, ephedrine and amphetamine also exert some direct **sympathomimetic action**.

individual tolerance   *See* **tolerance**.

indole alkaloids   Naturally occurring **alkaloids** containing an indole group in their chemical structures. They include bufotenine (from the skin

Bufotenine

Harmine

glands of toads of the *Bufo* species but also from many plants) and harmine (from *Harmala* species of plants). They possess hallucinogenic activity. (*See under* **psychotomimetic drugs**.)

indolealkylamines Synthetic or naturally occurring compounds, or derivatives of the latter, containing an indolealkylamine nucleus in their chemical structures. They include the **indole alkaloids** and also lysergide (LSD) and its derivatives. They possess hallucinogenic activity (*see* **psychotomimetic drugs**).

induction agent A drug administered, usually intravenously, to induce rapid general anaesthesia and thereby avoid distress to the patient. The anaesthesia may then be continued with an inhalation agent. Sodium thiopentone probably remains the most frequently used induction agent. Basal anaesthetic is an alternative name.

infiltration anaesthesia Local anaesthesia induced by injection of a **local anaesthetic drug** subcutaneously around sensory nerve endings to enable minor operations (e.g. tooth extraction) to be performed.

infusion Continuous injection (usually intravenously) of a solution of a **drug** over a period of minutes, hours or even days. The force may be supplied by gravity from a reservoir, or by an infusion pump.

The word also refers to a solution of the soluble constituents of a crude drug, or to the process of obtaining the solution, specifically by steeping the crude drug in the solvent. For example, tea is usually prepared for drinking by an infusion process, and the liquid, as drunk, is an infusion of tea leaves (Latin: *fundere*, to pour).

inhalational anaesthetic *See* **general anaesthetic drug**.

injection The introduction of a solution, or a suspension, of a substance (usually a **drug**) through a hypodermic needle into the body by one of several routes, e.g. intravenously, intramuscularly, subcutaneously, intraperitoneally, intrathecally (Latin: *jacere*, to throw).

inositol triphosphate A hydrolysis product of **phosphatidylinositol** 4,5-biphosphate that is released into the cytosol in response to the action of certain **agonists**. In the cytosol it functions as a **second messenger** for mobilizing intracellular Ca^{2+}. *See* **PI response**.
Berridge & Irvine (1984) *Nature* **312**, 315

inotropic action An action that results in a change in the peak tension or force of a contraction (Greek: *inos*, of muscle; *trepein*, to turn). Thus, a positive inotropic action results in a larger isometric contraction. For example, **adrenaline** exerts a positive inotropic action on cardiac muscle. (NB Adrenaline also exerts a positive **klinotropic action**.)

insecticides Substances that exhibit **selective toxicity** against the class Insecta. Insects of pharmacological relevance are flies, fleas, midges, mosquitoes, bugs and lice. Insecticides include chlorinated hydrocarbons such as dicophane (DDT), gamma benzene hexachloride (γ-BHC) and dieldrin, **organophosphorus anticholinesterases** such as malathion and dichlorvos, carbamate anticholinesterases such as carbaryl, dinitrophenols such as binapacryl, and organic insecticides of natural origin such as pyrethrum flowers and derris root. Insecticides are used in the bush to control insect vectors of disease, and by application to the skin to control infestation by fleas or lice. Malathion is the main drug currently used to control lice infestation (body lice and crab lice).

insulin The polypeptide hormone secreted by the B-cells of the islets of Langerhans in the pancreas (Latin: *insula*, island). Its deficiency or lack of activity gives rise to the disease diabetes mellitus.

interferon inducers *See* **interferons**.

interferons Antiviral single-chain glycoproteins (mol. wt. *c.* 20 000) that are synthesized in all mammalian cells when the appropriate genes are derepressed through exposure to an appropriate stimulus, of which virus infection is one. Interferons are believed to help contain viral infections until the immune system can be fully activated. When released from infected cells, interferons help to protect uninfected cells from subsequent viral-induced damage by inhibiting viral multiplication in those cells. The interferon interacts with a surface membrane **receptor** and induces an antiviral protein that interferes with the early translation of viral mRNA, without inhibiting normal cellular RNA translation. The protection appears to be mediated by a rise in the cellular content of **cyclic AMP**. Interferons are species-specific but nor virus-specific; that is, interferons induced in one species interfere with the multiplication of almost all viruses in that species, but have little antiviral action in unrelated species. At least three distinct interferons have been detected in different human cells.

Recombinant DNA technology is being used to induce bacteria to synthesize human interferons, and interferons are being tested, as **drugs**, for use not only in viral infections but also against some cancers. Additionally, interferons may be of value in patients whose immune systems have been suppressed by drugs prior to organ transplant.

Substances, in addition to viruses, that enhance the production of interferons by cells (interferon inducers) include double-stranded RNAs from several viruses, extracts of micro-organisms including bacteria, protozoa and fungi, certain plant extracts (e.g. kanamycin), some synthetic polymers (e.g. polymethylacrylic acid and poly I:C) and some relatively low molecular weight substances (e.g. tilorone and the substituted propanediamine coded CP-20,961).

interleukin-1   A polypeptide (or a group of closely related polypeptides) synthesized in, and released from, mononuclear phagocytes during the early stage of the inflammatory response. Interleukin-1 induces several metabolic and immunological changes that are characteristic of the acute phase of inflammatory or immunologically mediated responses, e.g. fever, increased synthesis of hepatic acute-phase proteins, increased white blood cell count, decreased serum iron and zinc levels, negative nitrogen balance.

interleukin-2   A **lymphokine** synthesized and secreted by some T-cells following activation with **antigen** or **mitogen** in the presence of monocyte-derived **interleukin-1**. Interleukin-2 permits long-term growth *in vitro* of T-cell populations serving helper and cytotoxic functions, and it augments natural killer cell activity. It is being evaluated for therapeutic use in patients with certain neoplasms or with acquired immune deficiency syndrome (AIDS).

interleukin-3   A substance derived from concanavalin A-stimulated lymphocytes which appears to be involved in the maturation of a stem cell subpopulation of T-cells.

intra-arterial injection   Injection into an artery.

intradermal injection   Injection between the skin layers.

intramuscular injection   Injection into muscle mass.

intraperitoneal injection   Injection into the peritoneal cavity.

intrathecal injection   Injection into the cerebrospinal fluid of the subarachnoid space.

intravenous anaesthetic   *See* **general anaesthetic drug**.

intravenous injection   Injection into a vein.

intrinsic activity   A term coined by Ariëns and his co-workers to describe that property of **agonists** which determines the strength of the pharmacological stimulus produced by **receptor** occupation. It is defined by the equations:

$$E = \alpha[DR]$$

and

$$\frac{E}{E_{max}} = \frac{\alpha[DR]}{[R_T]}$$

where α = intrinsic activity, E = effect observed and E_{max} = the maximal effect, $[DR]$ is the concentration of drug–receptor complex and R_T is the total number of receptors. $[DR]/[R_T]$ corresponds to the proportion of receptors occupied by drug. The relationship between response, drug concentration, $[D]$, and the dissociation constant (K_D) of the drug–receptor complex is given by:

$$\frac{E}{E_{max}} = \frac{\alpha[D]}{[D] + K_D}$$

For full agonists that produce the maximal response from occupation of receptors, $\alpha = 1$; for **dualists**, α is less than 1 but greater than 0; and for antagonists without agonist activity, $\alpha = 0$.

intrinsic efficacy A term proposed by R. Furchgott to denote the parameter of an **agonist** that determines the stimulus (S) produced when it occupies **receptors**. Thus, $S = \varepsilon[DR]$, where ε is intrinsic efficacy and $[DR]$ is the concentration of drug–receptor complexes. The relationship to Stephenson's **efficacy** factor is given by $e = \varepsilon[R_T]$, where e = efficacy and R_T is the total number of receptors.

intrinsic sympathomimetic activity A term used to describe the agonistic activity of some β-**adrenoceptor antagonists**; such drugs are therefore **partial agonists**. Examples of drugs with this type of activity include dichloroisoprenaline, alprenolol, oxprenolol and pindolol.

inverse agonist *See under* **benzodiazepine receptors**.

ion channel block Blockade of ionic current flow through membranes by chemical agents that bind to some components of the ion channels. A number of agents act selectively on particular channels. For example, **tetrodotoxin** and **saxitoxin** selectively block voltage-dependent Na^+-channels (*see* **voltage-dependent ion channels**), and blockade of such channels in cardiac muscle is the main mechanism of action of class I **antidysrhythmic drugs**. Tetraethylammonium and 4-aminopyridine block voltage-dependent K^+-channels, and **calcium channel blocking drugs** are selective for Ca^{2+}-channels.

Block of the **cholinoceptor**-linked cation channels at the motor endplate is a special case, in that some of the **drugs** capable of producing this effect exert their main pharmacological action at a different site. Examples of drugs which, in high concentrations, may block motor endplate ion channels include **barbiturates**, **local anaesthetic drugs**, phencyclidine, perhydrohistrionicotoxin and certain **antibiotics**. A surprising observation is that some **neuromuscular blocking drugs**, notably tubocurarine and gallamine, may block endplate ion channels under certain conditions. Their usual action is to block the recognition sites of the cholinoceptors, as illustrated on the left of the diagram (a), but they may also act to block ion channels that have first been opened by **acetylcholine**, as on the right (b). *See* **receptor-operated ion channels** for explanation of diagram.

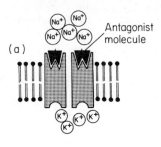 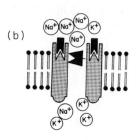

ionization constant   The ionization of anion-forming (acidic) or cation-forming (basic) drugs may be expressed:

$$AH \rightleftharpoons A^- + H^+$$

and

$$BH^+ \rightleftharpoons B + H^+$$

where AH and B are the non-ionized forms of acidic and basic drugs respectively, and the ionized forms are A^- (anion) and BH^+ (cation). The ionization constant (K_a) of these dissociation reactions is then given by:

$$K_a = \frac{[A^-][H^+]}{[AH]}$$

and

$$K_a = \frac{[B][H^+]}{[BH^+]}$$

The dimensions of K_a are molar.

Alternative names for ionization constant are dissociation constant or equilibrium constant. *See also* **Henderson–Hasselbalch equation**.

It is usually more convenient to express ionization constants as their negative logarithms, i.e. pK_a values. The pK_a values of some common basic drugs are: guanethidine 11·4, atropine 9·7, haloperidol 8·7, **morphine** 7·9, ergometrine 6·8, **histamine** 5·9, chlordiazepoxide 4·6, diazepam 3·3, colchicine 1·9, caffeine 0·8. And for some common acidic drugs: **cromoglycate** 2·0, aspirin 3·5, methotrexate 4·8, dicoumarol 5·7, azauridine 6·7, thiopentone 7·6, azaserine 8·6, ethosuximide 9·5.

ionophore   A substance that forms channels through a lipid membrane, including cell membranes, thereby allowing ions to traverse the membrane along their concentration gradient. Most of the exogenous ionophores are polyether **antibiotics** obtained from *Streptomyces* species. Most of them are straight-chain molecules in their uncomplexed form, but they become cyclized by head-to-tail hydrogen bonding in the presence of appropriate cations. Many ionophores are ion-selective. They are lipid-soluble, and the cyclized molecules may become stacked through the membrane, so forming an ion-selective channel. The ion selectivity is determined by the structural constraints in the antibiotic molecule.

Examples of ionophores include monensin (which is relatively selective for Na^+), valinomycin and nigericin (which are relatively selective for K^+), calcimycin (or A-23187, which is relatively selective for Ca^{2+}), and lasalocid (or X-537A, which is non-selective and transports Na^+, K^+ and Ca^{2+}). It should be noted that although these substances are antibiotics in the sense that they are produced by micro-organisms and exert toxic effects on other cells, they are not therapeutically useful as antibiotics, because they are also toxic to man. Nevertheless, in controlled doses some of them have been given clinical trials for conditions unconnected with infections (e.g. calcimycin is a cardiac **inotropic agent**).

The term ionophore may also be used to describe the ion channels already present in cell membranes that are voltage-dependent or coupled to receptors (*see* **voltage-dependent** and **receptor-operated ion channels**).

The term should *not* be used to describe drugs that facilitate ion movement through already existing ion channels. For example, the so-called **calcium channel activators** are not ionophores.

irin   A mixture of substances (now known to be **prostaglandins**) released from the iris and associated structures during inflammation of the eye.

irreversible receptor antagonist   An antagonist that forms a strong bond with the **receptors** such that the rate of dissociation of the antagonist–receptor complex is so slow as to be virtually zero. The antagonist may be regarded as irreversible, and the antagonism is not surmountable by increasing the concentration of **agonist**. The number of receptors available for interaction with the agonist is reduced, hence the maximal response is reduced. The occupation of the receptors by the irreversible antagonist can be reduced (i.e. the receptors can be protected from blockade) by the simultaneous presence of a high concentration of agonist or of a **competitive antagonist**.

If the proportion of receptors that are inactivated by an irreversible antagonist is designated r_i, the equation for the relationship between response and agonist concentration is:

$$E/E_{max} = [D](1 - r_i)/([D] + K_D)$$

(*see* **occupation theory** for explanation of terms.) The equation for the **Lineweaver–Burk plot** is:

$$\frac{E_{max}}{E}, \quad \text{i.e.} \quad \frac{1}{y} = \frac{K_D}{[D]} \frac{1}{1 - r_i} + \frac{1}{1 - r_i}$$

where E_{max} is the original maximal response, and it is assumed that the relationship between response and receptor occupancy is not changed. Graphs of response against agonist concentration and log concentration are shown below for various degrees of inactivation of receptors by an

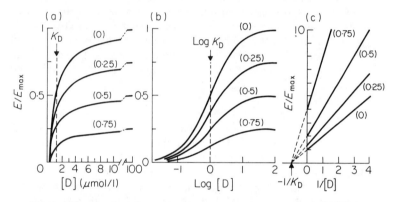

Effects of inactivation of receptors with an irreversible antagonist. The numbers in parentheses indicate the proportion of receptors inactivated (r_i). For the Lineweaver–Burk plot (c), K_D was arbitrarily taken as 1 μmol/1 and [D] was expressed in units of μmol/1. From Bowman & Rand (1980) *Textbook of Pharmacology*, 2nd Edition. Blackwell Scientific Publications, Oxford.

irreversible antagonist. The dissociation constant (K_D) is not altered and the half-maximal responses before and after inactivation of the receptors are produced by the same concentration of agonist. In the Lineweaver–Burk plot, the intercepts on the (E_{max}/E)-axis are at points corresponding to $1/(1 - r_i)$ and the lines intersect on the (1/[D])-axis at a point corresponding to $-1/K_D$.

irritant purgative   A purgative that stimulates peristalsis by an irritant action on the intestinal mucosa, or by directly stimulating sensory nerve endings, or by facilitating reflex action in the myenteric plexus. Irritant purgatives include castor oil (actually the ricinoleic acid derived therefrom), phenolphthalein and anthraquinones such as those in senna, rhubarb, cascara and aloes.

islet-activating protein   A protein present in pertussis (whooping cough) vaccine and also called pertussis toxin or islet cell stimulating protein. Islet-activating protein (IAP) was found to prevent **adrenaline-**

induced hyperglycaemia in rats by stimulating the release of **insulin** from the islets of Langerhans. The mechanism involves suppression of α_2-**adrenoceptor**-mediated inhibition of insulin release (i.e. disinhibition), and stimulation of β-adrenoceptor-mediated insulin release. The α_2-adrenoceptor-mediated inhibition of insulin release depends upon inhibition of adenylate cyclase; that is, the α_2-adrenoceptor is coupled to the N_i GTP-binding protein (*see* **adenylate cyclase**). IAP stabilizes N_i in its inactive state, so that it can no longer inhibit adenylate cyclase. Consequently the enzyme is stimulated via β-adrenoceptors and the increased **cyclic AMP** concentration enhances insulin release. (Cf. the effect of **cholera toxin** which stabilizes N_s in its active state—the end result is the same.)

More recent evidence shows that the action of IAP is not selectively on islet cells; in fact it enhances cyclic AMP formation in many cell types.

islet cell stimulating protein   *See* **islet-activating protein**.

isobol   A line on a graph joining up points of equal effect (Greek: *isos*, the same; *bolos*, effect). *See also under* **synergistic action**.

isoceptors   *See* **isoreceptors**.

isoenzymes   Different forms of an enzyme, usually occurring in different tissues. The isoenzymes of a particular enzyme catalyse the same reaction, but they differ in some of their properties. For example, they migrate differently on electrophoresis. The formation of isoenzymes usually involves different arrangements of subunits arising from two different genetic loci to form the active polymeric enzyme. For example, the enzyme lactate dehydrogenase is a tetrameric enzyme with two distinct subunits, designated H for heart and M for muscle. There are five isoenzymes arising from five different combinations of the two subunits in the tetramers. Thus, HHHH and HHHM occur in heart and erythrocytes, MMMM and HMMM occur in skeletal muscle and liver and HHMM occurs in brain and kidney.

The enzyme catalyses the reaction:

$$\text{Lactic acid} + \text{NAD} \rightleftharpoons \text{pyruvic acid} + \text{NADH}$$

The MMMM enzyme is about twice as active as the HHHH enzyme. The latter is inhibited by excess pyruvate but the MMMM enzyme is barely affected.

isometric   An adjective used to describe a muscle contraction in which the muscle length remains constant while the tension developed increases (Greek: *isos*, equal or unchanging; *metron*, measure).

isoreceptors A term (analogous to **isoenzyme** or isozyme) sometimes used in referring to subtypes of a more major class of **receptors**. (Isoceptors is an alternative name.) For example, β_1-adrenoceptors and β_2-adrenoceptors are isoreceptors of the general class of β-**adrenoceptors**.

isotonic An adjective used to describe a muscle contraction in which the load remains constant while the muscle shortens in length (Greek: *isos*, equal or unchanging; *tonos*, that which is stretched, hence tension). The term isotonic is also applied to solutions which have the same osmotic pressure. For example, 0·9% w/v NaCl solution is isotonic with mammalian blood plasma, and so does not damage the membranes of cells suspended in it.

isotonic solution A solution in which body cells (e.g. erythrocytes) can be bathed without causing a net flow of water across the cell membrane; i.e. the solution exerts the same osmotic pressure as the intracellular fluid (Greek: *isos*, equal; *tonos*, that which is stretched). Also used to denote a solution which has the same osmotic pressure as some other solution with which it is compared. For example, 0·9% w/v NaCl solution is isotonic with blood serum.

isozyme *See* **isoenzyme**.

Jardetzky's therapeutic characteristic A risk-benefit ratio derived from data obtained in laboratory animals and calculated from $LD_{2.5}/ED_{97.5}$. The $LD_{2.5}$ is the lethal dose in 2·5% of animals in a group, and the $ED_{97.5}$ is the effective dose in 97·5% of animals in a group (cf. LD_{50} and ED_{50}).

Jesuit's bark A name for the bark of various species of South American cinchona trees from which quinine and quinidine are obtained. Peruvian bark and cinchona bark are alternative names.

joro spider toxin (JSTX) A toxin from the venom glands of the Japanese joro spider (*Nephila clavata*). It has the property of blocking **glutamate receptors** in crustacea and mammals.

kainic acid An amino acid isolated from the Japanese seaweed *Digenea simplex*. It is a powerful stimulant of the central nervous system and appears to act at glutamate synapses. Its relationship to **glutamic acid** is indicated by the dotted line in the structure below. It greatly potentiates glutamate, and in large doses it causes destruction of postsynaptic cells that possess **glutamate receptors**. It is used as a pharmacological tool by neurobiologists to inactivate particular nerve centres in the brain. When injected into the corpus striatum of animals in small amounts, kainic acid produces a model of the disease Huntington's chorea.

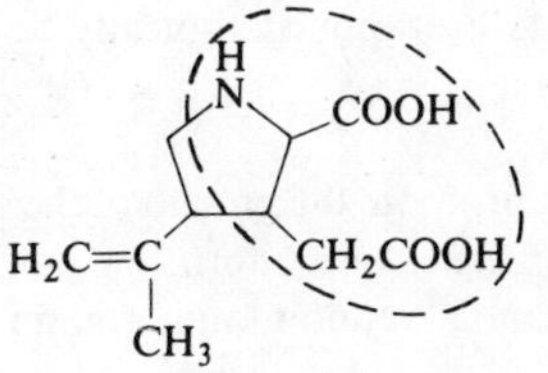

Kainic acid

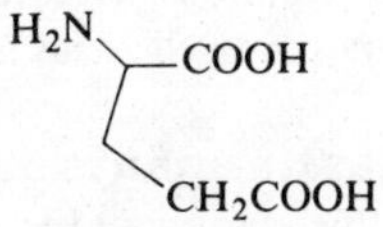

Glutamic acid

McGeer & McGeer (1979) In *Advances in Cytopharmacology*, Vol. 3 (Eds. Ceccarelli & Clementi). Raven Press, New York.
McGeer *et al.* (1978) *Kainic Acid as a Tool in Neurobiology*. Raven Press, New York.

kaliuresis (alternatively kaluresis)   *See* **kaliuretic action**.

kaliuretic action (alternatively kaluretic action)   An action that promotes kaliuresis; i.e. the excretion of potassium ions in the urine (Latin: *kalium*, potassium; Greek: *ouresis*, water-making). Many **diuretic drugs**, e.g. **thiazide drugs**, possess a kaliuretic action as an unwanted effect.

kallidin   A polypeptide, lysyl-**bradykinin**, formed by the action of **kallikrein** on a precursor in the plasma. Kallidin is rapidly converted to bradykinin by an aminopeptidase enzyme in plasma. The original kallidin was actually a mixture of bradykinin and lysyl-bradykinin but the name kallidin is now reserved for the latter.

[N]Lys–Arg–Pro–Pro–Gly–Phe–Ser–Pro–Phe–Arg[C]
Kallidin

kallikreins   Enzymes that act on **kininogens** to produce **kallidin** and/or **bradykinin**. They are also called kininogenases. In 1926, Frey and colleagues showed that the pancreas was a rich source of kallikrein, and the name is derived from this observation (Greek: *kallikreas*, pancreas). There are two types of kallikrein enzyme. Glandular kallikrein is formed from a precursor (glandular prekallikrein) in certain glands (salivary, sweat, lachrymal glands and exocrine pancreas) and released from the glands into the blood during secretory activity. The enzyme acts on kininogens I and II to produce kallidin and bradykinin. Plasma kallikrein is formed from plasma prekallikrein (Fletcher factor) under the influence of

117

the enzyme plasmin or Factors XII a or f of the clotting cascade. Plasma kallikrein acts only on kininogen II to form bradykinin.

keratolysis   *See* **keratolytic agents.**

keratolytic agents   An agent that promotes keratolysis, i.e. softening or peeling of the horny (keratin) layer of the epidermis (Greek: *keras*, horn; lysis, dissolution). Keratolytic agents are applied topically and include resorcinol, salicylic acid and sulphur.

keratoplastic agents   Agents that promote the growth of the superficial layers, the keratin, of the epidermis (Greek: *keras*, horn; *plassein*, to form). Such agents include coal tar, ichthamol, tretinoin and **vitamin** A and D ointment.

kindling   A term applied to a lasting change in brain function that results from repeated focal electrical stimulation and leads to a predisposition to epileptiform convulsions. Thus, low-intensity electrical stimulation of the amygdala of a laboratory rat applied for one or two seconds each day, although initially without apparent effect, eventually provokes bilateral clonic convulsions with loss of balance. The rat appears normal between convulsions, but even after many weeks without stimulation a convulsion appears when stimulation is applied. The mechanism underlying the effect is not understood, but the phenomenon provides a useful model of epilepsy which can be used to screen compounds for potential anti-epileptic activity.

kinetics   The study of the rates of reactions, for example the rate at which equilibrium is approached in an enzyme–substrate interaction.

kininogenases   *See* **kallikreins.**

kininogens   The polypeptide precursors of plasma kinins (**kallidin** and **bradykinin**). Kininogens are derived from the plasma α_2-globulin fraction. There are two kininogens, known as kininogen I (mol. wt. 57 000) and kininogen II (mol. wt. 19 700). Kinogen II is also called Fitzgerald factor.

klinotropic action   An action that results in a change in the rate of rise of tension in a contraction (Greek: *klinein*, to slope or to lean). Thus, a positive klinotropic action results in a faster rate of rise of tension.

   For example, **adrenaline** exerts a positive klinotropic action on cardiac muscle. (NB Adrenaline also produces a positive **inotropic action** on this tissue.)

Krebs solution   A **physiological salt solution** originally devised by Krebs in 1950 (*Biochim. biophys. Acta* **4**, 249) for bathing isolated mammalian tissues. It has the following composition (mmol/l): NaCl 94, KCl 4·7, $MgSO_4.7H_2O$ 0·45, $CaCl_2$ 2·5, KH_2PO_4 1·2, $NaHCO_3$ 22, glucose 13, pyruvic acid 3·1, fumaric acid 5·3, **glutamic acid** 3·1 (the acids are converted to the sodium salts by the $NaHCO_3$). The solution is bubbled with 5% CO_2 in oxygen. *See also* **Krebs–Henseleit solution**, which is often incorrectly called Krebs solution.

Krebs–Henseleit solution A **psysiological salt solution** originally devised by the authors in 1932 (*Hoppe-Seyler's Z. physiol. Chem.* **210**, 33). It is useful for maintaining mammalian tissues, especially when nerve-evoked responses are to be recorded. It has the following composition (mmol/l): NaCl 118, KCl 4·7, $CaCl_2$ 2·5, $MgSO_4.7H_2O$ 1·2, NaH_2PO_4 1·2 (but sometimes replaced by KH_2PO_4), $NaHCO_3$ 25, glucose 11·1. It is bubbled with 5% CO_2 in oxygen.

kynurenines Major metabolites of tryptophan on the pathway other than those that result in **serotonin** and tryptamine. The kynurenines include kynurenine itself, 3-hydroxy kynurenine, 3-hydroxyanthranilic acid, anthranilic acid, quinolinic acid, picolinic acid, xanthurenic acid, nicotinic acid and nicotinamide. Kynurenines have been implicated in the aetiology of stress-induced depression and in malignancy.
Lapin (1980) *Trends pharmacol. Sci.* **1**, 410

lachrymators Tear gases. *See* **incapacitating agents**.

β-lactam antibiotics Antibiotics containing a β-lactam group in their molecules: **penicillins, cephalosporins, cephalomycins**.

β-lactamases *See* **penicillinases**.

laetrile *See* **cyanogens**.

Lambert–Eaton myasthenic syndrome *See* **Eaton–Lambert myasthenic syndrome**.

Langendorff perfused heart preparation An isolated heart from a rabbit perfused through its coronary vessels. The perfusion cannula is tied into the aorta and the **physiological salt solution** under pressure is passed retrogradely into the aorta so that the aortic valves close. The fluid therefore passes through the coronary circulation and escapes from the inferior vena cava.

Contractions of the heart are recorded as well as outflow of fluid.

Consequently, the effects of drugs on frequency and force of beating and on coronary flow can be examined.

Langendorff (1895) *Pflügers Arch. ges. Physiol.* **190**, 280

Langmuir adsorption isotherm   *See* agonist–receptor interaction and occupation theory.

Latin square design   An arrangement of four items (e.g. four different treatments) in such a way as to minimize the effects of any progressive change in the sensitivity of the test system and to distribute spontaneous fluctuations in a random way amongst the four. The Latin square design is often used in **bioassays**, where the four treatments might be high and low doses of a standard known drug solution (SH and SL) and high and low volumes of a drug solution of unknown concentration which is being assayed (UH and UL). If SH, SL, UH and HL are designated A, B, C and D, then a typical Latin square design for administering the doses is:

A 1	B 2	C 3	D 4
B 5	A 6	D 7	C 8
C 9	D 10	A 11	B 12
D 13	C 14	B 15	A 16

Each dose occurs once, and once only, in each horizontal row and each vertical column.

α-latrotoxin   The major protein component of the venom of the black widow spiders (*Latrodectus* species, e.g. *L. tredecimguttatus, L. mactans, L. geometricus*). This protein acts on vertebrate nerve endings, causing them to discharge their neurotransmitters from their storage vesicles. The storage vesicles are subsequently depleted. *See*, for example, Tzeng & Siekevitz (1978) *Brain Res.* **139**, 190.

laudanum   The name originally given to preparations of or containing opium by the Swiss physician Paracelsus in the early 16th century. The name is derived from his high opinion of its medicinal value (Latin: *laudare*, to praise). Subsequently, the name laudanum, which is now obsolete, became restricted to the simple alcoholic tincture of opium.

laxative   A drug that produces emptying of the bowels (Latin: *laxare*, to loosen). Alternative names and their etymological origins are given under **aperient** and **purgative**.

LD$_{50}$ A term introduced by J. W. Trevan to denote the lethal dose of a drug in 50% of the animals in a group, i.e. the median lethal dose. The usual method of determining the LD$_{50}$ is to administer a range of doses (on a body weight basis), each to a group of 30 animals. The percentage mortality in each group may be plotted against the dose; a sigmoid curve is

obtained. The dose corresponding to 50% mortality (the LD_{50}) can be read off from the graph. The percentage kill plotted against the logarithm of the dose is also a sigmoid curve, but if the percentages are converted to probits (*see* **probit transformation**) the sigmoid curve is stretched into a straight line. The logarithm of the LD_{50} then corresponds to a probit of 5. Trevan (1927) *Proc. roy. Soc. B* **101**, 483

lectins   Sugar-binding proteins or glycoproteins of non-immune origin which are devoid of enzymatic activity towards the sugars to which they bind and which do not require free glycosidic hydroxyl groups in these sugars for their binding. Lectins have the properties of agglutinating certain cells, stimulating mitotic division in lymphocytes and/or precipitating complex carbohydrates. They are isolated from a wide variety of natural sources including seeds, roots, bark, fungi, bacteria, seaweeds, sponges, molluscs, fish eggs, body fluids of invertebrates and lower vertebrates, and mammalian cell membranes. Their precise physiological roles are unknown but they are valuable tools in a number of biological studies, such as blood-grouping, mitogenic stimulation of lymphocytes, fractionation of cells, isolation and purification of carbohydrate-containing molecules, and certain histochemical studies.

Concanavalin A (from jack beans) is a well-known example of a lectin. It has an affinity for terminal α-D-mannosyl and α-D-glucosyl residues.

legionnaires' disease   A severe form of pneumonia caused by a previously unrecognized bacterium which is now called *Legionella*. The disease owes its name to an epidemic that occurred in an hotel during a convention of American legionnaires.

lenitive   A drug that produces emptying of the bowels (Latin: *lenire*, to soften). Alternative names and their etymological origins are given under **aperient** and **purgative**.

leptocurares   A term coined by D. Bovet (Greek: *leptos*, slender) to denote the type of **neuromuscular blocking drugs** that produce block by depolarization. Bovet pointed out that the molecules of such drugs are thin and flexible with relatively small groups (usually methyl) on the quaternary nitrogens. Diagrammatically, the molecules might be represented as $Me_3 N^+ \sim N^+ Me_3$. Decamethonium ($Me_3N\text{---}(CH_2)_{10}\text{---}N^+ Me_3$) is typical. (Cf. **pachycurares** which produce non-depolarization block.)

letheon   An obsolete term for anaesthetic. *See* **anaesthesia**.

leukotrienes   A family of local hormones (*see* **autacoids**) formed in the body from essential fatty acids such as arachidonic acid by alternative pathways to the **prostaglandins**. Leukotrienes (LT) with four double bonds

121

arise from a common precursor, the unstable epoxide leukotriene A_4, which is formed from arachidonic acid by the action of 5-lipoxygenase. The leukotrienes may be divided into two groups according to their chemical structure: those that have a sulphur linkage and amino acid residues at C-6, and those that exist as dihydroxy acids. The first group includes leukotrienes C_4, D_4 and E_4, whereas leukotrienes A_4 and B_4 belong to the second group. The biological actions of the two groups differ. Thus $LT B_4$ and its isomers produce **chemotaxis**, **chemokinesis**, aggregation of polymorphonuclear leukocytes, exudation of plasma, and contraction of guinea-pig parenchyma. $LT C_4$, $LT D_4$ and $LT E_4$ produce contraction of smooth muscles including bronchoconstriction and vasoconstriction, exudation of plasma, and stimulation of **phospholipase**. The actions of $LT C_4$, $LT D_4$ and $LT E_4$ are antagonized by **FPL-55712**. Leukotrienes are probably responsible for many of the signs and symptoms of hypersensitivity states, and of the inflammatory reaction. The structure of one member of the family, LTC_4, is shown below as an example; it is probably a major constituent of the **slow reacting substance of anaphylaxis** (**SRS-A**) (*see* Piper (1983) *Trends in pharmacol. Sci.* **42**, 75).

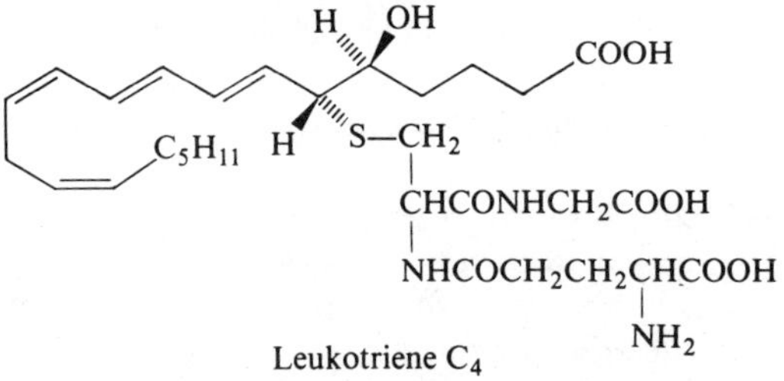

Leukotriene C_4

Leukotrienes take their name from the kind of blood cells (leucocytes) in which they were originally found, and the conjugated series of three double bonds ('trienes') that they contain.

leupeptin An inhibitor of the enzyme **calpain 1**.

levarterenol The official *United States Pharmacopeia* name for $(-)$-**noradrenaline** (*l*-norepinephrine).

ligand An atom or molecule that binds to a larger molecule at a specific site. For example, both **acetylcholine** and α-**bungarotoxin** are ligands for the **nicotinic cholinoceptors** at the neuromuscular junction in skeletal muscle (Latin: *ligare*, to bind).

Lineweaver–Burk plot A graph of the reciprocal of the reaction rate $(1/v)$ in an enzyme reaction against the reciprocal of the substrate concentration $(1/s)$. The intercept of the extrapolated line with the abscissa gives the value of $-1/K_m$, and hence K_m, which is the dissociation constant for the complex of enzyme and substrate, i.e. the Michaelis–Menten constant (*see* **Michaelis–Menten equation**). The intercepts of the lines with the ordinate give the reciprocal of the maximal rate $(1/V)$ of the reaction for each concentration of enzyme. This procedure was first devised by Lineweaver and Burk in 1934.

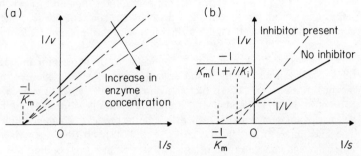

(a) Lineweaver–Burk plot of the reciprocal of the reaction rate $(1/v)$ against the reciprocal of the substrate concentrations $(1/s)$. The intercept of the extrapolated lines with the abscissa gives the value of $-1/K_m$ and is independent of the enzyme concentration. The intercepts with the ordinate give the reciprocal of the maximal rate $(1/V)$ of the reaction for each concentration of the enzyme.
(b) Competitive enzyme inhibition, Lineweaver–Burk plot. The maximum obtainable rate, $1/V$, is the same whether the inhibitor is present or not.

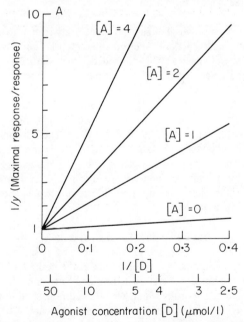

Lineweaver–Burk plots: reciprocal of response against reciprocal of agonist concentration $(1/[D])$ in the presence of various concentrations of antagonist $([A])$.

123

In the presence of a competitive inhibitor of the enzyme, the graph of $1/v$ against $1/s$ is still a straight line. The maximum rate of reaction obtainable in the presence of the inhibitor is the same as in its absence. The slope of the line of the inhibited reaction is steeper. The intercept on the abscissa ($1/v = 0$) is $-1/(K_m[1 + i/K_i])$ in the presence of the inhibitor (i = concentration of inhibitor, and K_i = dissociation constant for enzyme–inhibitor complex); i.e. the inhibitor has increased the apparent K_m for the substrate.

A Lineweaver–Burk plot is also applicable to drug–receptor interactions. The reciprocal of the response (y) expressed as a fraction of the maximal response (i.e. $1/y$) is plotted against the reciprocal of the **agonist** concentration ($1/[D]$) and gives a straight line with the slope of K_D in the absence of antagonist and a steeper slope in the presence of an antagonist. The lines intercept on the $1/y$ axis, when $1/[D] = 0$ (that is, with an infinitely high concentration of agonist) at a point corresponding to the maximal response ($1/y = 1$).

lipofuscin   An insoluble pigment that accumulates in some ageing tissues. It is formed from malondialdehyde which polymerizes with itself and some other tissue breakdown products. Malondialdehyde is formed during the auto-oxidation of membrane polyunsaturated lipids in a chain reaction started by **free radical** formation.

lipomodulin   An anti**phospholipase** protein closely related to, and possibly a precursor of, **macrocortin**. J. Axelrod and co-workers discovered that the inhibitory effect of **glucocorticoids** on leucocyte chemotaxis was due to the formation of a glycoprotein which they named lipomodulin.

liposomes   Microscopic phospholipid vesicles used as drug carriers. Liposomes are composed of naturally occuring phospholipids and are therefore non-immunogenic and biodegradable. The liposome containing the drug may be taken up into cells by endocytosis and there fuse with a lysosome, it may fuse with the cell membrane and release its contents intracellularly, or it may become adsorbed to the cell surface and the drug may slowly diffuse across the lipid boundaries to the inside of the cell. *See also* **drug delivery system**.

loading dose   A large initial dose given so that the effective concentration in the **biophase** is reached quickly. This is followed by smaller maintenance doses given to maintain the concentration at the desired level. The size of the maintenance doses is therefore determined by the rate of elimination of the **drug**. Examples of drugs which are often administered in the form of a large loading dose followed by smaller maintenance doses include **sulphonamide** antimicrobial drugs and **cardiac glycosides**. The administration of the initial loading dose of a cardiac glycoside is termed digitalization.

local anaesthetic drug A **drug** that is used to produce **anaesthesia** in a localized region of the body. The drugs act by blocking voltage-dependent Na^+ channels (*see* **voltage-dependent ion channels**) in axonal membranes and thereby abolishing conduction of the nerve impulse. They also block voltage-dependent K^+ channels, but it is the block of Na^+ channels that abolishes the action potential. The original local anaesthetic drug was the now virtually obsolete cocaine (an **alkaloid** from coca leaves), and the convention is to give all local anaesthetic drugs names that end in '-caine'; hence, procaine, lignocaine (called lidocaine in USA), benzocaine, etc.

The localization of the anaesthetic effect is achieved partly by the properties of the drug and partly by its formulation, but mainly by the route of its administration. Local anaesthetic drugs may be applied to the surface of the skin or mucous membrane (surface anaesthesia), by injection around sensory nerve endings (infiltration anaesthesia), by injection near a large nerve trunk (nerve block anaesthesia), by injection into the epidural space (epidural anaesthesia), or into the subarachnoid space (intrathecal or spinal anaesthesia). When used specifically to prevent pain sensation, local anaesthetic drugs may be called local analgesic drugs.

Many local anaesthetic drug molecules have a general structure of the following sort:

They have pK_a values (*see* **ionization constant**) such that at body pH a substantial number of molecules is in each form, i.e. ionized and non-ionized. The non-ionized molecules are lipid-soluble and allow penetration of lipid barriers en route to the site of action on the inside of the axon membrane, but the ionized form is probably the form which interacts directly with the Na^+ and K^+ channels.

local analgesic drug *See* **local anaesthetic drug**.

local hormones *See* **autacoids**.

Locke solution A **physiological salt solution** originally devised by Locke in 1901 (*Zbl. Physiol.* **14**, 670) for perfusing the isolated mammalian heart. It has the following composition (mmol/l): NaCl 154, KCl 5·4–5·6, $CaCl_2$ 1·1–2·2, $NaHCO_3$ 1·8–6·0, glucose 5·5–11·1. It is gassed with air or with oxygen.

Iodoxamides Compounds with a **cromoglycate**-like action in inhibiting mediator release from **mast cells**. They include iodoxamide ethyl and iodoxamide tromethamine.

$$CH_3CH_2-O-\overset{\overset{O}{\|}}{C}-\overset{\overset{O}{\|}}{C}-NH-\underset{\underset{CN}{}}{\overset{\overset{Cl}{}}{\bigcirc}}-NH-\overset{\overset{O}{\|}}{C}-\overset{\overset{O}{\|}}{C}-O-CH_2CH_3$$

Lodoxamide ethyl

loop diuretics Diuretic drugs that act on the loop of Henle in the nephron. They include frusemide (furosemide in USA), ethacrynic acid, triflocin and bumetanide. These drugs inhibit active Cl^- reabsorption in the ascending limb of the loop. They are also called high-ceiling diuretics because they can increase diuresis even in patients who are already responding maximally to other diuretic drugs.

lubricant laxatives Agents that produce emptying of the bowels by softening the stools. Examples of lubricant laxatives include liquid paraffin (liquid petrolatum), **surfactants** such as dioctylsodium and paloxalkols, and (in suppositories) glycerine or soft soap.

luteolytic agents Agents that, in one way or another, inhibit the corpus luteum's action to secrete progestogens. Several chemically distinct drugs possess this type of activity in addition to other actions. They include the anabolic androgen oxymetholone, which inhibits luteinizing hormone-releasing hormone, aminoglutethimide and cyclofenil which inhibit progesterone synthesis, and prostaglandin $F_{2\alpha}$, which causes involution of the corpus luteum. A luteolytic agent that was free from other effects might serve as a useful contraceptive drug.

Luxuskonsumption A term coined by Neumann et al. (1902, *Arch. Hyg. Berlin* **45**, 1) to describe the observation that when a normal individual increases his food intake (Latin: *luxus*, excess) there is an initial increase in weight and then a new plateau is reached despite continued overeating. The 'missing' energy is clearly not stored as fat, but is believed to be burnt off in **brown fat**, that is, as 'dietary-induced thermogenesis'.

lymphokine A **biological response modifier** produced by activated lymphocytes that acts to modulate the immune system.

lymphotoxins Protein factors that mediate the cytotoxic actions of sensitized T-lymphocytes. Lymphotoxins probably play a part in the rejection of allogenic grafts and cell-mediated antitumour responses.

lysosomes Subcellular organelles containing enzymes that break down larger molecules (carbohydrates, proteins, nucleic acids) into simpler substances that can be oxidized in the mitochondria. The lysosome membrane protects the rest of the cell from these enzymes. Lysosomes play a part in many cellular reactions to disease, and some drugs have the property of stabilizing the lysosomal membrane, thereby preventing the damage that ensues from the release of its enzymes. Such drugs include chloroquine, cortisol and indomethacin, although it is not supposed that this action does more than contribute in a minor way to their therapeutic actions.

lysozyme An enzyme that catalyses the hydrolysis of β-1,4-glycoside links of N-acetylneuraminic acid residues in sialic acids of the cell walls of many bacteria. It therefore exerts bactericidal action. It is present in lachrymal secretion, saliva, nasal mucus, gastric secretion and milk, and serves to protect against bacterial infection.

MAC value Minimum alveolar concentration of inhalational anaesthetic at 1 atmosphere pressure that produces immobility in 50% of patients or animals exposed to a noxious stimulus (Eber *et al.* (1965) *Anesthesiology* **26**, 756). This concentration is called 1 MAC. Because the dose-response curve of anaesthetics is steep, more than 99% of animals fail to respond to the stimulus at a dose of 1·1 MAC. Most inhalational anaesthetics are administered at a dose of about 1 MAC, and additional analgesia and relaxation are produced with adjuvant drugs (**analgesic drugs**, **neuromuscular blocking drugs**). However, nitrous oxide lacks potency to the extent that 1 MAC cannot be achieved at atmospheric pressure, and nitrous oxide is not in fact used as the sole agent, except perhaps for dental procedures and during the first stage of parturition.

McEwen solution A **physiological salt solution** originally devised by McEwen in 1956 (*J. Physiol.* **131**, 678). The essential difference from Krebs–Henseleit solution is the inclusion of sucrose to reduce oedema formation in the tissues. It is used to bathe isolated mammalian tissues, especially when nerve-evoked responses are to be recorded. It has the following composition (mmol/l): NaCl 130, KCl 5·6, $CaCl_2$ 2·2, $MgCl_2$ 0·5, NaH_2PO_4 1·0, $NaHCO_3$ 25, glucose 11·1, sucrose 13. It is bubbled with 5% CO_2 in oxygen.

McN-A-343 A compound (originally synthesized in McNeil Laboratories) that selectively stimulates a particular subclass of **muscarinic cholinoceptors**.

McN-A-343 stimulates muscarinic receptors on sympathetic ganglia. These receptors mediate excitation of the ganglion cells and a rise in blood pressure results. As well as being blocked by atropine, they are blocked by mianserin.

macrocortin

McN-A-343 (4-[*m*-chlorophenylcarbamoyloxy]-2-butyntrimethylammonium chloride)

The compound AH 6405 has similar actions.

AH 6405 (1,4,5,6-tetrahydro-5-phenoxypyrimidine)

macrocortin An endogenous glycoprotein (*c.* 40 000 daltons) inhibitor of the enzyme **phospholipase** A_2 which catalyses the release of arachidonic acid from membrane phospholipids. The synthesis and release of macrocortin is stimulated by **glucocorticoids** which inhibit **eicosanoid** synthesis by this mechanism. Macrocortin is so called because it is a large molecule originally obtained from rat macrophages, and because it mimics the effects of glucocorticoids (alternative names are renocortin and **lipomodulin** although lipomodulin may not be identical with macrocortin). *See also* **phospholipase** A_2 **inhibitors**.

macrolide antibiotics **Antibiotics**, the molecules of which contain a large lactone ring to which one or more sugars are attached. The main macrolide antibiotics are erythromycin (from *Streptomyces erythreus*), oleandomycin (from *Strept. antibioticus*), spiramycin (from *Strept. ambofaciens*) and triacetyloleandomycin which is prepared from oleandomycin. These antibiotics bind to the 50S ribosomal subunit of sensitive bacteria, but have much less ability to bind to the analogous 80S mammalian ribosomal subunit, which accounts for their **selective toxicity**.

maculotoxin The toxic principle from the venom of the Australian blue-ringed octopus (*Hapalochlaena maculosa*). Maculotoxin is in fact now known to be **tetrodotoxin**, so that the name is obsolete.

magic mushrooms In Britain refers to the indigenous liberty cap mushroom (*Psilocybe semilanceata*) which contains the hallucinogenic substance, psilocybin. From time to time the ingestion of these mushrooms by teenagers and even schoolchildren becomes a cult, and numerous cases of toxicity have occurred. Twenty to thirty medium-sized mushrooms are equivalent to about 12 mg psilocybin.

Magnus preparation of guinea-pig isolated ileum The preparation of an isolated segment of guinea-pig ileum for recording longitudinal contractions in an organ bath.

Magnus (1904) *Pflügers Arch. ges. Physiol.* **102**, 123

maintenance dosage   The series of relatively small doses that follow the **loading dose** in order to maintain an effective concentration in the **biophase**.

major tranquillizer   An alternative name for **neuroleptic drug**.

malignant hyperpyrexia   An inherited muscle disorder that gives rise, after an appropriate stimulus, to intense muscle spasm and a consequent severe, progressive, and often lethal rise in body temperature. The basic abnormality seems to involve an inadequate ability of the muscle sarcoplasmic reticulum to bind or rebind calcium ions firmly enough, and this leads to the muscle spasm. The rise in temperature follows from the enhanced muscle metabolism and the rupture of muscle cells with the release of pyrogenic substances. The main triggers of the syndrome are certain depolarizing agents, especially those used during **surgical anaesthesia**. The anaesthetic agent halothane (said to depolarize the muscle fibre membranes of patients with the disease, although not those of normal individuals) and the depolarizing **neuromuscular blocking drug** succinylcholine are particular culprits. The incidence of the disease in the population as a whole is small. Many of the patients with the disease remain unaware of any abnormality until they undergo an operation. The condition has been described as the only anaesthetic-related disease.

There is a high incidence of a closely related condition in certain strains of Landrace pig, and these pigs provide a model for studying the disease.

At present, the main means of controlling the condition when it unexpectedly occurs during an operation is with dantrolene sodium which acts to limit the release of Ca^{2+} from the sarcoplasmic reticulum.

malignant hyperthermia   *See* **malignant hyperpyrexia**.

mammotrophic drugs   Drugs that produce breast enlargement and galactorrhoea as unwanted side-effects in women (usually associated with amenorrhoea). The usual mechanism is through excessive secretion of prolactin from the pituitary, arising from interference with the hypothalamic dopaminergic mechanism that normally serves to inhibit prolactin release. Drugs with mammotrophic action include reserpine (which depletes dopamine stores), methyldopa (which is biosynthesized into methyldopamine which then partially replaces **dopamine**), and neuroleptic phenothiazines (which block **dopamine receptors**).

Excessive development of the male mammary glands, even to the functional state, is called gynaecomastia (Greek: *gynaikos*, woman; *mastos*, breast; i.e. woman-like breasts).

MAO   *See* **monoamine oxidase.**

marihuana   *See* **cannabis.**

mast cells   Cells with large basophilic granules containing **heparin** and **histamine**. They are present in the connective tissue around blood vessels and lymphatics, particularly in the lungs, liver and intestines. They have a similar structure to the basophil leucocytes of the blood. The release of histamine from mast cells following an immunological stimulus to the membrane is a basic pathological mechanism of allergic disease.

The term 'mast cells' is derived from the German '*Mastzellen*' (fodder cells, or cells concerned with fattening or nutrition), a name proposed by Paul Ehrlich in 1879 to indicate the function which he mistakenly attributed to them. H. H. Dale pointed out that, 'in its English translation, "mast cell" has no functional implication like that of the original German; and, in any case, a proper respect for priority and for Ehrlich's memory would make us retain the name he proposed, and which has passed into such general use'. Alternative, and now obsolete, names include *cellules isoplastiques, cellules a l'anglais, mastocytes, cellulas cebadas* and labrocyte.

Mast cells and basophils possess membrane **receptors** to which IgE **antibodies** bind. The signal to secrete histamine is the union of the receptor-bound IgE antibody with specific **antigen** present in the surrounding medium. In fact, two adjacent antibody sites must be bridged by antigen. This results in a sequence of membrane phospholipid breakdown and enzyme activation with the eventual formation of open Ca^{2+} channels. Influx of Ca^{2+} causes the exocytosis of histamine granules. **Cyclic AMP** is probably involved in the inactivation of the Ca^{2+} channels.

On antigen challenge, mast cells also release preformed **serotonin**, eosinophil and neutrophil chemotactic factors, and lysosomal enzymes, and they form and release **prostaglandins** (especially PGD_2), **leukotrienes** C, D and E (**SRS-A**), and platelet-activating factor (**PAF-acether**).

3-MCA   3-Methylcholanthrene: an agent (inducing agent) used to enhance the activity of **mixed function oxidases** (cytochromes P_{448} and P_{450}) in the livers of laboratory rodents prior to the preparation of a hepatic microsome system for use in tests for mutagenicity, such as the **Ames test**.

M-current   A current carried by outward-flowing K^+ ions passing through a particular class of calcium-independent, voltage-sensitive K^+ channels in the membrane of ganglion cells. It is inhibited by **acetylcholine** acting on **muscarinic cholinoceptors**, hence the term M-current. The M-current in frog ganglion cells, for example, is switched on progressively between $-70\,mV$ and $0\,mV$. It is non-inactivating and therefore forms a major component of the steady membrane conductance. Inhibition of the M-current by acetylcholine causes a slow membrane depolarization which does not directly activate the cell but which may facilitate the cell's response to signals mediated through **nicotinic cholinoceptors**.

Brown (1983) *Trends Neurosci.* **6**, 302

mean　The average value or arithmetic mean which is the sum of the measurements divided by the number of measurements

$$\bar{y} = \frac{\Sigma Y}{N}$$

where $\bar{Y}$ (Y-bar) is the mean, ΣY (sigma Y) is their sum, and N is the number of measurements.

mean channel open time　A measure of the mean time that an ion channel remains open under the influence of its activating stimulus, i.e. an **agonist** in the case of a **receptor-operated ion channel** or a voltage change in the case of a **voltage-dependent ion channel**. The first studies of this sort were made on the **cholinoceptor**-linked ion channels of the neuromuscular junction.

median　The statistic of central tendency that divides the sample into two equal-sized groups. For example, in the following measurements, arranged into rank order, there are five values of 2·0 or less and five values of 2·1 or more. The median therefore lies between 2·0 and 2·1. Had there been only the first nine measurements, the median would have been 2·0.

Measurements: 1·6 1·7 1·9 1·9 2·0 2·1 2·2 2·5 2·6 2·7

Generalizing, the median is at $(N + 1)/2$ in an odd-numbered rank and between $N/2$ and $(N + 2)/2$ in an even-numbered rank.

median effective dose　*See* ED_{50}.

median lethal dose　*See* LD_{50}.

membrane labilizing drug　A drug that causes an excitable membrane to discharge conducted action potentials or that lowers the threshold to other stimulating agents. In most instances the same drug exerts both actions in high and low doses respectively. Membrane labilizers include Ca^{2+}-complexing agents (such as sodium edetate), **veratrum alkaloids**, dicophane (DDT) and **batrachotoxin**. Most membrane labilizers act by delaying the closure of sodium channels, by lowering the membrane potential at which sodium channels open (i.e. increasing the sensitivity of the sodium channel gates to a fall in membrane potential), or in some instances by blocking voltage-dependent potassium channels.

membrane stabilizing drug　A drug that suppresses excitation of an excitable membrane without itself producing a change in the resting membrane potential. **Local anaesthetic drugs** and **tetrodotoxin** are examples of membrane stabilizing drugs.

mercurial diuretic drugs   A largely obsolete group of powerful **diuretic drugs** that are derivatives of mercuripropanol.

$$R—CH_2—CH—CH_2—Hg—X$$
$$|$$
$$O(H \text{ or } CH_3)$$

They increase the excretion of Na^+ and Cl^-. Examples of mercurial diuretic drugs include mersalyl and chlormerodrin.

metabolic inhibitors   Usually refers to agents that inhibit ATP production in the mitochondria. *See also* **electron transfer inhibitors** and **uncouplers of oxidative phosphorylation**. Additional metabolic inhibitors include compounds that act to disorganize mitochondrial structure (e.g. high doses of thyroxine), the antibiotic antimycin A (not used therapeutically) which inhibits the reaction between cytochromes b and c_1, arsenates which interact with ADP and so prevent ATP production, and the plant **alkaloid** atractylate which inhibits the release of ATP from the mitochondria.

metabolic tolerance   *See* **tolerance**.

metameter   A value that is obtained by transformation of an original datum. For example, in the use of log dose–probit relationships, the doses and the percentages responding in each group are the original data, and the log dose and probits are metameters. *See also* **quantal response** and **probit transformation**.

metaphilic effect   A change produced by **agonists** in the molecular structure of their **receptors** such that the **affinity** for certain **antagonist drugs** is increased. The degree of antagonism produced by antagonists that are affected in this way is increased if the antagonist and the agonist are applied together or if the antagonist is applied shortly after the agonist. *See* Rang & Ritter (1969) *Molec. Pharmacol.* **5**, 394.

methonium compounds   The name given to a series of polymethylene bistrimethylammonium compounds of the general structure $Me_3N^+—(CH_2)_n—^+NMe_3$. They were first studied pharmacologically by Paton and Zaimis and independently by Barlow and Ing in the late 1940s and early 50s. The two most important members of the series are hexamethonium (where $n = 6$) and decamethonium (where $n = 10$). Hexamethonium blocks transmission through autonomic ganglia by a non-depolarizing mechanism (probably receptor block plus **ion channel block**), whereas decamethonium blocks neuromuscular transmission in skeletal muscle by

depolarization block (although **phase II neuromuscular block** may also occur.

Note that, according to this definition, suxamethonium (the British official name for succinyldicholine) is a misnomer because it does not conform to the general structure given above.

methylxanthines *See* **xanthine alkaloids.**

Meyer–Overton hypothesis A hypothesis put forward by Meyer (1898) and Overton (1901) that sought to explain the mechanism of action of **general anaesthetic drugs** in terms of an interaction of the drug molecules with the lipids of neuronal membranes.

Michaelis–Menten constant *See* **Michaelis–Menten equation.**

Michaelis–Menten equation An equation, derived by Michaelis and Menten, which expresses the velocity of an enzyme reaction in terms of the substrate concentration. The equation is:

$$v = \frac{V}{(1 + K_m/s)}$$

where v = the reaction rate, V = maximal reaction rate, s = original concentration of substrate and K_m = the Michaelis–Menten constant.

In the first stage of an enzyme reaction, the substrate (s) reversibly combines with the enzyme to form a complex, thus:

$$\text{Substrate} + \text{enzyme} \underset{k_2}{\overset{k_1}{\rightleftharpoons}} \text{complex}$$

where k_1 and k_2 are the rate constants for the forward and backward reactions. The ratio of the constants, k_2/k_1, is K_m (the Michaelis–Menten constant), which is the dissociation constant for the complex. The **affinity** of the substrate for the complex is given by $1/K_m$. Thus, the lower the value of K_m, the greater the affinity between it and the substrate.

K_m is equal to the concentration of substrate (moles/litre) at which the reaction rate is half the maximal rate ($V/2$) with excess substrate. The value of K_m may be used to describe the activity of an enzyme for catalysing the reaction of a particular substrate.

The Michaelis–Menten equation predicts that the rate of formation (v) of the product, plotted against the substrate concentration (s), is a rectangular hyperbole, and the value of K_m can be read off from the point corresponding to 50% of the maximal rate.

The Michaelis–Menten equation can be rearranged thus:

$$\frac{1}{v} = \frac{1}{V} + \frac{K_m}{V} \times \frac{1}{s}$$

and the graph of $1/v$ v. $1/s$ gives a straight line, the **Lineweaver–Burk plot.**

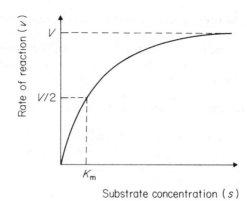

Substrate concentration (s)

Graph of rate of reaction (v) plotted against substrate concentration (s) gives a hyperbolic curve which approaches the maximal rate (V) asymptotically. The value of the Michaelis constant, K_m, can be read off the abscissa at the point corresponding to half the maximal rate, $V/2$. From Bowman & Rand (1980) *Textbook of Pharmacology*, 2nd Edition. Blackwell Scientific Publications, Oxford.

Mickey Finn   A drink composed of chloral hydrate dissolved in a strong alcoholic beverage (whisky, gin, etc.). It has been used with criminal intent as 'knockout drops', and is said to be named after a Chicago gangster of the 1920s.

microsomes   Small vesicles derived from disruption of the endoplasmic reticulum after homogenization of cells. The microsomes may be separated by ultracentrifugation. They contain many of the cell's oxidation–reduction enzymes and the haemoprotein known as **cytochrome P$_{450}$**. Microsomes derived from liver cells may be used to study drug metabolism *in vitro*.

migraine   A syndrome, the most common symptom of which is periodic severe headache which is vascular in origin and usually pulsative and unilateral in the initial phase. The headache is often accompanied by visual disturbance and sickness. Galen, in the second century AD, called the disease 'hemicrania' (Latin) to denote the common symptom of unilateral headache. Over the centuries, the term hemicrania has been gradually modified, thus:

hemicrania → emigranea → migranea → megrim → migraine.

milbemycins   A family of **macrolide antibiotics** (antibiotic B-41) which kill insects and mites. They are denoted by Greek letters and numbers, thus: milbemycins α_1, α_2, α_3, etc. and β_1, β_2, β_3, etc. The milbemycins are obtained from *Streptomyces hygroscopicus*, subspecies *aureolacrimosus*; some of them have been synthesized.

mineralocorticoid A **corticosteroid** that is relatively more powerful in its actions on electrolyte and water balance than on carbohydrate metabolism. Aldosterone is the most potent endogenous mineralocorticoid, although hydrocortisone has a significant effect because of its relatively high concentration. *See also* **glucocorticoid**.

minor tranquillizer *See* **tranquillizer**.

miotic drugs Drugs that produce miosis (meiosis) of the pupil (i.e. constriction of the pupil). (Greek: *meion*, smaller; *meiosis*, diminution). Such drugs include **parasympathomimetic drugs** such as pilocarpine, **anticholinesterase drugs** such as physostigmine, and **morphine**. Miotic drugs may be useful to lower intraocular pressure in open-angle glaucoma.

mitogen A substance that stimulates mitosis and therefore cell division. An example is the leucoagglutinin PHA-L, a lectin from red kidney beans, which stimulates mitotic division of isolated lymphocytes.

mixed-function oxidases (oxygenases) A term used to describe the liver microsome enzymes that catalyse oxidation reactions. They utilize molecular oxygen for the direct oxidation of the substrate, and they act on a wide range of substrates to cause cleavage of, for example, O–C or N–C bonds. Similar reactions catalysed by these enzymes may also occur in lung, kidney, small intestine, placenta and skin.

The essentials of the reaction are:

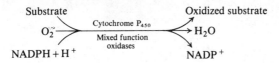

mode The most commonly occurring value in a series of measurements.

modulator A term applied to a chemical which appears to function physiologically at a synapse, not as a direct transmitter but rather to modify the responses to a transmitter. A number of neuropeptides appear to act in this way. Modulators may be released from separate axons or may be released as **co-transmitters**. A modulator, by itself, may not produce an observable effect on membrane properties, yet it may suppress or enhance the activity of a neurotransmitter. One mechanism whereby this might occur is if the modulator interfered with the opening of **voltage-dependent ion channels** that are brought into play only when the transmitter, through another mechanism, depolarizes the membrane.

monoamine oxidase (MAO) A mitochondrial enzyme (amine: oxygen oxidoreductase [deaminating] [flavin-containing], EC1.4.3.4) located be-

135

tween the outer and inner mitochondrial membranes. The outer membrane is freely permeable to the substrates for the enzyme. Monoamine oxidase activity is present in nearly all tissues, and is particularly high in the intestinal mucosa and liver. MAO catalyses the oxidative deamination of **catecholamines** and a wide range of other amines to form the corresponding aldehyde derivatives. FAD is a prosthetic group.

$$R-CH_2-NH_2 \xrightarrow[\substack{FAD \quad FADH_2}]{O_2 \quad MAO} \left[R-CH_2-\underset{\underset{}{\overset{\overset{OH}{|}}{NH}}} \right] \longrightarrow R-C\overset{O}{\underset{H}{\diagup}}$$

Amine substrate   Intermediate   Aldehyde

                hydroxylamine

H_2O

There are two forms of the enzyme, termed MAO-A and MAO-B, with different substrate specificities and inhibitor sensitivities. Both forms of the enzyme are active against tyramine. MAO-A, but not MAO-B, is active against **serotonin** and **noradrenaline**; MAO-B, but not MAO-A, is active against benzylamine and 2-phenylethylamine (and possibly **dopamine**, although this is controversial). In fact these specificities are relative rather than absolute, and the two enzyme forms are better distinguished by their sensitivity to inhibitors. MAO-A is relatively selectively inhibited by clorgyline, whereas MAO-B is relatively selectively inhibited by sergilene.

monoamine oxidase inhibitors (MAOI)   Drugs that inhibit the mitochondrial enzyme **monoamine oxidase**.

The first MAO inhibitor was discovered by **serendipity**. It was noted that the **antitubercular drug** isoniazid elevated the mood of depressed patients with tuberculosis. It was subsequently found that isoniazid had a similar antidepressant effect on non-tubercular patients and it was discovered that isoniazid inhibits MAO. The related drug, iproniazid (now obsolete), was then synthesized specifically as an **antidepressant drug**.

The main MAO inhibitors currently used clinically as antidepressant drugs are phenelzine, isocarboxazid and tranylcypromine. Isocarboxazid is also used in the control of angina, and another inhibitor, pargyline, is used as an **antihypertensive drug**. These drugs have the disadvantages that they inhibit a number of drug-metabolizing enzymes in addition to MAO, and so may potentiate other drugs given concurrently. They are also non-selective, in that they inhibit both forms of MAO, and they may give rise to what, for brevity, is called the '**cheese reaction**'. Most of the existing MAO inhibitors are irreversible in their inhibiting effects. Some are of the **suicide-substrate** type. Current research is aimed at developing selective reversible inhibitors in the hope that adverse reactions will be minimized. Caroxazone, cimoxatone and toloxatone are examples of newly developed selective, reversible inhibitors of MAO-A.

monoclonal antibody   An **antibody** of a single particular specificity. The principle of the method of preparation, summarized below, is based on work in Cambridge by Milstein and Kohler. Antibody-secreting cells (lymphocytes) from an immunized animal are fused with cells of a cultured myeloma cell line which, being cancer cells, are immortal. The fused hybrid cells are grown in a special medium in a number of wells for about two weeks and the supernatants are then tested for antibody activity. Clones that secrete the required antibody are then grown in bulk. The technique has many uses and vast potential, for example for differentiating **receptors** and **antigens** of various kinds, **radioimmunoassay**, drug-targeting, tissue-typing, specific treatment of infections and of cancers, destruction of D antigen of the rhesus system.

Animal injected with antigen
↓
Spleen cells removed
↓
Spleen cells fused to myeloma cells
↓
Hybrid cells grown in special medium
↓
Supernatants tested for required antibody
↓
Clones secreting required antibody
selected and grown in bulk

(Clone–Greek: $kl\bar{o}$n, a young shoot. Analogous to taking a cutting in botany; i.e. propagation vegetatively from a single cutting.)

monokine   A **biological response modifier** produced by monocytes.

mood stabilizer   A term used to describe the beneficial effect of lithium salts (usually lithium carbonate) in manic-depressive illness. Lithium salts taken orally are effective in normalizing a manic episode and in reducing the recurrence of attacks of manic-depressive illness. The mechanism of action is uncertain. Speculation is concerned with effects on neuronal membranes where Li^+ may partially replace Na^+, and on its ability to modify central turnover of **noradrenaline** and **dopamine**.

MOPET   An acronym for 3-methoxy-4-hydroxyphenylethanol, a break-down product of **dopamine**. The main metabolite is homovanillic acid.

MOPP   A particular combination of **anticancer drugs**: mustine, Oncovin (vincristine), procarbazine and prednisone. It is also known as MVPP.

morphia   *See* **morphine**.

morphinan derivatives   Drugs based on a morphinan nucleus.

Morphinan

Most of the important drugs in this group are **narcotic analgesics drugs** e.g. levorphanol. Morphinan itself is without activity.

The analgesic activity is confined to (−)-isomers. The (+)-isomer corresponding to levorphanol is called dextromethorphan. It has no analgesic activity but is a powerful cough suppressant (*see* **antitussive drugs**).

morphine   The main **alkaloid** of the opium poppy *Papaver somniferum*, and the prototype **narcotic analgesic drug**.

In 1803, a German pharmacist, Serturner, isolated the main alkaloid from opium and called it morphia, after Morpheus, the Greek god of dreams. The name morphine is now used in accordance with the convention that the names of alkaloids end in '-ine'.

morphine-like drugs   Drugs producing the type of analgesia produced by **morphine**. They are more commonly called **narcotic analgesic drugs**, **opioids** or **opiates**.

MPPP   1-Methyl-4-phenyl-4-propionoxy-piperidine, a 'street drug' with actions similar to those of pethidine (meperidine, Demerol). MPPP is often illegally synthesized by pushers and users with some chemical knowledge, and it is sometimes known as 'synthetic heroin'. Its special importance to toxicology and pharmacology is that it may contain, and may easily but accidentally be converted to, **MPTP**, which may have a role in the aetiology of Parkinson's disease.

MPTP   1-Methyl-4-phenyl-1,2,3,6-tetrahydropyridine. MPTP has the property of destroying neurones of the nigrostriatal pathway and thereby

MPTP   MPP$^+$

inducing irreversible parkinsonian signs and symptoms. It is a protoxin, being oxidized in a two-step process to 1-methyl-4-phenylpyridinium ion (MPP$^+$) before becoming active. The first step is catalysed by **monoamine oxidase** B. MPTP is toxic even after inhalation or skin contact. It is an occasional contaminant of industrial processes, and may be present in batches of **MPPP**, a street drug used by addicts.

mucolytic drug   A drug that reduces the viscosity of mucus. Examples include the sodium salt of acetylcysteine, bromhexine and guaiphenesin.

muricidal rats   A strain of rats that when presented with a mouse kill it by biting through the spinal cord (Latin: *murinus*, a mouse). Other rats ignore the mouse. Muricidal rats are sometimes used to study the actions of **drugs** on aggressive behaviour. For example, **tricyclic antidepressant drugs** may prevent muricidal behaviour. The action of the **antidepressant drugs** is dependent on the effect of **serotonin** on the amygdala. The tricyclic antidepressants block serotonin uptake.

muscarine   An **alkaloid** obtained from the poisonous mushroom *Amanita muscaria*. It is the prototype **parasympathomimetic drug** and has no **nicotinic actions**.

muscarinic cholinoceptors   A subclass of **cholinoceptors** (acetylcholine **receptors**) for which **muscarine** is a specific **agonist**. Muscarinic cholinoceptors are blocked by atropine, and in practice receptors have been defined as muscarinic more often on the basis that they are selectively blocked by small doses of atropine than that they are stimulated by muscarine.

Muscarinic cholinoceptors may be subdivided into at least three further subtypes, MI, MII and MIII receptors, on the basis of their interaction with agonists and antagonists. Birdsall and Hulme (1983) have tentatively defined them as follows (*see Trends pharmacol. Sci.* **4**, 459). MI receptors occur on nerve cell bodies including sympathetic ganglion cells (but not nerve terminals). Pirenzepine is a **competitive antagonist** and **McN-A-343** is a selective agonist. MI receptor activation may mediate closure of K$^+$ (M) channels. MII receptors occur in the heart, on some parasympathetic and sympathetic nerve terminals, and on dopaminergic SIF cells in cat sympathetic ganglia. Gallamine (and some other **neuromuscular blocking drugs**) are allosteric antagonists of MII receptors; 3-acetoxy-*N*-methyl-piperidine methiodide is an agonist. MII receptors may mediate inhibition of **adenylate cyclase**. MIII receptors occur on smooth muscle cells. 4-

Diphenylacetoxy-*N*-methylpiperidine methiodide is a competitive antagonist and acetyltropine methiodide an agonist. MIII receptors may be coupled to Ca^{2+} channels, may initiate the **PI response** or, in arteries, may cause the release of **EDRF** which in turn stimulates **guanylate cyclase**.

muscarinic receptors   *See* **muscarinic cholinoceptors**.

muscle relaxant drug   A **drug** that produces relaxation of striated (non-cardiac) muscle. The term does not imply a mechanism or a site of action and so may cover **centrally acting muscle relaxants** (e.g. baclofen), **neuromuscular blocking drugs** (e.g. tubocurarine), and drugs that interfere with the contractile mechanism (e.g. dantrolene sodium). The term is not usually used to include drugs that produce relaxation of smooth muscle.

mutagenic action   An action that produces an abnormality of genetic material so that a permanent change in inherited constitution (a mutation) occurs. Mutagenic actions of drugs are unwanted side-effects that may be associated with **carcinogenicity**. *See*, for example, **Ames test**.

mutagenicity tests   Tests to detect the propensity to produce genetic damage. Chemicals (e.g. agricultural chemicals, food additives, flame retardants, drugs) to which man and animals may be exposed are subjected to mutagenicity tests. The best known of these tests is the Ames test (or *Salmonella*–microsome test), but there are many others carried out on bacteria, yeasts, fungi, plants, insects, cultured animal cells (e.g. human lymphocytes or mouse lymphoma cells) or animals *in vivo* (e.g. mice, rats or hamsters). In many countries, legislation demands a range of tests comprising a bacterial gene mutation test, a test for chromosomal damage, and a gene mutation test on mammalian cells. Mutagenicity tests are not only valuable for predicting the potential to produce **genetic damage**, but may also act as useful pre-screens for potential oncogenicity (*see* **oncogen**).

MVPP   *See* **MOPP**.

myasthenia gravis   A relatively rare disease of neuromuscular transmission in which there is rapid fatigue on exercise. It may affect any muscle of the body, but those of the face and neck often show the first signs. Ptosis (dropping of the upper eyelids) is often characteristic as a result of fatigue of the striated muscle fibres of the levator palpebrae which normally hold up the eyelids. Myasthenia gravis is an autoimmune disease in which there are circulating **antibodies** to the motor endplate acetylcholine receptors. Cross-linking of **receptors** by **antibody** leads to degradation of the receptors, and the endplates in myasthenia gravis therefore have a much lower than normal receptor density. Drugs that facilitate neuromuscular transmission, especially **anticholinesterase drugs** such as neostigmine and pyridostigmine, are beneficial, and considerable improvement may be achieved by removing the circulating antibodies by plasmapheresis. (Greek: *mys*, muscle; *astheneia*, weakness. Latin: *gravis*, severe.)

myasthenic syndrome *See* **Eaton–Lambert myasthenic syndrome**.

mydriatic drugs Drugs that produce mydriasis (Greek: dilatation) of the pupil. Such drugs include atropine, ephedrine, and **cocaine**.

myoneural blocking drug *See* **neuromuscular blocking drug**.

NANC nerve fibres Non-adrenergic, non-cholinergic nerve fibres. Refers to peripheral efferent autonomic fibres whose transmitter is neither **noradrenaline** nor **acetylcholine**. The airways, the bladder, the gut and the genital smooth muscles are amongst the organs that receive such an innervation in addition to noradrenergic and cholinergic innervations. The transmitters of NANC nerves are in general unknown; there is clearly more than one. Putative transmitters include purine nucleotides and various peptides.

narcosis A state of reversible central nervous system depression to the point of insensibility or stupor (Greek: *narkē*, numbness).

narcotic analgesic drug A drug that produces **narcosis** (reversible depression of the central nervous system) as well as analgesia. Usually restricted to drugs of the **morphine** type, and a more precise, although perhaps less literal, definition is an agent producing naloxone-reversible analgesia.

narcotic drug Literally, a drug that produces **narcosis**; i.e. reversible insensibility or stupor (Greek: *narkotikos*, benumbing or deadening). In practice, the term is often used to mean a dependence-producing drug. No contradiction arises when dependence-producing drugs of the morphine type, for example, are referred to, because these drugs do produce depression of the central nervous system. However, the term is sometimes less appropriately applied to dependence-producing drugs such as **cocaine** or amphetamine which stimulate the central nervous system. The misuse of the term in so far as its literal meaning is concerned has arisen through the titles given to various drug-regulating bodies, such as the UN Commission on Narcotic Drugs and the Federal Bureau of Narcotics in the USA, which are concerned with a range of drugs of dependence, not all of which are narcotic in the literal sense.

narcotize To put an animal or a person under the influence of a **narcotic drug**, i.e. a drug that depresses the central nervous system.

nasal decongestant drug   A drug that diminishes the resistance to airflow through the nose that accompanies the common cold or hay fever. Such drugs are applied locally and act by producing vasoconstriction in the nasal mucous membranes (e.g. **sympathomimetic drugs** such as ephedrine, phenylephrine and xylometazoline) or by reducing secretions in the respiratory tract (e.g. **atropine-like drugs**).

natriuresis   The excretion of larger than normal amounts of sodium ion in the urine (Latin: *natrium*, sodium; Greek: *ouresis*, the making of water).

natriuretic drug   A drug that produces **natriuresis**. All of the therapeutically useful **diuretic drugs** are natriuretic.

natriuretic hormone   A humoral agent, probably a low molecular weight peptide, thought to be released or activated by extracellular fluid volume expansion. It is believed to inhibit sodium ion transport (antinatriferic activity) in the distal renal tubule by inhibiting renal Na^+, K^+-ATPase. *See also* **atriopeptins**.
Gruber *et al.* (1980) *Nature* **287**, 743

nematodes   Roundworms. The Nemathelminthes, including the class nematodes, are one of the two phyla of worms (the other is the Platyhelminthes or **platyhelminths**) that include those that are obligate parasites of man. Examples of parasitic roundworms include *Trichuris* (whipworm), *Enterobius* (threadworm), *Ascaris* (giant intestinal worm), *Necatur* (hookworm), and *Onchocerca* (blinding filaria).

nephrotoxic drugs   Drugs that may produce kidney damage as an unwanted effect. Such drugs include, amongst many others, the **antibiotic** gentamicin, the anaesthetic methoxyflurane, the antiarthritic group of gold salts, and the solvent carbon tetrachloride.

nerve gases   Certain organophosphorus **anticholinesterase drugs** developed for use as war gases in Germany during World War II, notably sarin, soman and tabun.

nerve growth factor (NGF)   A protein growth factor extracted from the salivary glands of several animals and from the venom glands of certain snakes. It is tissue-specific, causing marked proliferation of immature postganglionic sympathetic neurones and sensory neurones, but it is not species-specific. The original observation leading to its discovery in 1951 by Levi-Montalcini was that a transplant of a mouse sarcoma greatly promoted the growth of sensory and sympathetic ganglia in chick embryos. Nerve growth factor was one of the earliest growth factors to be discovered.

neuroleptanalgesia   A calm and indifferent state produced, in preparation for minor surgery, by the use of a combination of an **analgesic drug**
(e.g. fentanyl) and a **neuroleptic drug** (e.g. droperidol). The patient remains
conscious and is able to co-operate with the surgeon, but feels no pain and
is unconcerned by the procedure. Nitrous oxide and oxygen may be given
to produce additional light anaesthesia if it is thought necessary.

neuroleptic drugs   A class of **psychotropic drugs** used to control the signs
and symptoms of schizophrenia, mania and certain other neurotic and
personality disorders (from Greek words meaning support of the nervous
system). Chlorpromazine is the prototype of this class of drugs. The term
neuroleptic was adopted at the Second International Congress of Psychiatry in 1957 to designate drugs having actions and uses like those of
chlorpromazine. Other members of the class include thioridazine, fluphenazine, haloperidol, pimozide and reserpine. Alternative names for the
class include major tranquillizers, neuroplegics, psycholeptics, psycho-
plegics, antischizophrenics and antipsychotics.

neuromodulator   The term 'neuromodulator' has sometimes been used
to describe substances that by themselves have no observable actions on
target cells but are able to modify the release of transmitter from presynaptic terminals or the response of the target cell to released transmitter.
However, since neurotransmitters can in some instances act in this way,
and since other substances of non-synaptic origin, such as hormones, or
substances released locally from effector cells, such as **prostaglandins**, may
also function similarly, it is incorrect to make a strict distinction between
'neurotransmitters' and 'neuromodulators', and the latter term may have
only limited usefulness.

neuromuscular blocking drug   A **drug** that interrupts neuromuscular transmission by blocking **cholinoceptors** at the motor endplate of
striated (non-cardiac) muscle. An alternative name is myoneural blocking
drug, but this is a less preferred term because the order of transmission is
from nerve to muscle.

   On logical grounds, the term neuromuscular blocking drug might apply
to drugs that block transmission by any mechanism (pre- or postjunc-
tional) at any nerve–muscle junction (adrenergic or cholinergic, autonomic
or somatic). However, long use has sanctioned the definition given above.
The **curare** alkaloid, tubocurarine, is the prototype of drugs of this class,
and curare-like drug is another alternative name.

neuronal uptake of dopamine   Dopamine is taken up into **noradrenergic nerve fibres**. It causes **noradrenaline** release by displacement and some
is released as a **false transmitter**. The rest is converted to noradrenaline in
the vesicles under the influence of the enzyme **dopamine β-hydroxylase**.
   Dopamine is also taken up into **dopaminergic nerve fibres**, which do not
possess the enzyme dopamine β-hydroxylase. Uptake of dopamine is

blocked by the antiparkinson drug amantadine, but not by **tricyclic antidepressants**. *See also* **neuronal uptake of noradrenaline**.

neuronal uptake of noradrenaline   Also called uptake 1. A low-threshold, saturable, active uptake process present in noradrenergic axons and especially at nerve endings. It is responsible, through re-uptake, for inactivating a large proportion of the **noradrenaline** released from the nerve. The rate of uptake of noradrenaline is proportional to the concentration with low concentrations, but the process is saturated by about 1 μmol/l. The process is Na^+-dependent. Much of the noradrenaline taken up is then loaded into vesicles and is available for release by nerve impulses.

Adrenaline, **dopamine**, metaraminol and tyramine are also taken up by the process, although they do not have the same affinity for uptake as noradrenaline. Isoprenaline is not taken up.

Cocaine, methylphenidate, **tricyclic antidepressant drugs** and phenoxybenzamine are examples of **drugs** that block uptake 1. By causing noradrenaline to persist in the region of its **receptors**, they thereby potentiate it. However, this is not the only mechanism involved in the potentiation. Lithium carbonate, on the other hand, increases uptake 1 and thereby reduces the effects of injected noradrenaline.

neuropeptide Y   A 36-amino acid polypeptide first isolated from porcine brain. It coexists with **noradrenaline** in certain sympathetic nerve endings and it has been suggested that it may function as a **co-transmitter** with noradrenaline. It is a powerful vasoconstrictor and it has been proposed that it produces those vasoconstrictor responses to sympathetic nerve stimulation that are resistant to α-**adrenoceptor** blockade. (Note that this role has also been attributed to ATP.) Neuropeptide Y inhibits **cyclic AMP** accumulation in cerebral blood vessels.

neuroplegic drug   An alternative name for **neuroleptic drug**.

neurotensin   A tridecapeptide originally isolated from the bovine hypothalamus, but later found to have a characteristic distribution in the gastrointestinal tract, mainly within mucosal N-cells in the terminal ileum. Its pharmacological actions include vasodilatation, reduced gastric acid secretion, delayed gastric emptying, inhibition of gut motility, and stimulation of exocrine pancreatic secretion.

neurotoxin   Toxic substances with selective toxic actions on nervous tissue. They may be naturally occurring or synthetic. **Tetrodotoxin**, β-**bungarotoxin** and **dendrotoxin** are examples of naturally occurring neurotoxins. Semicarbazide (which selectively depletes **GABA** systems), 6-hydroxydopamine (which selectively destroys **noradrenergic nerve fibres**) and 5,7-dihydroxytryptamine (which selectively destroys **serotoninergic nerve fibres**) are examples of synthetic neurotoxins.

nicotine 3-(1-Methyl-2-pyrrolidinyl)pyridine, the main **alkaloid** present in tobacco leaves (*Nicotiana tabacum* and *N. rustica*, named after Jean Nicot who introduced tobacco into France in the 16th century). The naturally occurring form in tobacco is the (−)-S-isomer which is pharmacologically more active than the (+)-R-isomer. Nicotine is pharmacologically important, especially from the historical point of view, because it is the prototype drug used to define **nicotinic cholinoceptors**. Nicotine is the main active principle of tobacco smoke and of chewing tobacco, being mainly responsible for both the pleasurable effects of tobacco use and for dependence upon it.

Nicotine

nicotinic actions Actions brought about by stimulation of **nicotinic cholinoceptors**.

H. H. Dale in 1914 (*J. Pharmacol. exp. Ther.* **6**, 147) showed that the pharmacological actions of **acetylcholine** and related esters resembled those of either **nicotine** or **muscarine**. Acetylcholine itself produced both types of action. To an extent, therefore, its pharmacological actions resembled those of a mixture of nicotine and muscarine. Dale called the actions 'nicotine actions' and 'muscarine actions', and the adjectival forms ending in '-ic' naturally followed. The main peripheral nicotinic actions arise from stimulation of nicotinic cholinoceptors on the motor endplate of skeletal muscle, on autonomic ganglion cells, and on adrenal medullary cells.

nicotinic cholinoceptors Cholinoceptors (**acetylcholine** receptors) that are specifically sensitive to **nicotine** and related drugs. *See* **nicotinic actions** for origin of term. Cholinoceptors are not homogeneous and were classified into two main groups by H. H. Dale in the early years of this century. One group, sensitive to **muscarine**, are called **muscarinic cholinoceptors**. The other group is the nicotinic **receptors**. Traditionally, in pharmacology, receptors are classified according to the **agonists** that stimulate them, backed up by the antagonists that block them, but they are not classified in relation to the chain of events that they initiate, including any **second messengers** that may be involved. However, it happens that all nicotinic receptors, at least those in the periphery, are coupled to cation channels. Activation of the receptors causes the channels to open and the concentration gradients and equilibrium potentials of the cations are such that the cationic current flow that ensues causes membrane depolarization and therefore excitation. The main nicotinic receptors outside the brain are located on the motor endplates of skeletal muscle, on autonomic ganglion cells and on adrenal medullary cells. When activated (by acetylcholine released from the nerve or by any applied nicotinic agonist) they initiate contraction of the muscle, excitation of the postsynaptic cells, and release of **catecholamines** respectively.

Even nicotinic receptors as a subgroup of cholinoceptors are not homogeneous and may be classified into at least two further subdivisions, mainly on the basis of the antagonists that block them. Tubocurarine blocks all nicotinic receptors, but ganglionic nicotinic receptors are selectively blocked by **ganglion blocking drugs** such as trimetaphan, whereas motor endplate nicotinic receptors are selectively blocked by many **neuromuscular blocking drugs** such as gallamine and pancuronium. The methonium compounds also serve to point up the difference between the two types of nicotinic receptors, the ganglionic receptors being selectively blocked by hexamethonium (C6) and the motor endplate receptors selectively stimulated by decamethonium (C10). Accordingly, D. A. Brown describes the two classes as 'nicotinic (C6) receptors and nicotinic (C10) receptors'.

nicotinic receptors   *See* **nicotinic cholinoceptors.**

nictitating membrane   An extraocular structure (third eyelid) present in most mammals but vestigial in man, in whom it persists only as the semilunar fold in the nasal commisure. The membrane slides over the anterior surface of the eye and is composed of a sheet of cartilage covered with conjunctiva. In mammals, the membrane is retracted by two bundles of smooth muscle lying within the intraorbital space. The smooth muscle is innervated by motor postganglionic sympathetic fibres arising in the superior cervical ganglion. The special importance of the nictitating membrane to pharmacologists is that it (especially that of the anaesthetized cat) provides a convenient preparation for studying the actions of **drugs** on adrenergic mechanisms and on sympathetic ganglia.

In birds, reptiles and amphibia, the nictitating membrane is composed of striated muscle which closes it rapidly. In some species, such as the tortoise, the membrane is rapidly closed by striated muscle and slowly retracted by smooth muscle.

nitrogen mustards   A group of **alkylating agents** that alkylate various nucleophilic cell constituents, e.g. the 7N of guanine which is the main purine base of DNA that is alkylated. They have the general structure:

$$R-N\begin{array}{l} \diagup (CH_2)_2Cl \\ \diagdown (CH_2)_2Cl \end{array}$$

They are used as cytotoxic agents in cancer **chemotherapy**, and include such drugs as mustine, chlorambucil, melphalan and cyclophosphamide.

nitrosamines   Simple alkylamino compounds that are potent **oncogens.** They may be formed in the stomach after ingestion of nitrites. They are metabolized in the liver with the production of **alkylating agents** that are the active oncogens. For example, dimethylnitrosamine is hydroxylated to produce methylhydroxynitrosamine

$$O{=}N{-}N\overset{CH_3}{\underset{CH_3}{\diagdown}} \longrightarrow O{=}N{-}N\overset{CH_3}{\underset{OH}{\diagdown}}$$

Dimethylnitrosamine   Methylhydroxynitrosamine

nivalenol *See* **tricothecene mycotoxin.**

NMA receptors *See* **excitatory amino acid receptors.**

nociceptive reflex A withdrawal reflex (e.g. the flexor reflex of a limb) that protects the body from injury (Latin: *nocere*, to harm). Nociceptive reflexes (e.g. foot withdrawal in the **hot plate test**, tail flick induced by a spring clip) are often elicited in tests for pain-relieving activity of drugs. Hence the term **antinociceptive action.**

noise analysis An alternative name for **fluctuation analysis.**

non-competitive antagonist An **antagonist drug** that prevents the effect of an **agonist** by acting at a site different from that of the agonist; i.e., unlike the agonist, it does not combine with the recognition sites of the **receptors**. The antagonist may combine, reversibly or irreversibly, at an adjoining site, i.e. an allosteric site (Greek: *allos*, other), on the receptor protein. Modification of the adjoining site may prevent agonist–receptor interaction. The effect is analogous to removal of receptors. This type of non-competitive allosteric antagonism is thought to be produced, for example, by gallamine when it blocks cardiac **muscarinic cholinoceptors**. The antagonist may combine reversibly or irreversibly with another component of the system so that successful initiation of effect is prevented, even though the agonist combines normally with the receptor recognition sites. This is analogous not to removal of receptors, but to removal of response potential. An example might be the occlusion of a **receptor-operated ion channel** by an antagonist drug. The agonist combines with the receptor, but the response is prevented because the non-competitive antagonist plugs the associated ion channel. (*See* **ion channel block.**) In the presence of a non-competitive antagonist, the maximal response produced by the agonist is reduced but the agonist can act normally at receptor complexes that remain unaffected by the antagonist. The **affinity** of the agonist for the receptor and the potency of the agonist remain unaltered. The graphs below illustrate differences between a **competitive** and a non-competitive **antagonist**. If log dose–response curves for the agonist are plotted, a competitive antagonist shifts the curve, in parallel, to the right, but the maximal response remains the same, i.e. the potency of the agonist is diminished. A non-competitive antagonist depresses the maximal response, i.e. the **efficacy** of the agonist is reduced but there is no change in potency. If double reciprocal plots of agonist response in the absence and presence of antagonist are drawn (i.e. reciprocal of response against reciprocal of dose—not log dose; *see* **Lineweaver–Burk plot**), the lines intersect on the Y-axis if the response is competitive and on the X-axis if non-competitive.

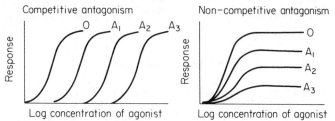

Log concentration–response curves for agonist in the absence (0) and in the presence of three concentrations (A_1, A_2 and A_3) of antagonist.

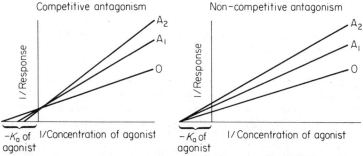

Double reciprocal plots for agonist in the absence (0) and in the presence of two concentrations (A_1 and A_2) of antagonist. K_a = affinity constant of agonist.

An antagonist might act at a remote site on a receptor complex in such a way as to produce a conformational change in the receptor recognition site that reduces its affinity for the agonist. In this case, the maximal response would be produced if sufficient agonist were added and the effect is better described as negative co-operativity (*see* **co-operativity**) than as non-competitive antagonism.

Antagonists that combine irreversibly with the receptor to produce an insurmountable block may also be described as non-competitive (although some authors describe them as '*irreversible competitive*'). Here they are defined under **irreversible receptor antagonist**.

non-competitive inhibition A type of enzyme inhibition in which the inhibitor combines equally well with the free enzyme and with the substrate–enzyme complex, both effects causing inhibition of the reaction.

The following equation may be derived in relation to non-competitive inhibition.

$$\frac{1}{v} = \frac{1}{V}(1 + K_m/s)(1 + iK_i)$$

where v = reaction rate, V = maximal reaction rate, K_m = Michaelis–Menten constant, s = original substrate concentration, i = concentration of inhibitor and K_i = the dissociation constant for the inhibitor–enzyme complex. Graphs of $1/v\ v.\ 1/s$ and $1/v\ v.\ i$ have the following forms (cf. **Lineweaver–Burk plot**).

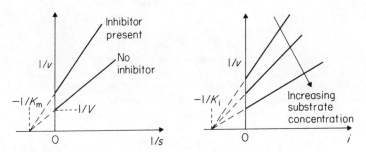

From Bowman & Rand (1980) *Textbook of Pharmacology*, 2nd Edition. Blackwell Scientific Publications, Oxford.

non-neuronal uptake of amines *See* extraneuronal uptake of amines.

non-parametric statistical tests
Tests that do not involve any assumptions about the conformity of the values to be analysed to a theoretical distribution. Thus, for example, if it is known that the differences in values obtained do not conform to a normal distribution, or if there is no information to suggest that they represent a sample from a normally distributed population, then analysis by non-parametric statistical tests is more appropriate than analysis by parametric statistical tests.

non-steroidal anti-inflammatory drug
A drug, not based on a steroid nucleus, that is used to control the inflammatory response. In general they act by inhibiting the synthesis of **prostaglandins**. Aspirin is the classical example but the group also includes other **salicylates**, pyrazolone derivatives such as phenylbutazone, indole derivatives such as indomethacin, anthranilic acid derivatives such as fenclofenac, and proprionic acid derivatives such as ibuprofen.

nootropic drugs
Drugs claimed to enhance learning, increase brain resistance to stress including hypoxia, and stimulate brain metabolism, especially in senile patients. Examples of such drugs include piracetam and pyritinol (Greek: *nous*, mind).

nor- A prefix in chemical nomenclature which seems first to have been used by Mathieson and Foster (1868, *J. chem. Soc.*, p. 358) as a contraction of 'normal'. They used the term noropianic acid (normal opianic acid) to denote the demethylated compound, and methylnoropianic acid for the monomethylcompound. Opianic acid is the dimethylcompound obtained by oxidation of the **opium alkaloid** narcotine.

Opianic acid

Since that time the prefix has generally been used by chemists to denote the compound in which one or two methyl groups of the parent compound have been replaced by H, or for the compound in which a $-CH_2-$ group has disappeared from a chain; i.e. the next lower homologue.

Pharmacologists, on the other hand, seem to enjoy and persist with the idea that 'nor' stands for the German '*N ohne Radikal*' (nitrogen without a radical), and this view probably arose as a mnemonic to help students remember the constitutions of **noradrenaline**, norephedrine, normorphine and so on. Even so, the prefix 'nor' is used for many compounds, in addition to noropianic acid, which contain no nitrogen at all (e.g. norpinic acid, noroestrone, norequilenin) and so the chemists' view is undoubtedly the correct one. (See correspondence between A. M. Woolman and J. H. Gaddum (1956) in *Nature* **177**, 1046.)

noradrenaline 4-(2-Amino-1-hydroxyethyl)-1,2-benzenediol: norepinephrine in the USA. The laevorotatory, i.e. *l* or (−) isomer is the chemical transmitter of **noradrenergic nerve fibres**. It has D absolute configuration.

noradrenergic nerve fibre A nerve fibre that releases **noradrenaline** as a neurotransmitter. *See* **adrenergic nerve fibre** for discussion of the restricted use of the suffix '-ergic'.

norepinephrine *See* **noradrenaline**.

normal distribution *See* **binomial distribution**.

notexin A polypeptide neurotoxin from the Australian tiger snake (*Note-*

chis scutatus scutatus). It acts to prevent the release of **acetylcholine** from **cholinergic nerve fibre** endings. (The toxin notechis II-5 is chemically related and comes from the same source. It has a similar action to notexin.)

NREM sleep   Non-rapid eye movement sleep. A phase of sleep characterized by stationary eyeballs under the closed lids, by regular breathing, heart rate and blood pressure, by more relaxed muscles than is the case during **REM sleep**, and by a predominance of large slow waves in the cortical EEG. Mundane thoughts, rather than true dreaming, are characteristic of mental activity during this time. There are normally about five or six periods of NREM sleep during a single night's sleep, each period lasting for 30–40 min. NREM sleep appears to play an important role in the maintenance of skeletal muscle function.

NSAID   *See* **non-steroidal anti-inflammatory drug.**

null hypothesis   In applying a statistical test to the comparison of two or more groups of samples in which the values exhibit random variation, the general principle is to assume, in the first instance, that the differences between the groups are attributable entirely to random variation. This is termed the null hypothesis.

The purpose of the statistical analysis is to establish the degree of probability with which such a difference can be expected. If the probability is high, there is no reason to conclude that the differences are other than can be ascribed purely to chance and the null hypothesis is accepted. The null hypothesis is never proved; it is merely not rejected. On the other hand, if the probability is low, then the possibility arises that the differences are not due to chance but are attributable to the differences in whatever treatments are being compared.

occupation theory   Theory, developed by a number of workers over the years (notably A. J. Clark, R. P. Stephenson and E. J. Ariëns), that holds that the response of a cell to an **agonist** is a function of the occupation of specific **receptors** by that agonist (cf. **rate theory**). Within occupation theory there are two broad subtheories concerning the relationship between receptor occupation and response.

1   *Linear relationship.*   Clark found that there were many instances of drug action in accord with the view that the effect observed (E) is linearly proportional to receptor occupancy, and that the maximal effect (E_{max}) is reached when the total number of receptors (R_T) is occupied.

That is to say that the proportion of receptors occupied by drugs, $[DR]/[R_T]$, is equal to the ratio of the effect produced to the maximal possible effect, E/E_{max}. ([DR] is the concentration of drug–receptor combinations.)

In terms of the dissociation constant of an agonist, K_D (*see* **agonist–receptor interaction**):

$$\frac{[DR]}{[R_T]} = \frac{[D]}{[D] + K_D}$$

Therefore:

$$\frac{E}{E_{max}} = \frac{[D]}{[D] + K_D}$$

This equation predicts that the plot of response as a fraction of the maximal response (fractional response) against the concentration of agonist is a hyperbolic curve starting from the origin and approaching E_{max} asymptotically, and the plot of fractional response against the logarithm of the agonist concentration is a symmetrical sigmoid curve.

When the concentration of agonist is such that the response obtained is half the maximal response, $[D]$ is equal to K_D. Thus, if the several assumptions implicit in the concept that $[DR]/[R_T] = E/E_{max}$ are valid, then the value of the dissociation constant for an agonist–receptor interaction can be read from the plot E/E_{max} against $[D]$ or E/E_{max} against $\log [D]$. That is to say, the dissociation constant (K_D) for the interaction of an agonist drug with its receptor sites is given by the concentration producing half the maximal response ($[D_{max}/2]$).

One problem with a general approach to the above treatment is that some drugs are incapable of producing the maximal response, no matter how large the concentration. Observations of this sort led to the designation of drugs as **partial agonists** or **dualists**, and to the concept of **intrinsic activity**.

2 *Non-linear relationship.* Stephenson drew attention to a number of results which were not in accord with the concept that the response was linearly proportional to the fraction of receptors occupied. He proposed that a maximal effect can be produced by some agonists when only a small proportion of the receptors is occupied. The remaining unoccupied receptors are so-called **spare receptors**. Stephenson used the term **efficacy** to denote the capacity of an agonist to produce a response once it occupies receptors.

odorivectors Odoriferous substances. For a given substance to be an odorivector it must possess the following properties:
1 It must have a vapour pressure that is sufficient to supply a concentration exceeding the threshold for excitation of the olfactory receptors.
2 It must be water-soluble in order to dissolve in the mucous layer covering the olfactory epithelium.
3 It must be capable of being adsorbed onto the olfactory epithelium.
4 It must also be lipid-soluble in order to penetrate the membrane of the olfactory cell.

5   It must normally be absent from the olfactory epithelium because the sense of smell rapidly adapts.

6   It must be capable of exciting the olfactory receptors.

oestrogen   A generic term for oestrus-producing steroids (Latin: *oestrus*, a gadfly; Greek: *oistros*, a vehement desire). In mammals other than human beings oestrus is the recurrent restricted time of sexual receptivity in females. It is marked by intense sexual urge. In human beings, oestrogen is formed in the ovary, the adrenal cortex, the testis and the fetoplacental unit. It is responsible for the development of the human female secondary sex characteristics and it acts on the female genitalia to produce an environment suitable for the development of the early embryo.

Oestrogens are used in **oral contraceptives**, as palliatives in postmenopausal breast cancer and cancer of the prostate, to inhibit lactation, in threatened abortion, and in severe menorrhagia.

oncogen   A substance that produces cancer. Hence oncogenicity, the capacity to produce cancer (Greek: *oncos*, growth).

oncogenes   Genes that, when expressed abnormally, may lead to cancerous growth. Oncogenes were first found in tumour viruses (viral oncogenes) but it is now known that normal vertebrate cells also possess such genes (cellular oncogenes). Indeed, during evolution, the viruses may have acquired them from vertebrates rather than vice versa. The normal function of the cellular oncogenes may be to direct the synthesis of enzymes or other proteins that play an essential role in cell growth and multiplication. One such enzyme is a protein kinase that phosphorylates tyrosine subunits in proteins; another is a DNA-binding protein that is essential for DNA replication. It is only when there is augmented expression of the genes (e.g. through viral infection) or inappropriate expression (e.g. caused by chemical mutagens or carcinogens or radiation), that the cell is overwhelmed and becomes transformed into a cancer cell.

Rous in the USA first demonstrated the existence of tumour viruses as long ago as 1910, although his work was largely ignored for many years. The virus studied by Rous caused a sarcoma to grow in chickens and is known as Rous sarcoma virus. It belongs to the family of retroviruses which have an RNA genome. Their RNA must be transcribed 'backwards' into DNA (hence the name retrovirus) in order for them to propagate. Not all tumour viruses are retroviruses, but research on retroviruses has provided the clearest information about oncogenes. So far, 17 retrovirus oncogenes have been detected, at least 16 of them being related to a cellular oncogene found in the DNA of vertebrates. The product of at least eight of the genes is a **protein kinase**, and six of these are known to phosphorylate tyrosine subunits. The protein kinases bind to the plasma membrane of the cell. Some of the oncogenes code for proteins that promote steps in the pathway described under **PI response** and stimulate cell multiplication in this way. For example, the oncogene *sis* (from a monkey sarcoma) codes for platelet-derived growth factor, and *erb B* (from a chicken sarcoma) codes for receptors for epithelium-derived growth factor; these growth factors stimulate receptors that are coupled to the specific **phosphodiesterase, phospholipase C**. The oncogene *ras* (from a rat sarcoma) may code for the GTP binding protein that triggers uncontrolled stimulation of the specific phosphodiesterase; *src* (from a chicken sarcoma) and *ras* (from a chicken sarcoma) may code for the protein kinases that phosphorylate **phosphatidylinositol** at the 4 and then the 5 positions of its inositol head (*see* **PI response**).

Interferons can modulate cell proliferation and differentiation in cultured cells, and slow the growth of tumours *in vivo*. There is evidence that in some instances they act by inhibiting the expression of cellular oncogenes, although this is not the only mechanism involved.

Bishop (1982) *Sci. Am.* **246**, 67

oncogenicity *See* **oncogen**.

on–off effects A term used to describe the disabling and sudden periods of akinesia that afflict many parkinsonian patients after long-term, formerly successful, therapy with levodopa. A considerable amount of research is being carried out into possible methods of alleviating the syndrome by drug treatment.

ontogenesis The development of the organism by cell growth and differentiation from the zygote onwards (Greek: *on*, existing; *gennan*, to produce; i.e. production of the existing form).

onycholysis A gradual separation of the nail from the nail bed, beginning distally and usually involving no more than one half of the nail.

It is an occasional unwanted effect of some drugs, such as benoxaprofen.

operant conditioning A technique that conditions an animal to operate a mechanism (e.g. striking a lever) to obtain a reward (e.g. a pellet of food).

opiate An analgesic drug derived from the opium poppy; e.g. **morphine**, codeine. Also includes morphine derivatives, such as heroin (diacetylmorphine) which is prepared from morphine (cf. **opioid**).

opiate receptors Receptors that specifically bind **opiates** and **opioids** and that mediate the various effects of opioids. Opiate receptors are not homogeneous and have been divided into a number of types designated mu (μ), delta (δ), kappa (κ), epsilon (ε) and sigma (σ). At the present time highly selective **ligands** for each type are not available, but a useful degree of selectivity for three of the receptor types is exhibited as follows:

mu. Sufentanil, morphiceptin and DAGO (Tyr–D–Ala–Gly–(Me)Phe–Gly-ol).

delta. DPDPE ([D-Pen^2, D-Pen^5]enkephalin) and DSLET ([D-Ser^2, Leu^5]enkephalin-Thr^6).

kappa. U50,488.

Goldstein & James (1984) *Trends pharmacol. Sci.* **5**, 503

Piercey *et al.* (1982) *Life Sci.* **27**, 971.

opioid An **analgesic drug** with pharmacological similarities to opium (**morphine**). Includes both synthetic **morphine-like drugs** (e.g. buprenorphine) and endogenous peptides (e.g. met-enkephalin). More specifically, it refers to any directly acting opioid receptor **agonist**, not from opium, that is stereospecifically antagonized by naloxone. An **opioid peptide** is an opioid drug that is a polypeptide. Met-enkephalin is an example. (The suffix '-oid' comes from a Greek word meaning like, or having the form of.)

opioid peptides Naturally occurring endogenous peptides that stimulate **opiate receptors**. These peptides belong to three families, each derived from a distinct precursor molecule. Pro-opiomelanocortin (POMC) is the precursor of β-**endorphin**, which has high affinity for opiate μ, κ and δ receptors. (NB POMC is also the precursor of corticotrophin.) Pro-enkephalin A is the precursor of met-enkephalin and leu-enkephalin, which have preferential **affinity** for opiate δ receptors. Some of the intermediate peptides in the processing of pro-enkephalin A (e.g. peptide E, BAM-22P) have high affinity for μ opiate receptors. Pro-enkephalin B is also a precursor of leu-enkephalin, but in addition is the precursor for a number of other peptides such as **dynorphin** 1-8, dynorphin 1-17, α-neo-endorphin and rimorphin which have a selective affinity for κ receptors.

opiopeptins A generic term proposed by E. Way to cover the three distinct families of endogenous **opioid peptides**: enkephalin family, **dynorphin** family and **endorphin** family.

opium alkaloids The **alkaloids** obtained from the dried exudate from the unripe seed capsules of the opium poppy *Papaver somniferum*. (The word opium is derived from Latin and Greek words meaning 'juice'.) The alkaloids with medicinal use are **morphine**, codeine, papaverine and noscapine (narcotine). The alkaloids are traditionally divided into two chemical classes: phenanthrene derivatives such as morphine and codeine (analgesic action, antitussive action) and benzylisoquinoline derivatives such as papaverine (smooth muscle relaxant, **phosphodiesterase inhibitor**, **dopaminomimetic**) and noscapine (cough suppressant).

oral contraceptives Contraceptive agents that are active after oral administration. Euphemistically called 'the pill'. At present, successful preparations are available only for females; oral contraceptives for males have not yet been satisfactorily developed. It had long been known that the high blood levels of **hormones** (**oestrogens** and progesterone) during pregnancy suppress ovulation, and the contraceptives work in a similar way by mimicking the ovulation-suppressant activity of endogenous hormones. Oral contraceptives are of three main types:

1 Combination products which contain an oestrogen and a progestogen in a fixed dose ratio.

2 Sequential preparations which also contain both hormones but the ratio of doses is varied throughout the menstrual cycle in an attempt to mimic endogenous changes.

3 Progestogen-only preparations.

Orbeli effect The Russian physiologist Orbeli showed in 1923 that stimulation of the lumbar sympathetic chain in the frog produced an increase in the contractions of the gastrocnemius muscle that had been fatigued by rapid stimulation of the motor roots. This is known as the Orbeli effect. **Adrenaline** and **noradrenaline** produce a similar defatiguing effect which is probably due to an action on the nerve endings through which **acetylcholine** release is increased plus an enhancing action on muscle contractility. The Orbeli effect probably has no physiological counterpart.

organophosphorus   anticholinesterases Anticholinesterase **drugs**, most of which conform to the general structure:

$$
\begin{array}{c}
\text{O (or S)} \\
\parallel \\
X\!-\!P\!-\!YR \\
\mid \\
Y'R'
\end{array}
$$

where R and R′ denote alkyl or aromatic groups or hydrogen, Y and Y′ are usually oxygen but may be sulphur and X is an easily hydrolysed group which may be organic or inorganic. Dyflos (DFP, diisopropylfluorophosphate) is an example:

$$
\begin{array}{c}
\text{O} \\
\parallel \\
F\!-\!P\!-\!O\!-\!CH(CH_3)_2 \\
\mid \\
O \\
\mid \\
CH(CH_3)_2
\end{array}
$$

These inhibitors phosphorylate the esteratic site of the enzyme and thereby inhibit it. Restoration of enzymatic activity is very slow, and for this reason these drugs are often called irreversible inhibitors. A few members have therapeutic uses (e.g. echothiopate in glaucoma), many are, or have been, used as insecticides, and some were developed as war gases (the so-called **nerve gases**).

osmotic agents Agents used to raise the osmotic pressure of the tissue fluids in order to withdraw water from the CSF when there is high intracranial pressure, or from the eye in glaucoma. Hypertonic dextrose, urea, mannitol, sorbitol and glycerol may be used for these purposes.

osmotic diuretics Agents that, when given intravenously or orally in hypertonic solution, are filtered by the glomerulus and produce an osmotic **diuresis** when the amount delivered to the tubules exceeds the capacity for their reabsorption. The reduced water reabsorption retards the reabsorption of sodium and chloride ions. Substances used as osmotic diuretics include mannitol (intravenously), isosorbide (orally), trometamol (intravenously) and urea (orally). Their value is limited.

ototoxicity Toxicity manifested in the functions of the ear (Greek: *ot*, ear). For example, aminoglycoside **antibiotics** may produce deafness as a consequence of damaging the eighth cranial nerve.

ovulatory stimulant drug Drugs that stimulate ovulation. They are used in appropriate cases of anovulatory infertility and include the **anti-oestrogen** drugs clomiphene, cyclofenil and tamoxifen.

oxotremorine A muscarinic **agonist** that acts centrally to produce tremor, hypokinesia and rigidity, and peripherally to produce pronounced parasympathomimetic effects. It has been used to produce these effects in animals in an attempt to mimic the symptoms of Parkinson's disease. **Antiparkinson drugs** of the atropine type block the effects of oxotremorine. *See also* **tremorine**.

oxytocic agents Agents that hasten evacuation of the uterus by stimulating contractions of the myometrium (Greek: *oxys*, keen or quick; *tokos*, birth). Such agents include oxytocin itself (a hormone from the neurohypophysis), and **prostaglandin** $F_{2\alpha}$ (dinoprost).

pachycurare A term coined by D. Bovet (Greek: *pachys*, thick) to denote the type of **neuromuscular blocking drugs** that produce non-depolarization block by acting as **acetylcholine** receptor antagonists. Bovet pointed out that the molecules of such drugs are bulky, either in the supporting skeleton, or in the groups attached to the quaternary nitrogens, or in both. Diagrammatically, the molecules might be represented as shown below. Tubocurarine and pancuronium are typical.

PAF-acether PAF refers to platelet-activating factor and PAF is the acronym by which the platelet-aggregating agent secreted by IgE-sensitized rabbit basophils on exposure to specific **antigen** was originally known. When it was discovered that the substance belongs to the class of ether lipids, one of which is 1-0-alkyl-2-acetyl-*sn*-glyceryl-3-phosphoryl-choline, the name was expanded to PAF-acether to denote its chemical identity. It is also known as AGEPC (acetylglyceryletherphosphoryl-choline being another way of writing the above systematic chemical name).

PAF-acether is an **autacoid** that in fact exerts many actions in addition to activating platelets. It is produced by platelets, endothelial cells, leucocytes (leukocytes in USA), **mast cells**, macrophages and kidney cells, and has effects on inflammatory cells, the respiratory system and the cardiovascular system. It is implicated in acute and chronic inflammation, asthma and vasoregulation.

palytoxin A neurotoxin isolated from a marine zoanthid *Palythoa toxica*

The structure of palytoxin.

and other *Palythoa* species. It is the most deadly non-protein toxin ever isolated. Its LD_{50} in mice is about 0·15 μg/kg by intravenous injection. It is therefore about 50 times more toxic than **tetrodotoxin**. Its structure has been determined.

panacea   A cure-all. After Panacea, one of the daughters of Aesculapius.

papaveretum   A solution of the total pure **alkaloids** of **opium** (*see* **opium alkaloids**) as the hydrochlorides for oral use or for subcutaneous or intramuscular injection.

paralytic shellfish poisoning   Toxicity arising from eating mussels, clams or scallops that have been feeding on certain dinoflagellates of *Gonyaulax* species in which **saxitoxin** or related substances are produced. The dinoflagellates are red in colour, and a high concentration in the sea gives rise to a so-called red tide. The dinoflagellate toxin is lethal to fish, but molluscs are resistant and can accumulate a considerable amount. Paralytic shellfish poisoning has occurred sporadically all over the world, with the possible exceptions of the Mediterranean and Red Sea areas. There was an outbreak in NE England and eastern Scotland in 1968, in which mussels (*Mytilus edulis*) were found to be contaminated with *Gonyaulax tamarensis*.

parameter   (Greek: *parametrein*, to measure one thing by another.) A technical term originally coined to have precise meanings in various branches of mathematics. It is included here because it is frequently misused in many disciplines, including pharmacology and medical science generally, simply to mean any measured factor. An acceptable meaning in medical science, arising through common usage, may be: a variable, the measurement of which is indicative of a function that cannot itself be precisely measured by direct methods. For example, measurements of changes in blood glucose and urine glucose may be parameters of drug effects on the function of the endocrine pancreas.

paraquat   A bipyridyl-type herbicide which is widely used. Many cases of human poisoning have been reported. Toxic effects include damage to lungs, liver, kidneys and heart. The most striking toxic effect is a delayed (several days) and potentially lethal lung toxicity involving a widespread proliferation of cells in the lungs.

$$H_3C—\overset{+}{N} \underset{}{\bigcirc}—\bigcirc\overset{+}{N}—CH_3$$

Paraquat

It has been proposed that paraquat undergoes a single-electron, cyclic reduction–oxidation with the formation of superoxide anions ($^{\cdot}O_2{}^-$) (*see under* **free radicals**). Superoxide is spontaneously transformed to **singlet oxygen** which attacks polyunsaturated lipids of the cell membrane to form lipid hydroperoxides which decompose to lipid **free radicals** which again attack the cell membranes so that a chain reaction occurs.

Treatment must be commenced as soon as possible after ingestion of paraquat. It includes gastric lavage and the use of cathartics and Fuller's earth to remove the paraquat from the gut, haemodialysis or haemo-perfusion to remove absorbed paraquat, and the administration of specially prepared paraquat antibodies.

Paraquat was used in Mexico to control the illicit growing of **cannabis**, and high concentrations were subsequently found in some marihuana cigarettes, although no cases of poisoning from this source have been documented. The structure of paraquat suggests that it will possess ganglion blocking and neuromuscular blocking activity, but there is no reason to suggest that such actions contribute to its toxicity.

parasympatholytic drug A term applied to drugs that block the actions of the parasympathetic nervous system and of **parasympathomimetic drugs**. It usually refers to drugs that act by blocking **muscarinic cholinoceptors**, i.e. **muscarinic receptor antagonists** or **atropine-like drugs**. It is not an ideal term because it implies that parasympathetic nerves or parasympathomimetic drugs are lysed (Greek: *lysis*, dissolution, loosening), which of course they are not.

parasympathomimetic action Parasympathomimetic is a term introduced by Barger and Dale to describe drug actions that resemble those of the parasympathetic nervous system. *See* **parasympathomimetic drug**.

parasympathomimetic drug This term must literally apply to any drug that produces **parasympathomimetic actions**. However, some restriction in meaning based on selectivity of action is necessary for the sake of precision. Responses to parasympathetic nerve stimulation could be produced by drugs that stimulate parasympathetic centres in the brain stem, either directly or reflexly, but no drugs that selectively act in this way are known. Drugs that stimulate parasympathetic ganglia (**ganglion stimulating drugs**) produce parasympathomimetic actions, but all of those known to act in this way also stimulate sympathetic ganglia. **Anticholinesterase drugs** produce pronounced parasympathomimetic effects and some writers describe them as parasympathomimetic drugs. However, they also facilitate transmission in skeletal muscle and are used clinically for these effects (anticurare agents, **myasthenia gravis**). In addition, they may enhance sympathetic activity by facilitating sympathetic ganglionic transmission and transmission to the adrenal medullae. Thus, by a process of elimination, only the more traditional **muscarinic receptor agonists** remain (i.e. **muscarine**, **acetylcholine**, **pilocarpine**, methacholine, carbachol, etc., but excluding, for example, **McN-A-343**), and the term parasympatho-mimetic drug seems best restricted to these. The fact that some muscarinic agonists also stimulate **nicotinic cholinoceptors** (e.g. acetylcholine, carbachol) does not exclude them, because the general effects produced are overwhelmingly parasympathomimetic; the nicotinic actions require much larger doses.

parenteral administration Literally means administration other than by the gut. However, it is usually taken to mean administration by injection.

parkinsonian side-effects Side-effects that resemble the signs and symptoms of Parkinson's disease, i.e. drug-induced parkinsonism. Parkinson's disease (described by James Parkinson, 1755–1824) is a hypokinetic disorder of movement associated with disease of the basal ganglia. In particular, there is degeneration of the **dopaminergic nerve fibres** of the nigrostriatal pathway, and most of the signs and symptoms (muscle rigidity, tremor, hypokinesia and weakness) arise from this. Drugs that block central **dopamine receptors** (**antipsychotic drugs**) or deplete the basal ganglia of **dopamine** (e.g. reserpine) may produce parkinsonian side-effects. *See also* **MPTP**.

partial agonist A term introduced by R. P. Stephenson to denote an **agonist** that fails to produce a maximal response of a tissue when all the **receptors** are occupied by it. Partial agonists also possess antagonistic activity in the sense that they reduce the response to more active agonists. Ariëns used the term **dualist** to denote the same properties, and the two terms are synonymous.

In Stephenson's terms, it may be said that when a partial agonist is producing the maximal response of which it is capable, all the receptors are occupied but the **efficacy** is such that the stimulus produced is inadequate to produce the maximal response potentially obtainable. In Ariëns terms it may be said that the **intrinsic activity** (α) of a dualist or partial agonist is less than one but greater than zero (i.e. $1 > \alpha > 0$).

passive anaphylaxis Anaphylactic susceptibility transferred to an animal not previously exposed to a particular **antigen** by administration of serum from a sensitized animal of the same or a closely related species. A short time elapses during which reaginic **antibody** from the donor's serum is fixed to reactive cells of the recipient, and then challenge with antigen produces **anaphylaxis**.

passive diffusion Simple diffusion of a solute down its concentration gradient under physical laws, without the participation of active or passive special transport mechanisms. The amount of an uncharged molecule (m) passively diffusing through an area (A) of an interface (e.g. a cell

161

membrane) in a given time (t) is given by **Fick's law**:

$$m = P_K A(C_o - C_i)t$$

where C_o and C_i are the concentrations of the solute on the outside and inside of the interface respectively, and P_K is the permeability constant.

passive immunity Temporary but immediate specific immunity acquired by injection of the appropriate **antibody** or of serum containing it. Antibody preparations used for producing passive immunity include botulinum antitoxin (animal sera containing antibodies to the toxins of *Clostridium botulinum* types A and B), diphtheria antitoxin (animal sera containing antibodies to the toxin of *Corynebacterium diphtheriae*) and tetanus antitoxin (immunoglobulin fraction of sera containing antibodies to the toxin of *Clostridium tetani*). Similar preparations are available for immunization against gas gangrene, leptospira, rabies, scarlet fever, and several venoms from snakes, spiders and scorpions.

patch clamp An electrophysiological technique invented by E. Neher and his colleagues at the Max Planck Institute in Göttingen. The technique, sometimes called patch clamp analysis, allows the study of the interaction of single membrane receptor molecules with transmitters or other substances in living intact cells, or in isolated patches of membrane. The polished tip of a glass micropipette (1–2 μm diameter) is pressed against the membrane to form an electric seal with a leak resistance of about 50 MΩ. Currents flowing through the patch of membrane isolated under the tip must then flow into the pipette. When an appropriate **agonist** is placed in the pipette, the receptor-gated channel in the isolated patch of membrane is activated and its conductance may be recorded.

A modification of the technique provides greater adherence between the micropipette and the membrane, so that the leak resistance is greatly increased and the background noise correspondingly reduced. With this technique, single-channel currents as small as 1–2 pA can be resolved.

Pavlov pouch A pouch formed of a segment of the stomach prepared under anaesthesia, usually in the dog, for studying gastric secretion and the effects of drugs upon it. The mucosal surface is accessible via a cannula or fistula that passes through the abdominal wall. The pouch is separated from the main part of the stomach by a mucosal septum and the muscle layers and innervation remain intact. This type of pouch was developed and used by the Russian physiologist Pavlov in his experiments on conditioned reflexes. *See also* **Haidenhain pouch**.

pA$_x$ value The negative logarithm (p) of the molar concentration of antagonist (A) in the presence of which the potency of the **agonist** is reduced by x times; that is x times more agonist is required to produce a given response in the presence than in the absence of the antagonist.

The value of measuring antagonist potency in this way was developed by H. O. Schildt. Following his lead, it has become common practice to determine pA_2 and pA_{10} values of antagonists against various agonists. The dissociation constant for a **competitive antagonist** (K_A) is given by the concentration of the antagonist with which the ratio of concentrations of agonist (D) producing equal responses in its presence $([D_A])$ and absence $([D_0])$ equals two. That is, $[A]_2 = K_A$ and therefore $pA_2 = -\log K_A$.

For competitive antagonism, it can be shown that $\log (x - 1) = \log [A]_x - \log K_A$. If we substitute 10 for x, then:

$$\log 9 = \log [A]_{10} - \log K_A$$

but

$$\log [A]_{10} = -pA_{10}$$

and

$$-\log K_A = +pA_2$$

Therefore, rearranging:

$$pA_2 - pA_{10} = \log 9 = 0.95$$

Thus, if $pA_2 - pA_{10}$ for an antagonist is close to 0.95, the result is compatible with, although it does not prove, competitive antagonism. The table below shows two examples.

	pA_2	pA_{10}	Difference
Atropine v acetylcholine, guinea-pig ileum	9.0	8.1	0.9
Mepyramine v histamine, guinea-pig ileum	9.4	8.4	1.0

PCP *See* **angel dust.**

pD₂ value The negative logarithm of the concentration of **agonist** drug (D) that produces half of the maximal response, i.e. $pD_2 = -\log[D]_{max/2}$.

pD_2 values are measures of **affinity** of agonists for their **receptors**. The practice of expressing affinities in this way was introduced by Ariëns and van Rossum and their colleagues. *See also* **affinity.**

penicillin amidase An enzyme that catalyses the hydrolysis of the side-chain acid group of penicillin with the production of the inactive **6-aminopenicillanic acid**. A few organisms (e.g. a few *Escherichia* and *Alcaligenes* species) produce this enzyme and owe their resistance to **penicillin** to it.

The enzyme may be used commercially to produce large quantities of 6-aminopenicillanic acid from penicillins. This acid is used as a starting point for the synthesis of other penicillins.

penicillin resistance The resistance of normally sensitive strains of bacteria to the killing effect of **penicillins**. Resistance may be present from the start or it may be acquired after exposure to the drug. Resistance is a consequence of the presence, in the bacteria, either of the enzyme **penicillinase** or, more rarely, of the enzyme **penicillin amidase**, both of which destroy penicillin.

penicillinase inhibitors   Drugs that inhibit the enzyme penicillinase and thereby prevent bacterial resistance to β-lactam antibiotics. Clavulanic acid, from *Streptomyces clavuligerus*, is the main example of a penicillinase inhibitor.

Clavulanic acid

penicillinase-resistant pencillins   *See* **penicillinases**.

penicillinases   Enzymes that have the property of catalysing the hydrolysis of **penicillin** with the production of inactive penicilloic acid. The enzymes (also known as *β*-lactamases) are both constitutive and inducible in bacteria; that is, the bacteria may already possess the enzymes or they may be induced after exposure to the drug. Penicillinases constitute the main mechanism through which bacteria are resistant to penicillins. However, a few are resistant because they possess the enzyme **penicillin amidase**. Penicillinases are elaborated by a range of different bacteria including penicillin-resistant *Staphylococci*, some strains of *E. coli*, *Klebsiella*, *Proteus*, *Pseudomonas*, *Vibrio*, *Mycobacterium* and *Brucella*.

Certain partially synthetic pencillins (e.g. cloxacillin, oxacillin, nafcillin) are poor substrates for penicillinase and are hydrolysed only very slowly. They are called penicillinase-resistant penicillins.

Partially synthetic penicillins and **cephalosporins** may act as inducers of penicillinase even though they are themselves resistant to, or poor substrates for, the enzyme.

penicillins   A series of **β-lactam antibiotics** whose molecules consist of a thiazolidine ring (A) connected to a *β*-lactam ring (B) to which is attached a side-chain (R). They include, or are related to, benzylpenicillin itself, originally obtained by Alexander Fleming from the mould *Penicillium notatum*, but now, more productively, from an X-ray induced mutation of *P. chrysogenum*. Semi-synthetic penicillins are prepared from **6-aminopenicillanic acid**. They act on sensitive bacteria, mainly by inhibiting the transpeptidase reaction that is part of the process of cell wall synthesis. Many penicillins are inactivated by **penicillinase** enzymes produced by resistant bacteria. Those that are not (e.g. methicillin, nafcillin, oxacillin, floxacillin) are active against penicillinase-producing *Staph. aureus.* Their resistance to penicillinase is determined by the nature of the side-chain (R).

General structure of penicillins.

peptidergic nerve fibre A nerve fibre that releases a polypeptide as a neurotransmitter. *See* **adrenergic nerve fibre** for discussion of the restricted use of the suffix '-ergic'. More than 30 polypeptides have been localized in nerve endings and have been given the status of putative transmitters. These include a number of peptides formerly thought to be confined to the pituitary such as vasopressin, oxytocin, corticotrophin and growth hormone, hypothalamic releasing hormones such as somatostatin, thyrotrophin-releasing hormone and corticotrophin-releasing hormone, **opioid peptides** such as enkephalins, **dynorphin** and kyotorphin, gut hormones such as gastrin, motilin, secretin, **vasoactive intestinal peptide**, **substance P** and cholecystokinin, circulating hormones such as **angiotensin**, **atriopeptin**, calcitonin and glucagon, and a number of miscellaneous peptides such as bombesin, **neuropeptide Y**, **neurotensin**, proctolin, substance K and **calcitonin gene-related peptide**.

percutaneous absorption Absorption through the skin.

perhydrohistrionicotoxin *See* **histrionicotoxin**.

Perhydrohistrionicotoxin

pertussis toxin *See* **islet-activating protein**.

pessary A dosage form, a medicated suppository, for insertion into the vagina. Also an instrument inserted into the vagina to support the uterus or as a contraceptive device (Greek: *pessos*, an oval stone used as a counter in a board game. Latin: *pessarium*, a plug).

phantastica   *See* **psychotomimetic drugs.**

pharmacodynamic tolerance   *See* **tolerance.**

pharmacogenetics' Originally, the study of genetically determined variations that are initially revealed by the effects of drugs (Vogel 1959), but now generally regarded as also including the wider study of genetic determinants of drug action. Four examples that come under the broad heading of pharmacogenetics are the following.
1   Slow and fast metabolizers of isoniazid arising from low and high amounts of a metabolizing enzyme which is an hepatic *N*-acetylase that exhibits genetic polymorphism.
2   Plasma cholinesterase, for which four separate genes occur at one locus. The action of the **neuromuscular blocking drug** suxamethonium (succinylcholine) is normally rapidly terminated by plasma cholinesterase, but in patients with one of the unusual enzymes its action may be prolonged to different extents.
3   The acute porphyrias. Patients with the genetic trait may be precipitated into severe attacks following drug use, e.g. **barbiturates**, alcohol, **oral contraceptives** and many others.
4   **Malignant hyperpyrexia** precipitated by halothane and succinylcholine during surgical anaesthesia.

pharmacokinetics   The mathematical analysis of the time-courses of absorption, distribution and elimination of drugs (Dost, 1953).

pharmacology   The branch of medical science that deals with the mechanisms of action, uses and unwanted effects of drugs (Greek: *pharmakon*, drug; *logos*, study).

phase I neuromuscular block   Identical with **depolarization block**. Called phase I because under some circumstances, and in some species, a second phase (**phase II neuromuscular block**) develops with different characteristics. The two phases are most obvious in isolated guinea-pig muscle, where they are separated by a brief period of complete recovery.

phase II neuromuscular block   A second phase of neuromuscular block sometimes produced by **depolarizing neuromuscular blocking drugs** with characteristics that are different from those of the first phase (**phase I neuromuscular block**). Its occurrence and the extent to which it is manifested differ in different species and under different conditions. *In vivo* it may be influenced by the anaesthetic used and by other drugs used during anaesthesia. The two phases are most obvious in isolated guinea-pig muscle, in which they may be separated by a brief period of almost complete recovery of the twitch tension. More usually, the one merges gradually into the other.

Superficially phase II block resembles that produced by a non-depolarizing blocking drug such as tubocurarine, in that it can be antagonized by neostigmine. However, there is little evidence regarding the underlying mechanism. It is not a consequence of **receptor desensitization** nor of **ion channel block**. Suggested explanations include the possibility that in the particular species the depolarizing drug acts as a **partial agonist** rather than a full **agonist**, and that the effect is therefore the same as **dual block** as described by Zaimis. Another possibility is that the nerve terminals become depolarized by the drug, so that the nerve spike is diminished and conduction may even cease in some terminal branches. The transmission block would then be partly a consequence of reduced transmitter release. A third possibility is based on the observation that prolonged depolarization of the endplate triggers off extra activity of a ouabain-sensitive electrogenic Na^+ pump that restores the membrane potential to normal. This occurs to different extents and at different times (i.e. during the period of maximum drug effect or only during recovery from block) in different species. If membrane potential is restored while the depolarizing drug is still in contact with the **receptors**, the block will persist but will no longer exhibit the characteristics of **depolarization block**.

phenanthrene alkaloids *See* **opium alkaloids**.

phenothiazines Drugs whose molecules have a phenothiazine nucleus.

Phenothiazine

Such drugs include analgesic phenothiazines (e.g. methotrimeprazine), **centrally acting muscle relaxant** phenothiazines (e.g. dimethothiazine), and neuroleptic phenothiazines (e.g. chlorpromazine). The last are those most commonly described simply as 'phenothiazines'.

phenylethylamine-β-hydroxylase *See* **dopamine-β-hydroxylase**.

phenylpiperidine analgesics Narcotic analgesic drugs whose molecules contain a phenylpiperidine nucleus. Pethidine (meperidine in USA) is the best known.

General structure of phenylpiperidine analgesics. In pethidine, $R = CH_3$.

pheromones   Substances generated and secreted by one individual that induce a physiological effect in another. They often act in extremely low concentrations and at large distances, and usually through the olfactory sense. The so-called **Bruce effect** is a well-studied example of pheromone-induced behaviour. Other examples include the attraction of dogs to a bitch on heat, and the mating behaviour of many insects. Pheromones are exploited in agriculture to modify the behaviour of farm animals beneficially. There is evidence that human mating behaviour may also be influenced by pheromones, but as yet the phenomenon has been less thoroughly studied than in some animals.

Certain members of the wild potato family secrete an air-borne substance that repels greenfly, and this substance also is described as a pheromone, even though, unusually, two different species are involved.

phocomelia   A congenital abnormality in which the hands or feet are attached to the trunk by a single small bone rather like the flippers of a seal (Greek: *phoke*, seal; *melos*, limb). Phocomelia is one of the fetal abnormalities produced by the **teratogen** thalidomide.

phorbol esters   The parent alcohol of tumour-promoting esters in croton oil (from *Croton tiglium*, family Euphorbiaceae). The tumour-promoting phorbol esters act as analogues of **diacylglycerol** and cause long-lasting stimulation of **protein kinase C**. *See* **PI response**.

1-0-Tetradecanoylphorbol-13-acetate, TPA, a tumour-promoting phorbol ester.

phosphatidylinositol   A membrane phospholipid in which inositol is esterified to the phosphate of a phosphatidic acid. The two fatty acids that are esterified to the glycerol of the phosphatidic acid are usually stearic and arachidonic in phosphatidylinositol. Phosphatidylinositol is especially important in **pharmacology** because of its role in certain **second messenger** systems. *See* **PI response.**

Phosphate is added at positions 4 and 5 to produce phosphatidylinositol 4,5-biphosphate.

phosphodiesterase inhibitors Refers to cyclic nucleotide phosphodiesterase inhibitors. (*See* **phosphodiesterases**). The first known cyclic nucleotide phosphodiesterase inhibitor was theophylline (*see* **xanthine alkaloids**) and many subsequently produced synthetic inhibitors are chemically related to theophylline. Theophylline has actions, especially on Ca^{2+} movements, that are independent of phosphodiesterase inhibition. Synthetic compounds are more selective in their actions. Many phosphodiesterase inhibitors have been developed as cardiac inotropic agents (*see* **inotropic action**); they are also vasodilators. They include buquineran and carbazeran. Inhibitors that are relatively selective in inhibiting **cyclic AMP** destruction, as distinct from **cyclic GMP** destruction, are available, and the converse is also true. These **drugs** are currently known only by code numbers. The former are both inotropic and vasodilator, whereas drugs that selectively cause cyclic GMP accumulation are vasodilator but do not affect contractions of the mammalian heart.

phosphodiesterases Enzymes that catalyse the hydrolysis of phosphodiesters such as cyclic nucleotides and **phosphatidylinositol** 4,5-biphosphate.

Cyclic nucleotide phosphodiesterases occur as a number of **isoenzymes**, exhibiting distinct kinetic properties, substrate specificities and cellular localizations. Three basic forms of the enzyme occur in mammals. One is membrane-bound with a high **affinity** for **cyclic AMP**. The other two forms are cytosolic and are capable of hydrolysing both cyclic AMP and **cyclic**

GMP. One of these has about equal affinities for cyclic AMP and cyclic GMP, and cyclic GMP stimulates the hydrolysis of cyclic AMP. The other displays a higher affinity for cyclic GMP than for cyclic AMP, and is dependent upon **calmodulin** for activity. Another classification depends upon the order of emergence from a particular type of chromatography column (DEAE-cellulose). Types I and II (PDE I and II) have a lower K_m (*see* **Michaelis–Menten equation**) value for cyclic GMP (i.e. a higher affinity) than for cyclic AMP and the reverse is true for type III (PDE III). Type II is distinguished from type I in that cyclic GMP stimulates the hydrolysis of cyclic AMP. Type I is calcium-dependent. It seems that type III may correspond to the membrane-bound form and types II and III may be cytosolic. However, different separation techniques give different forms of the enzyme, and it is difficult to correlate them one with another. Furthermore, under certain conditions, the conversion of one form into another has been observed.

The **phospholipase C** that is coupled to the receptor and involved in the **PI response** is also a phosphodiesterase. This enzyme catalyses the conversion of phosphatidylinositol 4,5-biphosphate to inositol triphosphate and **diacylglycerol**.

phospholipase A$_2$ inhibitors Drugs that inhibit the enzyme phospholipase A$_2$ (phosphatide-2-acyl-hydrolase, EC 3.1.1.4) which specifically hydrolyses the 2-acyl linkage of phosphoglycerides to produce a free fatty acid and a lysophosphoglyceride. In mammalian cells the phosphoglycerides are the main source of arachidonic acid for the synthesis of **prostanoids**.

Inhibitors of the enzyme include:

1   A series of n-alkylphosphorylcholines which alkylate the active site.

2   Ca^{2+}-chelating compounds such as edetate which remove Ca^{2+}, a necessary co-factor, from the enzyme.

3   Cholesterol and **general anaesthetic drugs** which modify the properties of the surrounding lipids of the membrane.

4   **Local anaesthetic drugs** which possibly act through their ability to block Ca^{2+} binding sites on **calmodulin**.

5   Certain **butyrophenones** which produce a **non-competitive** enzyme **inhibition**.

6   **Glucocorticoids** which cause the release of a proteinaceous phospholipase A$_2$ inhibitor called **macrocortin** from macrophages and neutrophils.

phospholipases Enzymes that catalyse the hydrolysis of phospholipids. They are present in lysosomes, in the cell membrane and in the outer membrane of mitochondria. Phospholipases A$_1$ and A$_2$ catalyse the removal, respectively, of the 1-acyl group and the 2-acyl group from glycerophospholipids; the products are known as lysophosphatides. These enzymes are concerned in the remodelling of membrane phospholipids.

Phospholipase A_2 (probably activated by a Ca^{2+}-**calmodulin** complex) catalyses the hydrolysis of **phosphatidylinositol** with the release of arachidonic acid and subsequent **prostanoid** synthesis. *See also* **phospholipase A_2 inhibitors.**

Phospholipase C catalyses the breakdown of phosphatidylinositol 4,5-biphosphate in the so-called **PI response.**

photosensitivity Abnormal reactivity of the skin to sunlight, leading to erythema, rash, blisters, etc. Some **drugs** (e.g. benoxaprofen) and other chemicals (e.g. anthracene, porphyrins, neutral red) may give rise to photosensitivity. The underlying mechanism often involves the take-up of the chemical into lysosomes, which then become sensitive to those wavelengths of light absorbed by the chemical. The lysosomal membrane ruptures and the released enzymes give rise to the photosensitization. Photosensitization is one of the symptoms of the diseases known as porphyrias, in which porphyrins, derived from abnormalities in haemoglobin or cytochrome synthesis, are present in large amounts.

phrenic nerve–hemidiaphragm preparation from the rat An isolated half segment of the diaphragm of the rat with phrenic nerve attached. This is a skeletal muscle preparation which is set up in an organ bath and stimulated through its phrenic nerve.

Bülbring (1946) *Brit. J. Pharmacol.* **1**, 38

physical dependence *See* **drug dependence.**

physiological salt solutions Solutions of salts containing essential ions such as Na^+, K^+, Mg^{2+}, Ca^{2+}, Cl^-, HCO_3^- and $H_2PO_4^-$ and glucose, and bubbled with air, oxygen or carbogen (depending upon their buffering capacity). They are isotonic with extracellular fluid and of an appropriate pH. They may be used at room temperature or at any higher temperature up to and including normal body temperature. They are used to maintain isolated tissues by immersing, perfusing or superfusing them. They are of several different compositions usually denoted by the name of the scientist who first devised them. Hence, **Ringer solution, Tyrode solution, Locke solution, Krebs solution, Krebs–Henseleit solution, McEwen solution.**

physostigmine The prototype reversible **anticholinesterase drug.** It is an **alkaloid** obtained from the Calabar bean (the seed of *Physostigma venenosum*). Also called eserine.

phytoalexins Antibiotic substances from higher plants. Phytoalexins form part of the defence mechanism of plants against their parasites. Their antibiotic spectrum is directed mainly against fungi. They include pisatin from the pea (*Pisum sativum*), phaseolin from the French bean (*Phaseolus* spp.), and rishitin from the potato (*Solanum tuberosum*).

phytohaemagglutinins Plant **lectins.**

PI response   Several **agonists** that produce smooth muscle contraction by releasing intracellularly bound Ca^{2+} (e.g. **acetylcholine** on **muscarinic cholinoceptors** in smooth muscle) initially cause the turnover of inositol phospholipids. Numerous other agonist-induced cellular processes that require the release of intracellular Ca^{2+} may likewise involve a PI response (e.g. pancreatic cells, islet B-cells, platelets, vasopressin on ganglia, **angiotensin** on adrenal cortex, photons on photoreceptors). The concept that the breakdown products of the inositol lipids act as **second messengers** in the transduction mechanisms that bring about the various Ca^{2+}-dependent cellular responses was originally developed by M. R. and L. E. Hokin, R. H. Michell, and M. J. Berridge and others. The membrane inositol phospholipids are derived from **phosphatidylinositol** (PI) and accordingly this type of second messenger system became known as the PI response. However, it now seems more probable that the receptor is coupled not to phosphatidylinositol but, through an enzyme, **phospholipase** C, to phosphatidylinositol 4,5-biphosphate.

PI in the inner leaflet of the plasma membrane is phosphorylated first at the 4 position of its inositol head and then at the 5 position, by two specific kinase enzymes, to give phosphatidylinositol 4,5-biphosphate. The phosphates are then removed by phosphomonoesterase enzymes with the regeneration of PI. These apparently futile cycles go on continuously. A probable sequence of events consequent upon **receptor** activation is as follows. An altered conformation of the receptor protein perturbs the membrane in such a way that the phosphatidylinositol 4,5-biphosphate is brought into contact with a specific **phosphodiesterase**, phospholipase C. A GTP-binding protein is also involved in the coupling of the receptor to the enzyme (cf. the receptor-coupled activation of **adenylate cyclase** in **cyclic AMP** production). Phospholipase C catalyses the breakdown of phosphatidylinositol 4,5-biphosphate into **inositol** 1,4,5-**triphosphate** and **diacylglycerol**. Inositol triphosphate then enters the cytosol and acts on an intracellular receptor in the endoplasmic reticulum to cause the release of Ca^{2+}. (Mitochondrial Ca^{2+} is probably not released.) Evidence suggests that about 15 calcium ions are released by each inositol triphosphate molecule.

The diacylglycerol acts within the plane of the membrane to stimulate the enzyme **protein kinase** C, which in turn stimulates a membrane Na^+/H^+ carrier that expels H^+ in exchange for Na^+ so that cytosolic pH rises. A rise in pH coupled with a rise in cytosolic Ca^{2+} are two essential factors in cell proliferation. Protein kinase C is both a phospholipid-dependent and a Ca^{2+}-dependent enzyme. Phosphatidylethanolamine and phosphatidylserine enhance its activity, whereas phosphatidylcholine and sphingomyelin are inhibitory. Diacylglycerol increases its affinity for Ca^{2+}.

Diacylglycerol may be acted upon by the enzyme diacylglycerol lipase, one of the products being arachidonic acid which is the starting point for **prostaglandin** synthesis. It appears that unstable intermediates in prostaglandin synthesis (arachidonic acid peroxide and prostaglandin endoperoxide) may activate **guanylate cyclase** with the production of **cyclic GMP**. Cyclic GMP phosphorylates protein kinase G, which in turn inhibits inositol phospholipid turnover, presumably by phosphorylating and thereby inactivating one of the enzymes involved (probably phospholipase C). The guanylate cyclase–cyclic GMP system may thus serve as a brake in a feedback control mechanism that prevents over-response.

Several **phorbol esters** are potent **tumour promoters**. They act as non-metabolizable analogues of diacylglycerol and therefore remain in the membrane for prolonged periods, causing long-lasting activation of protein kinase C, and therefore repeated cell division. Some other tumour promoters may also act by stimulating protein kinase C, although not by the same mechanism as that of phorbol esters. Such tumour promoters include mezereum (from *Daphne mezereum* and related species), teleocidin and Aplysia toxin. Certain **oncogenes** may act by coding for various factors that stimulate different steps in the cascade of reactions termed the PI response.

There is also evidence that certain inhibitory responses that clearly do not in themselves involve calcium ion mobilization may be associated with phosphoinositide turnover, e.g. muscarinic receptor-mediated negative chronotropic and inotropic effects in the heart (*see* **chronotropic response, inotropic action**), and reduction of the **M-current** in sympathetic ganglia and hippocampus. It may be that all muscarinic receptors, whether excitatory or inhibitory, are coupled to phosphoinositide metabolism. Possibly calcium ion mobilization is a prerequisite even in inhibitory responses. The free calcium ions may then act to stimulate an enzyme or release some mediator that directly triggers the inhibitory response. The vasodilator action of acetylcholine is an example. Muscarinic receptor activation causes the calcium-dependent release of a substance (**EDRF**) that produces relaxation of the smooth muscle.

Nishizuke (1894) *Nature* **308**, 693

Berridge & Irvine (1984) *Nature* **312**, 315

Brown & Masters (1985) *Trends pharmacol. Sci.* **5**, 417

PIT A compound, 2,2′-pyridylisatogen, developed by M. Hooper and colleagues as an antagonist of ATP at **purinoceptors**. Unfortunately, it lacks specificity of action.

pK_a *See* **ionization constant**.

placebo A pharmacologically inactive substance or preparation (e.g. starch or lactose tablets) given to satisfy a patient's psychological need for drug therapy. Placebos are used as controls in trials to determine the efficacy of medicinal substances.

The word comes from Latin and literally means 'I will please', thus a drug given to please the patient.

plasticity A retained ability of a cell to change its adult phenotype. An adult cell is usually fully differentiated and normally unchangeable. However, some cells retain the ability to change under certain circumstances, and are said to exhibit plasticity. For example, sympathetic **adrenergic nerve fibres** cultured in the presence of factors present in non-neuronal cells may become cholinergic. They are said to exhibit neuronal plasticity. If cultured alone, they remain adrenergic neurones.

Platyhelminthes Flatworms. The Platyhelminthes are one of the two phyla of worms (the other is the Nemathelminthes; *see* **nematodes**) that include those that are obligate parasites of man. Examples of parasitic flatworms include trematodes (flukes) such as *Fasciolopsis buski* and certain schistosomes, and cestodes (tapeworms) such as *Taenia saginata* (the beef tapeworm), *Taenia soleum* (the pork tapeworm) and *Diphyllobothrium latum* (the fish tapeworm).

Poisson distribution When the average frequency of occurrence of a random event is known and is constant from sample to sample, the distribution of observed events is described by the Poisson distribution.

$$P = \frac{\lambda^x . e^{-\lambda}}{x!}$$

where e is the base of natural logarithms, x is the observed number of events per sample and λ is their average frequency or Poisson factor.

polyamines Amines with more than two amino groups. The main ones are spermidine and spermine. Spermidine and spermine were first found in semen (hence their names), but in fact they occur in most tissues. They are powerful growth stimulators of micro-organisms and cultured mammalian cells. They exert several actions on nucleic acid metabolism which probably underlie their effects on growth. Spermidine and spermine are synthesized in the body from the amino acid ornithine. (*See* reactions illustrated below.)

polymyxins A group of antibacterial polypeptide **antibiotics** produced by the growth of different strains of the soil bacterium *Bacillus polymyxa*. They are denoted by letters and numbers, i.e. polymyxins A, B_1, B_2, C, D_1, D_2, E_1, E_2, M. Of these, only polymyxin B (i.e. $B_1 + B_2$) and polymyxin E (i.e. $E_1 + E_2$, also called colistin) are sufficiently non-toxic for therapeutic use. Polymyxins are bactericidal on most Gram-negative bacteria. They act by binding to the plasma membrane and causing leakage of essential small molecules.

positive inotropic effect *See* **inotropic effect**.

post-coital contraceptive Large doses of stilboestrol (25 mg twice a day for five days) commencing not more than 72 hours after coitus is

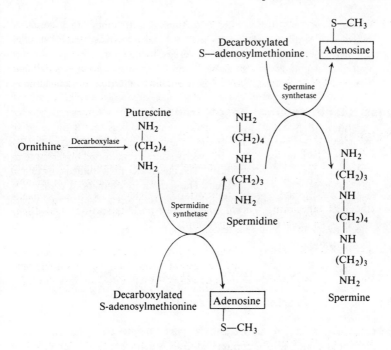

effective as a contraceptive, probably because it increases the rate of tubular transport of the ovum so that it arrives in the uterus when the blastocyst is not sufficiently developed and the endometrium is not yet prepared for implantation. Stilboestrol is ineffective if implantation has already occurred, that is it does not have **abortifacient** action. If implantation has already occurred, there is a risk of cancer in the offspring. Consequently, stilboestrol is approved for use as a post-coital contraceptive only under supervision and in cases of rape or incest. Other **oestrogens** have similar effects to stilboestrol, and the progestogen norethisterone is also effective.

post-tetanic augmentation of contractility   After a tetanus of a fast-contracting skeletal muscle, a single stimulus (applied to the nerve or the muscle) evokes a greater twitch than before the tetanus. The phenomenon is related to '**Treppe**' and takes a few minutes to wear off. It is probably the result of the tetanus causing a temporary post-tetanic facilitation of Ca^{2+} release from the sarcoplasmic reticulum, and consequently a greater interdigitation of actin and myosin during subsequently evoked twitches. Post-tetanic augmentation of contractility of this type does not occur in focally innervated slow-contracting muscle fibres, such as those of the cat soleus muscle.

post-tetanic decurarization   The temporary antagonism of tubocurarine block that occurs after a tetanus is interpolated in a series of twitches. A similar effect occurs during blocks produced by other non-depolarizing **neuromuscular blocking drugs**. It is a consequence of the fact that after a tetanus each single nerve impulse releases more **acetylcholine** than before the tetanus. *See also* **post-tetanic facilitation of transmission**.

post-tetanic facilitation of transmission A general pheno-menon at all synapses and neuroeffector junctions is that a single nerve impulse releases more transmitter (excitatory or inhibitory) during the few minutes after a period of high-frequency stimulation (loosely referred to as a tetanus) than it did previously. The effect was first studied in skeletal muscle, hence the use of 'tetanic'. The temporarily enhanced transmitter release is probably caused by an accumulation of Ca^{2+} in the axoplasm during the high-frequency stimulation. The metabolic pumps and binding mechanisms then require a few minutes to restore the axoplasmic Ca^{2+} concentration to normal.

post-tetanic potentiation Either **post-tetanic facilitation of trans-mission** or **post-tetanic augmentation of contractility**, or a combination of both. Usually applied to skeletal muscle.

potassium-sparing diuretic drugs **Diuretic drugs** that cause Na^+ loss and water loss accompanied by little or no abnormal K^+ loss. Potassium-sparing diuretic drugs include amiloride, triamterine and the **aldosterone antagonist drug** spironolactone.

potentiate To make more potent. If this definition is borne in mind, statements such as 'physostigmine potentiates **acetylcholine**' are seen to be appropriate, but statements such as 'Physostigmine potentiates cardiac slowing' are less acceptable. *See also* **synergistic action**.

potentiation *See* **synergistic action**.

Prinzmetal's angina *See* **variant angina**.

probit transformation It has been established that the Gaussian distribution (*see* **binomial distribution**) describes the frequency distribution of **quantal responses** to many **drugs**. A Gaussian frequency distribution curve can be converted to an S-shaped cumulative frequency curve, and this in turn can be converted to a straight line when plotted on a probability scale.

Deviations from the mean in standard deviation units corresponding to various probabilities (i.e., proportions of responders) can be read from published tables.

$$NED = \frac{x - \mu}{\sigma}$$

where NED is the normal equivalent deviation of the proportion responding ('normal' here refers to normal or Gaussian distribution), x is the deviation from the mean, μ is the population mean and σ is the population standard deviation.

The NED of any percentage less than 50 is negative, and for arithmetical convenience positive numbers are preferable. For this reason 5 is added to the NED so that all numbers are positive, and these positive numbers are called probits, and the procedure is a probit transformation.

i.e.
$$\text{Probit} = 5 + \frac{x - \mu}{\sigma}$$

When the probits of the percentages responding in each group are plotted against the logarithms of the doses a straight line is obtained.

procarcinogens A substance that is converted to a carcinogen or **oncogen** in the body. An example is 2-naphthylamine which is not itself carcinogenic but which is metabolized in the liver with the production of 2-amino-1-naphthol and 2-naphthyl-hydroxylamine which are **alkylating agents** and powerful carcinogens.

procyclidine *See* **angel dust**.

prodrug A substance that gives rise to a pharmacologically active metabolite, although not itself active (i.e. an inactive precursor). Examples of prodrugs that were not designed as such are prontosil, which is converted to the antibacterial agent sulphonilamide, and chloral hydrate, which is converted to the sedative–hypnotic agent trichlorethanol. In some instances, a prodrug is deliberately synthesized to improve drug delivery. An example is the compound ibuterol which is an esterified form of the **bronchodilator agent** terbutaline. Ibuterol is itself inactive. Esterification prevents metabolism in the gut wall and therefore increases absorption after oral administration. The lungs are especially rich in esterase enzymes, and the active terbutaline is therefore released within the lung tissue to a greater extent than elsewhere.

pro-opiomelanocortin (POMC) A large polypeptide present in the pituitary. It is the precursor of β-**endorphin** and of corticotrophin.

propanediol carbamates Drugs that are derivatives of dicarbamic acid esters of 1,3-propanediol.

$$\begin{array}{ccc} & R_1 & R_3 \\ & | & | \\ H_2N{-}CO{-}O{-}CH_2{-} & C{-}CH_2{-}O{-}CO{-}NH \\ & | & \\ & R_2 & \end{array}$$

R_1 and R_2 are usually propyl and methyl respectively. The main examples are the **sedative drugs** meprobamate, tybamate and carisoprodol.

propionamides   Drugs based on a propionamide (propionic acid amide) nucleus (CH_3—CH_2—CO—NH_2). The **anti-epileptic drug** beclamide is an example.

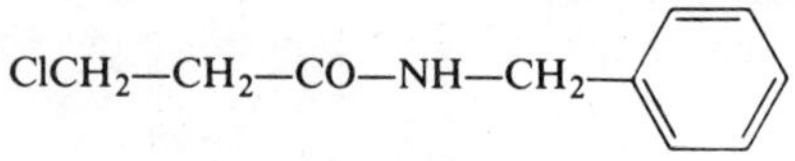

$$ClCH_2-CH_2-CO-NH-CH_2-\hspace{-0.5em}\bigcirc$$

Beclamide

prostacyclin   *See* **prostaglandins**.

prostaglandin synthase   Fatty acid cyclo-oxygenases, or simply **cyclo-oxygenases**.

prostaglandin synthase inhibitors   *See* **cyclo-oxygenase inhibitors**.

prostaglandins   A series of endogenous 20-carbon unsaturated carboxylic acids with a cyclopentane ring. They are analogues of so-called prostanoic acid (the name of the acid is derived from prostaglandin and not vice versa). The prostaglandins are **autacoids** that produce a broad spectrum of pharmacological effects. They may be synthesized in virtually every tissue by a range of stimuli. Vane and his co-workers showed that inhibition of their synthesis is the basis of the action of aspirin and other **non-steroidal anti-inflammatory drugs**.

Prostaglandins were detected in the 1930s as smooth muscle stimulating and inhibiting substances present in human semen and seminal fluid. Von Euler named them 'prostaglandin' in the mistaken belief that they came specifically from the prostate gland. The name has been retained.

The prostaglandins are derived from 20-carbon essential fatty acids present in and released from cell membranes—dihomo-γ-linolenic acid, arachidonic acid and 5,8,11,14,17-eicosapentaenoic acid. Arachidonic acid is the most important precursor in mammals. It is released from

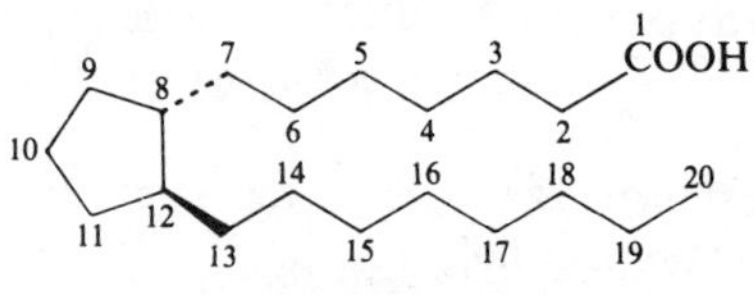

Prostanoic acid

membranes by the enzyme **phospholipase** A_2. Arachidonic acid is subsequently converted to the primary prostaglandins under the influence of a complex of microsomal enzymes, the first of which is fatty acid **cyclo-oxygenase**.

The prostaglandins (PG) are given trivial names according to their structures, by letters that denote the type of ring, by numbers that indicate the number of double bonds in the chains, and by α or β to denote the configuration of the 9-hydroxyl group on the ring of the F series (always α in naturally occurring PGs).

The ring structures of the six primary prostaglandins are shown below. (E = originally partitioned in ether; F = originally partitioned in phosphate buffer, Swedish: *fosfat*.)

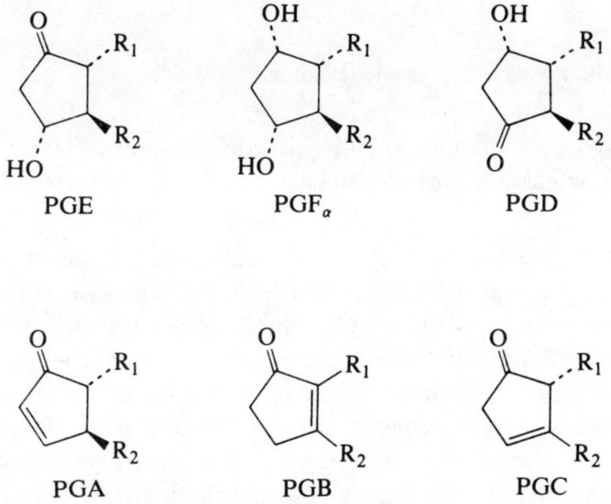

An example of a complete structure is given below for PGE_2, which has two double bonds in the side-chains.

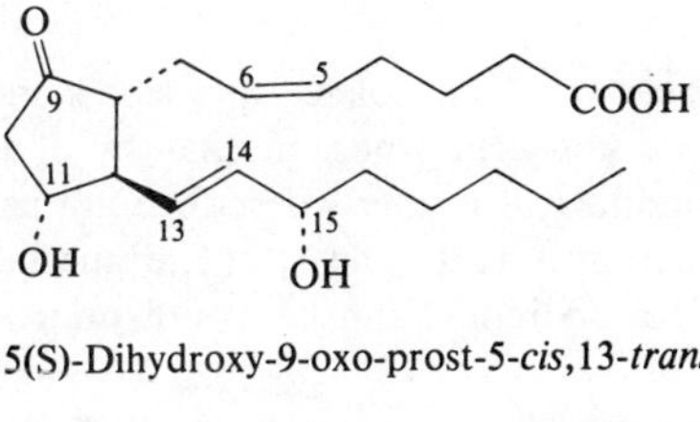

PGE_2 (11α,15(S)-Dihydroxy-9-oxo-prost-5-*cis*,13-*trans*-dienoic acid)

PGD_2 is the most potent bronchoconstrictor prostanoid. It also causes chemokinesis and vasodilatation. It is the major prostanoid released by lung mast cells and probably plays a major role in the pathogenesis of asthma.

Two additional unstable but highly active prostaglandins may be formed from intermediates by further enzyme action: **thromboxane A_2** (TXA_2) by thromboxane synthetase in platelets, and prostacyclin (PGI_2)

by prostacyclin synthetase in blood vessel walls. The ring structures of these two are:

TXA   PGI

prostanoic acid *See* **prostaglandins**.

prostanoids Both natural and synthetic substances that are analogues of prostanoic acid. *See* **prostaglandins**.

protein kinase C A Ca^{2+}- and phospholipid-dependent enzyme that is activated by **diacylglycerol** formed in the cell membrane during the turnover of inositol phospholipids. Diacylglycerol greatly increases the apparent **affinity** of protein kinase C for Ca^{2+}. Activated protein kinase C plays an important role in various cellular functions including cellular proliferation. *See* **PI response**. Protein kinase C is permanently activated by certain tumour-promoting agents, including **phorbol esters**, and this effect may underlie their co-carcinogenic action.
Nishizuka (1984) *Nature* **308**, 693

protein kinases Enzymes that phosphorylate proteins. Protein kinase A is **cyclic AMP**-dependent, protein kinase G is **cyclic GMP**-dependent and **protein kinase C** is Ca^{2+}-dependent.

protoplasmic poison An obsolete expression sometimes formerly used to describe a depressant drug whose mechanism of action was unknown: for example, quinidine was formerly described in this way with respect to its depressant action on the heart. (The mechanism of action of quinidine—to block sodium channels—is now more clearly understood.)

psoralens Naturally occurring constituents of certain plants (Greek: *psora*, itch). They are also called furocoumarins and they have the property of inducing pigmentation. They stimulate the melanocyte response to UV light. They are used to treat vitiligo, a disorder of the skin in which melanocyte function ceases in patches, resulting in depigmentation and loss of hair colour. They are also used as accelerators in suntan lotions in some countries, although they may produce toxic side-effects, including **photosensitivity**. Methoxsalen is an example of a psoralen.

Methoxsalen (8-methoxypsoralen)

psychedelics *See* **psychotomimetic drugs**.

psychic dependence *See* **drug dependence**.

psychoactivators An alternative name for **psychostimulant drugs**.

psychoanaleptic drugs An alternative name for **psychostimulant drugs**.

psychodysleptics *See* **psychotomimetic drugs**.

psychoenergizers An alternative name for **antidepressants drugs** of the class of **thymerectic drugs**.

psycholeptic drug An alternative name for **neuroleptic drug**.

psycholytics *See* **psychotomimetic drugs**.

psychomotor stimulants An alternative name for **psychostimulant drugs**.

psychoplegic drug An alternative name for **neuroleptic drug**.

psychosedative drug An alternative name for **tranquillizer**.

psychostimulant drugs Drugs that elevate mood and reduce fatigue even when mood is not depressed. Many of them have a secondary depressant effect, and most are capable of producing **drug dependence**. Alternative names include psychoanaleptic drugs, psychoactivators, psychotonics, psychomotor stimulants. The main examples are amphetamine and related drugs, and **xanthine alkaloids** and derivatives such as caffeine.

psychotogenics *See* **psychotomimetic drugs**.

psychotomimetic drugs Drugs that produce acute hallucinations and psychotic reactions. Many are naturally occurring and have a long tradition of use for quasimedical, religious and social purposes. Some have a limited use in psychiatric medicine. Several of them have a widespread non-medical (and usually illegal) use. Alternative names for the class include hallucinogens, psychotogenics, psycholytics, psychodysleptics, psychedelics, psychotoxics, eidetics and phantastica.

Three main groups of drugs belong to this general class: indolyl-alkylamines such as lysergide (LSD), phenylalkylamine derivatives such as mescaline and drugs with atropine-like actions such as phencyclidine (PCP, **angel dust**).

psychotonics An alternative name for **psychostimulant drugs**.

psychotoxics *See* **psychotomimetic drugs**.

psychotropic drugs Drugs used in the treatment of mental disturbances, and that produce acute reactions resembling those occurring in mental diseases. The term is derived from Greek words meaning 'mind turning'. The subclasses of psychotropic drugs are lithium salts, **tranquillizers** and **neuroleptic, thymoleptic, thymerectic, psychostimulant** and **psychotomimetic drugs**.

ptomaine poisons *See* **cadaverine**.

purgative A drug that produces vigorous emptying of the bowels, and which may be used to remove poisons from the alimentary canal, to prepare patients for sigmoidoscopy or radiological examination of the colon, to remove parasites after killing or paralysing them with another drug, to empty the bowel before surgery, or to counteract a constipating effect of another drug. There is no justification for the routine use of purgatives in the treatment of asymptomatic infrequency of defaecation. Examples of purgative drugs include senna, cascara, rhubarb (*Rheum palmatium*), aloes and phenolphthalein. Alternative names for purgative, sometimes used to denote increasing severity of action in the order given, are aperient (Latin: *aperire*, to open), lenitive (Latin: *lenire*, to soften), laxative (Latin: *laxare*, to loosen), evacuative (Latin: *e*, from; *vacuare*, to empty), purgative (Latin: *purgare*, to purify), cathartic (Greek: *kathartikos*, making completely clean).

purine receptors *See* **purinoceptors**.

purinergic nerve fibre A nerve fibre that releases a purine nucleotide or nucleoside (e.g. ATP, ADP, AMP, adenosine) as a neurotransmitter. *See* **adrenergic nerve fibre** for discussion of the restricted use of the suffix '-ergic'.

purinoceptors Cell membrane **receptors** that specifically bind purine nucleotides (ATP, ADP, AMP) or adenosine. These substances exert pronounced pharmacological actions (e.g. ATP is a powerful vasodilator) that are quite distinct from their roles in intermediary metabolism and nucleic acid synthesis.

Purinoceptors exist in at least two subtypes, but the nomenclature used by different authors is somewhat confusing. Burnstock first classified purinoceptors into P_1-purinoceptors and P_2-purinoceptors. P_1-receptors are more sensitive to adenosine than to ATP, whereas P_2-receptors are more sensitive to ATP. P_2-receptors are blocked by ANAPP$_3$ (aryl azido aminopropionyl ATP) or by α,β-methylene ATP.

Van Calker and Londos and their co-workers classified purinoceptors according to how they are coupled to **adenylate cyclase**. A_1 or R_i receptors mediate inhibition of adenylate cyclase, whereas A_2 or R_a receptors activate adenylate cyclase. (All of these are P_1 according to Burnstock's classification.) The A_1 and A_2 receptors may be characterized pharmacologically on the basis that $N6$-phenylisopropyl adenosine (PIA) is more potent than $5N$-ethylcarboxamide adenosine (NECA) on A_1 receptors, whereas the reverse order of potency is exhibited on A_2 receptors.

The problem is complex. *See*, for example, Satchell (1984) and Stone (1984) *Trends pharmacol. Sci.* **5**, 340 and 492 respectively.

putrescine The amine (1,4-butanediamine: $NH_2(CH_2)_4NH_2$) derived from the decarboxylation of ornithine. Putrescine is found in all cells and is the precursor of spermidine which exerts several actions on the control of nucleic acid metabolism. *See* **cadaverine** for the origin of the name.

pyrogen tests *See* pyrogens.

pyrogens Substances that cause a rise in body temperature. They may arise from micro-organisms (viruses, bacteria, moulds, yeasts), especially Gram-negative bacteria, in which case they are high molecular weight lipopolysaccharides. That produced by certain strains of *Escherichia coli* is effective in raising body temperature in doses as low as 1 ng/kg. The bacterial pyrogens act by causing the release of an endogenous pyrogenic lipid–polypeptide complex from polymorphonuclear leucocytes and monocytes, and this in turn activates **prostaglandin** synthesis in the hypothalamic temperature-regulating centres.

The steroid substance aetiocholanolone (a stereoisomer of androsterone) is a potent pyrogen in man. It is a normal intermediary metabolite in man, but abnormally excessive production may be responsible for some fevers. It acts in a similar way to bacterial pyrogens.

Tests for the presence of pyrogens in fluids for injection are an important part of quality control in the pharmaceutical industry. The tests depend upon injecting the fluid intravenously into rabbits.

pyrrolizidine alkaloids Alkaloids of the general structure shown below in which the R groups are H or OH. They were originally identified as constituents of ragwort (*Senecio jacoboea*) and are also called senecio alkaloids. In fact they occur in various plant families including species of Graminae, Leguminosae and Boraginaceae. The pyrrolizidine alkaloids produce an acute hepatocellular toxicity and liver tumours after chronic exposure.

The common comfrey (*Symphytum officinale*, Boraginaceae), a popular herbal remedy for a variety of complaints, has recently caused concern because of its content of pyrrolizidine alkaloids, although no cases of human toxicity have been reported.

quantal release of transmitter Release of neurotransmitter in discrete units (quanta) of uniform size. For example, the release of **acetylcholine** by nerve impulses at the neuromuscular junction is in whole number multiples of the amount estimated to be contained in a single quantum. The amount released spontaneously and detectable by electrophysiological techniques is also released quantally, a single quantum at a time. However, a further larger amount is spontaneously released in a non-quantal manner.

The quantum of transmitter is regarded by many as that contained within a single storage vesicle.

quantal response A response that is capable of existing in only one of two states. For example, dead or not dead in a test to find the lethal dose, and convulsions or no convulsions in an insulin **bioassay**. The response is measured as the percentage of animals responding in each group. If the percentage responding in each group is plotted against the logarithm of the dose given to each group an S-shaped curve is produced. The curve is converted into a straight line by rescaling the percentages into units called probits (*see* **probit transformation**).

quinolines Drugs possessing a quinoline nucleus in their molecules. The **anti-inflammatory drugs** cincophen and neocincophen are examples. *See also* **hydroxyquinolines**.

Quinoline

quinolinic acid *See* **excitatory amino acid receptors**.

radioimmunoassay An assay technique that depends upon competition between a radiolabelled **antigen** and unlabelled antigen for a specially prepared **antibody**. (**Monoclonal antibodies** are now being used more and more frequently.) The method was initially developed by Yalow and Berson in 1960 for assaying **insulin**, but it has since been used for assaying many polypeptides, and other substances, including **drugs**.

A radiolabelled pure antigen (*Ag, e.g. insulin) is prepared, for example by attaching ^{131}I to tyrosine in the molecule. When this reacts with antibody (Ab) the following reaction occurs:

$$*Ag + Ab \rightleftharpoons *AgAb$$

When unlabelled antigen (Ag, i.e. unlabelled insulin in this example) is added to the incubation medium, the amount of *Ag and Ab remaining constant, then:

$$*Ag + Ag + Ab \rightleftharpoons *AgAb + AgAb$$

and the ratio *AgAb/*Ag decreases with increase in the amount of unlabelled Ag. Obviously, a method must be available to separate *Ag from *AgAb (often a method depending on paper chromatoelectrophoresis is used).

A standard curve is first established showing the decrease in the percentage of labelled antigen bound by antibody in the presence of increasing known amounts of unlabelled free antigen. The percentage bound is then determined under identical conditions using the serum or other biological fluid containing the antigen to be assayed. The corresponding values are read from the standard curve. Clearly the biological fluid must not modify the immunological behaviour of the antigen or interfere in any other way with the reactions.

The technique may also be used to assay non-polypeptide drugs or other substances. For example, digoxin or **cyclic AMP** may be assayed in this way. In this case the substance is used as a **hapten** (H) by covalent linkage to a protein. Antibodies are raised to the unlabelled hapten–protein complex and the antibody is separated off. A constant amount of labelled hapten (*H) is then mixed with different known amounts of unlabelled hapten and interacted with a constant amount of the antibody. The more unlabelled H in the mixture, the less *HAb will be formed, and a standard curve is prepared from the data obtained.

The result obtained when the body fluid, or other solution of the unlabelled hapten to be assayed, is added to the labelled hapten and antibody can then be interpreted as concentration of unlabelled hapten by reference to the standard curve.

radiomimetic drugs Drugs whose effects on cells resemble those of X-radiation. **Alkylating agents** are sometimes described as radiomimetic.

radiosensitizing drugs Drugs that increase the sensitivity of hypoxic cells (e.g. those in the ischaemic regions of tumours) to X-rays or γ-rays. Oxygen itself may act in this way. Being electrophilic, oxygen may prevent repair of tumour tissue molecules that have been damaged by expulsion of electrons during irradiation.

Drugs thought to have an action like oxygen include **vitamin** K and certain nitro-imidazoles such as the antiprotozoal and antianaerobe drug metronidazole.

randomization Assignment to experimental groups in such a way that the groups are initially comparable in all those respects that might influence the outcome of the experiment. To take a simple case as an example, suppose that two drugs are to be compared in two groups (one for each drug) of subjects (animals or human beings). Simple ways of allocating the subjects randomly to the two groups are to assign them alternately, to toss a coin or throw a die, or to make use of published tables of random numbers. It would be incorrect, for example, to fill up one group and then to start on the next with the subjects as they arrive or, if animals, as they are picked from the cage. In these instances the most venturesome or least shy human beings would predominate in one group, as would the most docile and therefore more easily handled animals. While these behavioural differences might not have any obvious direct bearing on the responses being measured, they might be allied to factors that do influence the responses.

See also **Latin square design** for a method of randomization of a number of doses of a drug.

Random is not synonymous with haphazard. A random process is characterized by the occurrence of events such that the probability of occurrence of an event in a given time interval is always constant, and the occurrence of an event in one time interval is independent of its occurrence in other non-overlapping time intervals.

rate theory A theory first developed by W. D. M. Paton in the years 1959–61 which holds that the response to an **agonist** is a function of the rate of occupation of its **receptors**, as distinct from the proportion of receptors occupied (**occupation theory**). It can be deduced that:

$$A_{eq} = \frac{k_2}{1 + K_D/[D]}$$

where A_{eq} = the rate of association per receptor at equilibrium, k_2 = the rate constant for dissociation, K_D is the dissociation constant and [D] is the concentration of drug.

Paton proposed that:

$$E = \phi A$$

where E = response, ϕ = a factor relating the intensity of stimulation to the response produced, and A = the rate of association per receptor. It follows from the penultimate equation that as the concentration of drug, [D], is increased $A_{eq} \rightarrow k_2$. The maximal equilibrium response is therefore given by $E_{eq\,max} = \phi k_2$. Since the maximal equilibrium response is proportional to the rate constant for dissociation, drugs that dissociate rapidly will tend to be potent agonists, whereas drugs that dissociate slowly from the receptors will produce small or negligible responses and will be **partial agonists** or antagonists. Rate theory is generally inconsistent with recent observations and has largely been abandoned as a working hypothesis.

rausch A stage of light general anaesthesia, traditionally with ether (ether rausch), only to the point at which if questioned sharply the patient fails to reply (German: *Rausch*, intoxication).

receptor desensitization Loss of the ability of an **agonist** to activate a **receptor** (i.e. loss of **intrinsic activity** or **efficacy**) as a consequence of prolonged application of that or a related agonist.

The phenomenon of receptor desensitization has been studied most extensively in relation to the **nicotinic cholinoceptors** at the neuromuscular junction, but a similar phenomenon occurs at many other types of receptor, e.g. **histamine receptors, serotonin receptors, adenosine receptors,** etc.

When **acetylcholine** or another nicotinic agonist is applied to the motor endplates in high concentrations for prolonged periods under *in vitro* conditions, the endplate membrane does not remain at the level of depolarization initially produced. Instead, the response declines to reach a steady level which may be only a small fraction of the original effect; that is, the membrane potential may return virtually to its resting level despite continued application of the agonist. The phenomenon was first described by Fatt, Katz and Thesleff in the 1950s. Neuromuscular transmission remains blocked despite the recovery of the membrane potential. The waning response is said to be caused by receptor desensitization; it seems that the receptors assume an abnormal conformation that is still capable of combining with an agonist, but the combination is incapable of opening the associated ion channel. A scheme that qualitatively accounts for both activation and desensitization is as follows.

$$n\text{Ach} + \text{R} \underset{k_2}{\overset{k_1}{\rightleftharpoons}} \text{Ach}_n\text{R} \underset{\alpha}{\overset{\beta}{\rightleftharpoons}} \text{Ach}_n\text{R*}$$

$$k_7 \Big\updownarrow k_8 \qquad\qquad\qquad k_3 \Big\updownarrow k_4$$

$$n\text{Ach} + \text{R}_D \underset{k_6}{\overset{k_5}{\rightleftharpoons}} \text{Ach}_n\text{R}_D$$

where R represents the receptor macromolecule, n is the number of acetylcholine molecules that combine with it, Ach_nR is the acetylcholine–

receptor complex associated with a closed channel and Ach_nR^* that associated with an open, active channel, R_D denotes desensitized receptor, and Ach_nR_D denotes the inactive complex between acetylcholine and a desensitized receptor; k_{1-8}, α and β are the rate constants for the various reactions. The contribution of receptor desensitization, if any, to the type of block produced by **depolarizing neuromuscular blocking drugs** is controversial; it is probably irrelevant.

Other mechanisms may also give rise to receptor desensitisation in other systems. For example, there may be **down-regulation of receptor** numbers, or the receptors may become less efficiently coupled to a particular enzyme (e.g. **adenylate cyclase**) that they normally activate.

receptor-operated ion channels Receptor systems in which the **agonist** recognition site and an ion-specific channel are probably part of the same protein complex. Binding of the agonist to the recognition site induces a conformational change in the channel protein. The conformational change results in the opening of an ion-specific channel. The appropriate ion then diffuses through the membrane down its concentration gradient and the current carried by the ions alters the membrane potential. In some instances, for example in the case of Ca^{2+} channels, the change in membrane potential caused by the inward Ca^{2+} current may be relatively small, but the influx of Ca^{2+} may have other, more important effects. The Ca^{2+} may activate the contractile mechanism directly, or it may act as an amplifier by causing the release of intracellularly bound Ca^{2+}. On the other hand, it may exert the opposite effect by causing the opening of Ca^{2+}-operated K^+ channels. Efflux of K^+ then hyperpolarizes the membrane and inhibits cellular activity.

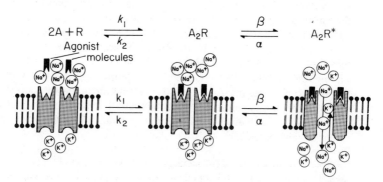

Diagrammatic representation of the interaction of an agonist (e.g. acetylcholine) with endplate cholinoceptors. Agonist molecules combine with the recognition sites of the receptor and induce a conformational change that results in the opening of a cation channel allowing the diffusion of Na^+ and K^+. The interaction is represented by the reaction equation at the top in the conventional way. (Note that the agonist molecules and the ions are drawn disproportionately large for clarity.)

Examples of receptor-operated ion channels include those **muscarinic cholinoceptors** and α-**adrenoceptors** that are coupled to Na^+ channels (influx of Na^+ depolarizes the membrane), α-adrenoceptors that are coupled to Ca^{2+} channels (activation of Ca^{2+}-operated K^+ channels), motor endplate **nicotinic cholinoceptors** coupled to cation (Na^+, K^+, Ca^{2+}) channels (the net effect is an influx which depolarizes the membrane), and **GABA receptors** coupled to Cl^- channels (influx of Cl^- hyperpolarizes and therefore inhibits the postsynaptic cell, but this is not always the response—*see* **GABA receptors**). The diagram represents the functioning of a motor endplate nicotinic cholinoceptor. *See also* **receptor-response coupling**.

receptor–response coupling   The chain or cascade of events that is triggered by an **agonist** interacting with its **receptors** and which finally results in cellular response. Each step in the chain usually constitutes an amplification process, in the sense that more and more ionic or molecular interactions are progressively involved. For example, one agonist molecule might interact with, and thereby activate, more than one receptor. The conformational change induced in the receptor system by only one or two agonist molecules may subsequently allow the transmembrane flux of many ions, or may activate many enzyme molecules. Each activated enzyme molecule may then catalyse the modification of many molecules of its intracellular substrate and so on.

There are a limited number of receptor–response coupling mechanisms and these are summarized below.

1 *Receptor coupled to ion channel.*   Interaction of the agonist with the recognition site causes a conformational change in the system such that an ion channel opens through the membrane (*see* **receptor-operated ion channels**). Examples include **acetylcholine** on motor endplate **nicotinic cholinoceptors**: a cation channel is opened, leading mainly to the influx of Na^+ and consequent endplate depolarization that triggers off an action potential which eventually releases Ca^{2+} from the sarcoplasmic reticulum, so that cross-bridges between actin and myosin are formed. Another example is the action of **GABA** on hippocampal **GABA receptors**. Chloride channels are opened in the postsynaptic cell membrane, and the influx of Cl^- hyperpolarizes, and thereby inhibits, the postsynaptic cell.

In some instances the receptor-activated influx of Na^+ produces a membrane depolarization that causes the opening of voltage-dependent Ca^{2+} channels (*see* **voltage-dependent ion channels**). Influx of Ca^{2+} may then, in conjunction with **calmodulin**, activate or support the contractile mechanism. There are also instances (e.g. **noradrenaline** on gut α-**adrenoceptors**) in which the receptor is coupled to a Ca^{2+} channel; influx of Ca^{2+} then causes the opening of Ca^{2+}-operated K^+ channels. Efflux of K^+ then hyperpolarizes, and thereby inhibits, the cell.

2 *Receptor coupled to an enzyme.*   Interaction of the agonist with the recognition sites causes a conformational change in the system such that

the receptor protein complex in turn causes a conformational change in (thereby activating) an enzyme. Often a GTP-binding protein is also necessarily involved in the enzyme activation. Examples include the various receptors, such as β-adrenoceptors, that are coupled to **adenylate cyclase** in the membrane. Activation of adenylate cyclase leads to the formation of many molecules of **cyclic AMP** which phosphorylate a **protein kinase** that in turn may phosphorylate a number of cellular proteins that modify the cell's activity. Some receptors (e.g. α_2-adrenoceptors) may be negatively coupled to adenylate cyclase (i.e. may inhibit its activity). (*See* **adenylate cyclase.**) Similar mechanisms may lead to the activation of membrane guanylate cyclase in some instances. Another example of this type of system is the coupling of certain receptors (e.g. gut **muscarinic cholinoceptors**) to the membrane phosphodiesterase, **phospholipase** C, involved in the **PI response**.

Insulin receptors may constitute an example of a different kind of receptor mechanism, but as yet there is not sufficient known about them to categorize them adequately. Insulin receptors are protein in nature and present in the cell membrane with their recognition sites directed outwards. When insulin combines, there is first a conformational change in the receptor protein, and then a small peptide is released from it which may be an intracellular mediator of insulin action. Phosphorylation of a 40S ribosomal subunit as a result of insulin action has been described. After binding of insulin, there is a rapid increase in the membrane permeability to glucose and amino acids, possibly as a consequence of the oxidation of sulphydryl groups in the plasma membrane, and there is activation of pyruvate dehydrogenase and glycogen synthetase, increased protein synthesis, and inhibition of lipolysis and hepatic gluconeogenesis. Cyclic nucleotides are not involved in the increased membrane permeability, and the identity of the **second messengers** involved has not yet been determined.

3 *Intracellular steroid receptors.* Steroid hormones penetrate cell membranes and combine with specific receptor-binding phosphoproteins in the cytosol. Each type of steroid hormone (**corticosteroids**, **androgens**, **oestrogens**, progestogens) is selectively bound by a different binding protein, and the binding sites are regarded as the receptors. Phosphorylation of the receptor protein is necessary before binding can occur. On binding, the binding protein undergoes a conformational change and the loss of part of the protein. The modified hormone–receptor binding protein then enters the cell nucleus, and interacts specifically with sites on the chromosomes to unmask certain cistrons. These are transcribed into messenger RNAs which enter the cytoplasm and direct the synthesis of specific proteins. In effect, therefore, the steroid hormones induce the expression of genes for enzymatic proteins and thereby alter cellular function and structure.

receptors Recognition sites on macromolecular complexes that selectively bind and interact with particular neurotransmitters, **hormones** or **agonist** drugs and which, as a consequence of the binding, trigger off a cellular response. This latter transducing function is a necessary part of the definition in order to differentiate receptors from other binding sites. Many types of receptor systems are situated in the cell membrane with their recognition sites directed outwards; the intracellular receptors for steroid hormones are exceptions. Most receptors are protein or glycoprotein in nature.

Langley (1906) and Ehrlich (1913) are regarded as first formulating the concept of receptors in the sense that they proposed that pharmacological actions resulted from the physicochemical interaction of drugs with specific receptive sites. Ehrlich did not separate receptors from **antibodies** and considered antibodies to be the prototypes of receptors. Dale (1914) was first to begin to classify receptors, and Gaddum (1936), Clark (1937) and Schild (1957) were the first to apply mathematical treatments to drug–receptor interactions. Until relatively recently, receptors were hypothetical structures, necessary to the pharmacologist to explain drug action, but nevertheless unknown. More recently, techniques have become available for visualizing many receptors, for isolating them, and for determining their chemical structures. Some types have been isolated and inserted into artificial membranes, and some have been induced to develop in the membranes of oocytes that do not normally possess them, by injecting the appropriate messenger RNA. The result is that a great deal has now been learned about their regulation, their biosynthesis and degradation, and about their transducing functions (*see* **receptor–response coupling**).

A receptor system as a whole can be regarded as consisting of at least two components, a recognition site (usually taken as synonymous with receptor) which binds the agonist, and an effector system which both senses and responds to the binding of the agonist. The response of the effector system is invariably a conformational change in the protein of which it is composed, and this in turn triggers the chain of events (receptor–response coupling) that leads to activation or inhibition of cellular function. The recognition site of the receptor shares many properties with the recognition site of an enzyme, but there is one obvious functional difference. Whereas the enzyme catalyses an alteration in its substrate, it is the agonist that induces an alteration in its receptors.

Receptors are named according to their endogenous agonist (**adrenoceptors, cholinoceptors, dopamine receptors, GABA receptors, glucocorticoid** receptors and so on) or to the first exogenous agonist found to activate them (e.g. **opiate receptors, benzodiazepine receptors**, digitalis receptors) whether or not an endogenous **ligand** is subsequently discovered. Each class of receptors may then be subdivided into a number of types and subtypes according to the order of potency of a range of agonists, both endogenous and synthetic.

The term 'receptor' is also used in a physiological sense as an abbreviated form of sensory receptor. The context usually makes the meaning obvious in the particular case.

Receptor **antagonist drugs** also combine with specific receptor recognition sites, but the combination does not result in a conformational

191

change in the associated protein, i.e. antagonist drugs lack **efficacy** or **intrinsic activity**. They merely act to prevent the interaction of the receptor with an agonist.

recombinant DNA technology   Commonly called genetic engineering. A battery of techniques that depend upon the following discoveries.

1   Certain enzymes, class II restriction endonucleases, can be used to cleave the DNA molecule at sequence-specific sites, so that DNA fragments containing a particular gene can be cut from the rest of the molecule.

2   A particular messenger RNA extracted from a tissue can be used to make a complementary copy of the relevant gene (a cDNA) by a process of RNA-directed DNA synthesis in which the retrovirus enzyme reverse transcriptase is used.

3   DNA fragments produced as under 1 or 2 can be joined (recombined) to produce a biologically functional hybrid DNA molecule. This may be achieved by inserting the DNA fragment (i.e. recombining it) into a bacterial plasmid. Bacterial plasmids made in this way are denoted by the letter ρ, by the initials of the originator(s) and by an experimental number. For example, the plasmid pSC101 (made by Stanley Cohen) was the first plasmid used in recombinant DNA work. Plasmids are taken up by bacteria and integrated with their DNA. Bacteria containing the appropriate DNA fragment can then be cultured to produce clones with multiple copies of the incorporated DNA fragment.

4   After breaking up a DNA molecule with the aid of restriction endonucleases, the fragments may be separated on a gel by electrophoresis. The fragments are then denatured with alkali to make them single-stranded and the gel is 'blotted' with a filter to which the single-stranded fragments become firmly bound. This is known as a 'Southern blot' after the scientist, E. M. Southern, who developed the technique. A probe, e.g. a radioactive fragment of DNA that is complementary to the fragment of interest, may then be passed over the filter. The probe will hybridize with the fragment of interest, and in this way (e.g. by autoradiography of the filter) it is possible to localize and identify the particular gene.

The techniques of recombinant DNA technology are of value in prenatal diagnosis, whereby certain genetic disorders in the fetus can be detected in early pregnancy. They are also used to cause bacteria to synthesize human proteins for medical use, such as **interferons**, antihaemophilic globulin, and **hormones** (e.g. **insulin** and **somatostatin**) and also **antigens** to infective micro-organisms, e.g. hepatitis B viral antigen.

rectus abdominis muscle of frog   The two rectus abdominis muscles of the frog (*Rana temporaria, R. pipiens* or *R. esculenta*) run each side of the midline of the abdomen wall from the sternum to the fork. An isolated rectus abdominis muscle, set up in frog **Ringer solution** and attached to a tension or length recorder may be used to study the action of drugs with the **nicotinic actions** of **acetylcholine**, and their antagonists. The muscle is a striated muscle containing many multiply innervated fibres and so it responds to nicotinic **agonists** with a sustained **contracture**.

redox   potential   Reduction/oxidation   potential.   A   measure   of   a compound's ability to reduce or to oxidize other compounds. A high negative redox potential signifies an effective reducing capacity (electron or hydrogen donor). A high positive redox potential is characteristic of an effective oxidizing agent (electron or hydrogen acceptor). The inner membranes of mitochondria possess specialized energy-coupling systems in which electrons at a high negative redox potential (e.g. of NADH, standard redox potential $- 0.32$ V) are obtained from substrate oxidation and are then transferred through a series of redox components of decreasing redox potential. Oxygen is the ultimate electron acceptor. The energy released during this change in potential is coupled to the generation of a transmembrane electrochemical gradient of protons which can be used for a variety of purposes (heat, generation of transmembrane ion gradients, membrane potential, ATP synthesis).

renocortin   *See* **macrocortin**.

respiratory stimulant drugs   Drugs that stimulate breathing. They are also called **analeptic drugs** (Greek: *analeptikos*, restorative). These drugs stimulate both the respiratory and vasomotor centres in the medulla and so increase the depth of breathing and the blood pressure. In doses not much larger they stimulate other brain centres and may therefore produce convulsions. Their medicinal use is limited and is surrounded by controversy. Examples of such drugs include nikethamide, leptazol (pentylenetetrazol), bemegride, doxapram and prethcamide.

retinoids   Synthetic analogues of **vitamin** A. Some authors include the natural forms of vitamin A (retinol or vitamin A_1 and 3-dehydroretinol or vitamin A_2) in the definition. Retinol (vitamin A alcohol) may be

Etretinate

Isotretinoin

193

converted in the body to retinal (vitamin A aldehyde) or retinoic acid (vitamin A acid). Synthetic analogues include etretinate and isotretinoin. The main use of these compounds is in dermatology, where they exert beneficial effects in a number of skin diseases including psoriasis and inherited disorders of keratinization.

reversible anticholinesterase drug An **anticholinesterase** drug that dissociates relatively rapidly from the enzyme. Some reversible anticholinesterases are alternative substrates for the enzyme. They are carbamyl esters (e.g., physostigmine, neostigmine, pyridostigmine, carbaryl) which are hydrolysed by the enzyme to release an alcoholic or phenolic moiety and leave a carbamylated enzyme which is far more stable than the acetylated form transiently produced when **acetylcholine** is hydrolysed. Hence, the enzyme is temporarily inhibited. Others are not hydrolysed by the enzyme but simply bind to it reversibly. Ambenonium is a bisquaternary substance which binds with high **affinity**. Edrophonium binds only briefly and is rapidly eliminated by the kidneys. The carbamyl ester type inhibits both acetylcholinesterase and butyrylcholinesterase to similar degrees. Ambenonium and edrophonium are relatively more selective for acetylcholinesterase.

Reversible anticholinesterase drugs are used to augment cholinergic function, for example in glaucoma, paralytic ileus, atony of the bladder, **myasthenia gravis**, and when antagonizing non-depolarizing neuromuscular blockade. Physostigmine, from the **Calabar bean**, was the first drug of this type to be discovered.

Reye syndrome A syndrome characterized by vomiting and lethargy which may progress to delirium and coma in children (mostly aged between 5 and 16) recovering from viral infections, particularly influenza, chicken pox or measles. There is a non-inflammatory cerebral oedema with fatty degeneration of the liver and kidneys. About 1000 cases occur each year in the USA. Death results in 20–30% of cases and permanent brain damage in many more. In many instances Reye syndrome has been associated with the use of aspirin and other **salicylates** to control the symptoms of the viral infection, and there is a strong suspicion that Reye syndrome is the result of a salicylate–viral disease interaction. However, interactions of viruses with other chemical agents (e.g. some fertilizers, pesticides, paints, or their vehicles, and **aflatoxins**) have also been implicated.

ricin A toxic glycoprotein isolated from castor bean (*Ricinus sanguineui*, Euphorbiaceae). The molecule consists of a neutral chain (mol. wt. *c.* 32 000 daltons) and an acidic chain (mol wt. *c.* 34 000 daltons) connected by S–S bonds (cf. **abrin**). The neutral chain inhibits protein synthesis and the acidic chain serves to bind the molecule to cells. Ricin has been proposed as a chemical warfare agent, and has been used for political

assassinations. **Monoclonal antibodies** against ricin have been prepared.
Olnes *et al.* (1974) *Nature* **249**, 627

Ringer solution   A **psysiological salt solution** originally devised by Sidney
Ringer in 1894 (*J. Physiol.* **17**, 6) for maintaining the beat of the frog's
heart. It is commonly used for other amphibian tissues also, but is
unsuitable for mammalian tissues. It has the following composition
(mmol/l): NaCl 103–111, KCl 1–1·9, $CaCl_2$ 0·9–1·1, NaH_2PO_4 0–0·1,
$NaHCO_3$ 1·2–2·4, glucose 0–11·1. It is bubbled with air.

Ringer solution was the first physiological salt solution to be devised,
and as a mark of respect the word 'ringer' is often used as synonymous with
physiological salt solution; hence Tyrode's ringer, Locke's ringer, Krebs'
ringer and so on.

Ringer–Locke solution   *See* **Locke solution**.

rubefacients   Substances applied to the skin as **counter-irritants**. The
name refers to their action in causing vasodilatation in the skin (Latin:
ruber, red; *facere*, to make). They include methylsalicylate, capsaicin and
oil of turpentine.

ryanodine   An **alkaloid** extracted from *Ryania speciosa* Vahl. It is used as
an insecticide.

It exerts apparently opposite effects on skeletal muscle and on cardiac
muscle. In skeletal muscle, the most obvious effect is a powerful **contracture**
which is believed to be the result of impaired sequestration of Ca^{2+} by the
sarcoplasmic reticulum. In cardiac muscle, it depresses the evoked
contractions (a negative **inotropic action**), probably through inhibiting the
release of Ca^{2+} from intracellular stores (chiefly the sarcoplasmic
reticulum).

St Anthony's fire (St Anthony b. AD 251)   Applied to the burning
sensation which is a feature of **ergotism**.

salicylates   Drugs that are derivatives of salicylic acid. Aspirin (acetyl-
salicylic acid) is the prototype. (Aspirin is the official name in most
countries but is a trade name in a few.) Aspirin and related drugs inhibit
cyclo-oxygenase and thereby reduce **prostaglandin** synthesis. Salicylates are
anti-inflammatory, **antipyretic** and **analgesic drugs**. In small doses they
inhibit platelet stickiness because they inhibit **thromboxane** synthesis before
prostacyclin (*see* **prostaglandins**) synthesis. The bark of trees belonging to
the willow family contains salicylates or substances from which salicylates
are easily derived (salicin and saligenin). The botanical name for the willow

family is the Salicaceae, and the word salicylate is derived from this. Extracts of willow bark have been used medicinally since ancient times, although their more recent use in arthritis, pain and fever is said to stem from the 18th century when the Rev. Edward Stone in England used

COOH
OH

Salicylic acid

powdered willow bark to treat his parishioners for the ague. Hoffman of the Bayer Company first synthesized aspirin which was introduced into medicine in 1899. In the UK, more than 2 million kg of aspirin, an average of about two tablets per week per head of population, are consumed per year.

salicylism A syndrome arising from the consumption of high doses of aspirin and related **salicylates**. It consists of dizziness, tinnitus, vomiting, mental confusion and hyperventilation, which tends to produce respiratory alkalosis, although this may be counteracted by the metabolic acidosis and ketosis directly produced by aspirin itself.

saline purgatives Soluble inorganic salts, or the salts of inorganic cations, which are barely if at all absorbed from the gut and which therefore stimulate defaecation through their osmotic effect, which increases the bulk of the colon contents by retaining water. Examples include Epsom salts (magnesium sulphate) and Glauber's salt (sodium phosphate).

Salmonella-microsome test *See* **Ames test**.

sauvagine A linear polypeptide (40 amino acids) isolated from the skin of the South American frog *Phyllomedusa sauvagei*. It produces pronounced vasodilatation in some vascular beds and a consequent fall in blood pressure. It also stimulates the release of corticotrophin and β-**endorphin** from the pituitary but inhibits the relase of prolactin, GH and TSH.

saxitoxin A potent non-protein toxin. Its name is derived from the fact that it was first isolated from the Alaskan butterclam, *Saxidomus giganteus*, but in fact it originates not in the clam but in the dinoflagellates, *Gonyaulax catanella*, that a variety of clams and mussels may ingest when climatic conditions are such that they occur in vast numbers. Saxitoxin gives rise to **paralytic shellfish poisoning**. It acts to block voltage-dependent Na^+ channels (*see* **voltage-dependent ion channels**) in nerve fibre membranes by a mechanism resembling that of **tetrodotoxin**. In addition, it has a weak neuromuscular blocking action, possibly related to the fact that its molecule possesses two positively charged nitrogens. Tetrodotoxin contains one guanine group, whereas saxitoxin contains two.

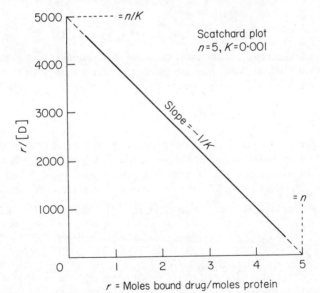

Saxitoxin

Scatchard plot A commonly used graph constructed to analyse data relating to the binding of ions and drugs and other molecules to proteins, including binding to **receptors**. It was first used by Scatchard in 1949. The equation for the Scatchard plot is derived from the law of mass action, and is:

$$\frac{r}{[D]} = \frac{n}{K} - \frac{r}{K}$$

where r = the ratio of bound drug to total protein, $[D]$ = the concentration of drug, K = the dissociation constant, and n = the number of

A theoretical Scatchard plot from the above equation, assigning the values shown for n and K. A straight line plot indicates that the binding sites are identical and independent of each other. From Bowman & Rand (1980) *Textbook of Pharmacology*, 2nd Edition. Blackwell Scientific Publications, Oxford.

identical separate binding sites. The Scatchard plot of $r/[D]$ against r is a straight line with an intercept on the $r/[D]$ axis, when $r = 0$, of n/K, a slope of $-1/K$ and an intercept on the r axis of n.

A curvilinear Scatchard plot indicates that there is more than one type of binding site, and that the different types differ in their dissociation constants for binding with the substance under investigation.

Schildt equation   An equation, devised by H. O. Schildt, that describes the effect of a **competitive antagonist** at equilibrium. The essential feature of competitive antagonism is that the effect of the antagonist, A, can be overcome by raising the **agonist**, D, concentration. The log concentration–response curve is shifted to the right by the competitive antagonist, but the curves all have the same shape, and the same maxima, and the linear portions are parallel to that for the agonist alone. The degree of the shift to the right is proportional to the antagonist concentration, and the **affinity** of the antagonist for the **receptors** is inversely proportional to the antagonist–receptor dissociation constant, K_A.

The values of K_A can be determined from the concentrations of agonist producing equal responses in the absence, $[D]_0$, and presence, $[D]_A$, of antagonist. Since the responses are equal, the receptor occupancy by the agonist is assumed to be the same, and it can be shown that:

$$\frac{[D]_0}{[D]_0 + K_D} = \frac{K_A[D]_A}{K_D K_A + K_D[A] + K_A[D]_A}$$

where K_D is the dissociation constant of the agonist. Taking reciprocals and dividing by the denominators:

$$1 + \frac{K_D}{[D]_0} = 1 + \frac{[A]K_D}{[D]_A K_A} + \frac{K_D}{[D]_A}$$

which reduces to:

$$\frac{[D]_A}{[D]_0} - 1 = \frac{[A]}{K_A}$$

i.e. the Schildt equation.

When the concentration of antagonist, $[A]_2$, is such that $[D]_A = 2[D]_0$, then $[A]_2 = K_A$. That is, the value of the dissociation constant for the antagonist is given by the concentration of the antagonist with which the ratio of concentrations of agonist producing equal responses in its presence, $[D]_A$, and absence, $[D]_0$, equals 2. (*See also under* **pA$_x$ value**.)

Schildt plot   For data that comply with the **Schildt equation**, a straight line graph (a Schildt plot) is obtained when log (dose ratio $-$ 1) is plotted against log of antagonist concentration, i.e. log $([D]_A/[D]_0 - 1)$ against log $[A]$ in the symbols used under Schildt equation. Such a plot can be used to find the pA_2 value (*see under* **pA_x value**), since the intercept on the log [A] axis will occur when $[D]_A/[D]_0 = 2$, and therefore:

$$\frac{[D]_A}{[D]_0} - 1 = \log 1 = 0$$

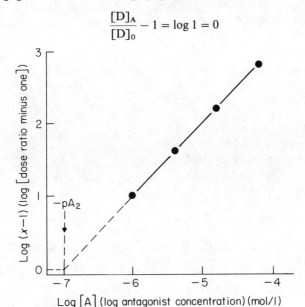

Method of finding pA_2 from concentration ratios of agonist giving equal responses in the presence $([D]_A)$ of concentration [A] of antagonist and in the absence of antagonist $([D]_0)$.

schistosomicidal drugs Drugs used to kill parasitic schistosomes. Schistosomes are platyhelminths (flatworms) belonging to the trematodes or flukes (as distinct from the tapeworms). Three species of schistosomes are parasites of man: *Schistosoma haematobium* is common throughout Africa, *S. mansoni* is common in both Africa and tropical South America, and *S. japonicum* is confined to the Far East including Japan, the Philippines and China. The intermediate hosts are aquatic snails which release free-living cercariae into the water. These are capable of penetrating human skin and entering the blood vessels where they grow to adult forms and lay eggs that pass out with the faeces or urine.

The human disease produced is schistosomiasis (or bilharziasis); it is associated with liver damage and bladder or rectal lesions. The main schistosomicidal drugs include antimony potassium tartrate, niridazole, stibophen, stilbocaptate, hycanthone and lucanthone.

Schultz–Dale reaction *See* **Dale–Schultz reaction**.

sclerosing agents Agents used to produce inflammation and therefore fibrosis and hardening of the walls of the submucosal veins in haemorrhoids or varicose veins, thereby increasing their strength or obliterating them (Greek: *sclerosis*, hardness).

The usual sclerosing agents are 5% phenol in almond oil, sodium tetradecylsulphate solution, sodium morrhuate, or quinine and urea hydrochloride.

scorpion venoms   The venoms from dangerous scorpions such as:
Androctonus australis Hector
A. mauretanicus mauretanicus
Buthus accitanus paris
B. occitanus tunetanus
Leiurus quinquestriatus quinquestriatus
Centruroides suffusus suffusus
C. sculpturatus
Tityus serrulatus

About 40 low molecular weight protein toxins have been isolated from scorpion venoms. In general, the toxins act to prevent the closure of sodium channels (i.e. block inactivation) and to block potassium channels in axonal membranes. The result is a greatly prolonged action potential and an enhanced release of neurotransmitters.

Zlotkin, Miranda & Rochat (1978) In *Arthropod Venoms* (Ed. Bettini), p. 317. Springer–Verlag, Berlin.

sea anemone toxins   Polypeptide toxins obtained from sea anemones (*e.g. Condylactis gigantea* or *C. aurantiaca*). They block the closure of sodium channels in excitable membranes (i.e. block sodium inactivation) without much effect on their opening.

Narahashi, Moore & Shapiro (1969) *Science* **163**, 680

second messengers   A term coined to describe the role of **cyclic AMP** in **hormone** action. The hormone (the first messenger) stimulates its specific **receptors** with the result that **adenylate cyclase** is activated and cyclic AMP is formed. The cyclic AMP (the second messenger) then phosphorylates **protein kinase** which, through a further chain of events, brings about the various cellular responses. The term is now widened to include all intermediate factors in the cascades of events that lie between receptor activation and cellular response (*see* **receptor–response coupling**); thus, Ca^{2+}–**calmodulin**, **cyclic GMP**, Na^+, K^+, Cl^-, **inositol triphosphate**, **diacylglycerol**, etc. may all be regarded as second messengers. The term, though useful, loses precision as more is learned about intervening events in receptor–response coupling. For example, stimulation of arterial **muscarinic cholinoceptors** causes the release of **EDRF** which in turn stimulates **guanylate cyclase** to catalyse the production of cyclic GMP. In this example, EDRF might thus be called the second messenger and cyclic GMP the third messenger, but this would mean that the numbers would have to be changed as more is learned about intermediate factors. Consequently there is a tendency to use the term 'second messenger' for all intervening factors after the initial receptor activation. Possibly a term such as 'intermediate messengers' would be more useful.

second-order kinetics   When there are two reactants, and the reaction proceeds at a rate which is proportional to the products of their concentrations, the kinetics are of the second order: there is no simple relationship between the concentration of one of the reactants and time.

sedative drugs   Drugs used to sedate, that is to calm, anxious and restless patients without causing sleep. Sedatives taken at bedtime may, however, encourage sleep without actually causing it. Drugs that produce sleep are called hypnotics and in many, although not all, instances the sedative drugs in larger doses can be used as hypnotics. Sedative drugs also include anti-anxiety drugs, and there is little if any meaningful difference between the terms 'sedative' and 'minor **tranquillizer**'. Formerly the most commonly used sedative drug was phenobarbitone, but its use for this purpose is now discouraged. The main sedative drugs are now the **propanediol carbamates** such as meprobamate and **benzodiazepines** such as chlordiazepoxide and diazepam.

selective toxicity   The property of a useful therapeutic antimicrobial agent, or of a pesticide or herbicide, that allows it to be toxic to the species that it is required to eradicate without harming other species. The selective toxicity of a chemotherapeutic agent is determined by its ability to inhibit some essential process in the parasite that may be absent or not essential to the host, or if it is capable of affecting an essential process in the host it does not gain access to the site of action in the host's cells. The most clear-cut example is the action of **penicillin** in destroying the cell wall of susceptible bacteria, a structure that is not present in mammalian cells.

senecio alkaloids   *See* **pyrrolizidine alkaloids**.

serendipity   The faculty of making useful discoveries by accident. The term was coined by Horace Walpole on the basis of the Persian fairy tale *The Three Princes of Serendip* in which the heroes repeatedly made unintentional discoveries. (Serendip is an ancient name for Sri Lanka.)

Serendipity has played an important part in pharmacology, many new types of drugs having been discovered in research programmes that were designed to search for compounds with quite different kinds of activity. For example, chlorpromazine and its transquillizing activity were discovered in a programme designed to search for new **antihistamine drugs**.

serotonin   5-Hydroxytryptamine (5-HT). More than a century ago it was observed that the serum from coagulated blood contains a vasoconstrictor substance that is not present in plasma. The substance, now known to be 5-hydroxytryptamine, is released from platelets which are broken down in the clotting process. It has been termed 'vasoconstrictine' and 'vasotonin' to denote its action, and 'thrombocytin' to denote its source. In 1948 it was isolated in pure form from serum and called serotonin. The following year it was chemically identified. Its systematic chemical name is 3-(2-aminoethyl)-5-hydroxyindole. The preferred trivial name should probably be serotonin, since it allows easily derived terms, such as serotoninergic, and it is common practice to use early descriptive names to denote endogenous chemicals (e.g. **histamine**, **adrenaline**), rather than the more cumbersome chemical names. Serotonin is commonly commercially available as the stable creatinine sulphate salt.

In man, about 90% of the total serotinin occurs in enterochromaffin cells in the gut; most of the remaining 10% is in platelets and in the brain.

The biosynthesis of serotonin is from tryptophan, and it exerts a wide range of pharmacological effects; it probably functions as an **autacoid**. It constricts most blood vessels but dilates those in skeletal muscle and the coronary vessels; it increases tone and motility of the small intestine, partly directly and partly by stimulating or sensitizing local afferent nerve fibres; it inhibits contractions of the stomach and colon; it produces contraction of bronchial, uterine, and other smooth muscles of the male and female genital tract. Serotonin probably plays a role as a neurotransmitter, especially in the central nervous system. It is particularly abundant in the neurones of the raphe nuclei in the midbrain where its role is concerned both with mood (limbic system projections) and with sleep (cortical projections).

$$HO \quad \overset{CH_2-CH_2-NH_2}{\underset{N_H}{}}$$

Serotonin

Serotonin also serves as the precursor for the synthesis of the hormone melatonin in the pineal gland.

serotonin antagonists   Drugs that antagonize **serotonin** by blocking **serotonin receptors**. Such drugs include lysergide or LSD (a **partial agonist**), bromolysergide (BOL), methysergide, cyproheptadine (also an **antihist-amine drug**), pizotifen, benanserin, cinanserin, ketanserin and (amongst other actions) many **phenothiazine drugs**. A new class of serotonin antagonists, which are indoletropanyl or indolehomotropanyl esters (e.g. ICS 205–930), has been developed. They act selectively on so-called M-receptors, and some are effective in extremely low concentrations (as low as 10^{-14} M). *See* Richardson *et al.* (1985) *Nature 1985*, **316**, 126. *See also* **serotonin receptors**.

serotonin receptors Receptors specifically sensitive to **serotonin**. The events involved in **receptor–response coupling** have not been fully elucidated for serotonin receptors, but it seems that in vertebrates cellular excitation produced by serotonin is, in many cases, a consequence of depolarization arising from increased Na^+ conductance followed by the opening of voltage-dependent Ca^{2+} channels (*see* **voltage-dependent ion channels**), whereas cellular inhibition is a consequence of membrane hyperpolarization arising from increased K^+ conductance. However, in some instances, serotonin may operate Ca^{2+} channels, may activate the **PI response** or may stimulate **adenylate cyclase**.

There are subtypes of serotonin receptors, but the number of subtypes and their characteristics are not as clear as for some other receptor classes.

An older classification by Gaddum defined D and M serotonin receptors in the gut. Serotonin causes contraction of the guinea-pig ileum through two mechanisms—a direct stimulant action on the smooth muscle which is blocked by dibenamine (hence D receptors), and an indirect action on the intramural nerve plexus which results in **acetylcholine** release from the postganglionic nerve endings. This latter action is blocked by **morphine** (hence M receptors). It is now known that morphine acts to prevent the release of acetylcholine rather than block the receptors. However, the fact that the 'M receptors' are not blocked by dibenamine is an indication that they are of a different type. More recent work has designated an excitatory neuronal 'M-like' receptor (similar, but not identical, to Gaddum's M receptor) mediating depolarization of sympathetic ganglia and of afferent vagal fibres, and an increase in transmitter release from autonomic **noradrenergic nerve fibres**. 2-Methyl-5-HT is a selective **agonist** for this M-like receptor, and compounds designated MDL 72,222 and ICS 205-930 are selective antagonists. An inhibitory neuronal receptor, designated HT_1 (or 5-HT_1, or S_1), that mediates inhibition of **noradrenaline** release in dog saphenous vein, and of transmitters from brain slices and synaptosomes has been designated. These receptors appear to be regulated by guanine nucleotides. 5-Carboxamide tryptamine, methysergide and the compound 8-hydroxy DPAT are agonists at the HT_1 receptor, but selective antagonists are not yet available. HT_2 (or 5-HT_2, or S_2) receptors appear to correspond to Gaddum's D receptors. They are not regulated by guanine nucleotides. HT_2 receptors mediate excitation of cerebral cortical neurones, bronchoconstriction, vasoconstriction, and platelet aggregation. Antagonists at HT_2 receptors include methysergide, metitepine, ketanserin and pizotifen. HT_2 receptors in the cerebral cortex may be labelled by tritiated spiroperidol, which is a **dopamine antagonist** at many sites. Thus, three different receptor subtypes have so far been designated, HT_1, HT_2 (or D), and 'M-like', but this is clearly an oversimplification.

serotonin uptake inhibitors Drugs that inhibit the uptake of serotonin into platelets and into **serotoninergic nerve fibre** endings. A high-affinity uptake process that allows accumulation of serotonin against a large concentration gradient is present in these structures. The process resembles that for **neuronal uptake of noradrenaline** and both are inhibited by **tricyclic antidepressant drugs**. In addition, some drugs are capable of selectively inhibiting serotonin uptake. Examples include citalopram and fluoxetine.

serotoninergic nerve fibres Nerve fibres that release **serotonin** as a neurotransmitter. Serotoninergic nerve cell bodies are located in the raphe nuclei of the pons and upper brain stem, the area postrema, and the caudal locus coeruleus. Serotoninergic fibres project to the cerebral cortex, the limbic system, the thalamus and the cerebellum.

sialodacryoadenitis (Greek: *sialon*, saliva; *dacryon*, tear; *adenos*, gland.) A viral disease of the rat caused by a coronavirus. There is inflammation of the salivary and lachrymal glands, and swelling of the Harderian gland, which causes the eye to protrude and which may prevent closure of the eyelids. Each bout of the disease lasts for about a week, and a rat may have several attacks during its life.

singlet oxygen The outer orbitals of the oxygen molecule possess two unpaired electrons. An arrangement in which both electrons occupy the same orbital and the electron spins are paired is in the singlet state and known as singlet oxygen. It is not a **free radical** but may be considered a related species.

SMON Subacute myelo-optic neuropathy. A set of neurological disorders associated with the repeated ingestion of halogenated **8-hydroxyquinolines** (e.g. clioquinol) which are used in the treatment of intestinal amoebiasis. The occasional occurrence of SMON and other unwanted effects has discouraged the use of halogenated 8-hydroxyquinolines for relatively trivial complaints such as traveller's diarrhoea.

sociopharmacology 'The use of the methods of social psychology to elucidate the action of drugs, and the use of drugs to illuminate the variables of social functioning' (Joyce, 1984). Most work in the field to date has been concerned with the influence of social factors upon drug response rather than with that of drugs upon social behaviour.

The term was first used by Lennard (1965) in *Psychological Approaches to Social Behaviour* (Eds. Leidermann & Shapiro), p. 127. Tavistock, London.

Joyce (1984) in *Measuring the social benefits of medicine* (Ed. Teeling Smith), p. 146. Office of Health Economics, London.

SOD *See* **superoxide dismutase.**

solanaceous alkaloids The **alkaloids** of the medicinal solanaceous plants *Atropa belladonna* (deadly nightshade), *Hyoscyamus niger* (black henbane), and *Datura stramonium* (thorn apple). The main alkaloids are (−)-hyoscine (scopolamine) and (−)-hyoscyamine. Atropine is racemic hyoscyamine; racemization occurs during the extraction process.

somatic mutation theory of cancer The theory proposed by Bauer and Boveri that the induction of cancer is the consequence of a mutation arising in somatic (non-germinal) cell tissue which subsequently leads to uncontrolled division of the mutated cells to produce tumours.

somatostatin A tetradecapeptide first detected in the hypothalamus by its ability to inhibit the release of growth hormone. Subsequently it was detected in other regions of the central nervous system and in some peripheral organs such as the thyroid, the pancreas and the stomach. It inhibits the secretion of several pituitary hormones and several gastro-intestinal and pancreatic secretory products. It stimulates **mast cells** by an action resembling that of compound 48/80.

It is present in some peripheral nerve fibres including some that innervate the frog heart.

$$\overbrace{}^{\text{S—S}}$$
Ala–Gly–Cys–Lys–Asn–Phe–Phe–Trp–Lys–Thr–Phe–Thr–Ser–Cys

It may serve as a neurotransmitter or a **co-transmitter** in parts of the central nervous system.

spare receptors For a highly active **agonist** with a high **efficacy**, the maximal response is produced by a concentration that does not occupy all the **receptors**. The receptors remaining unoccupied are termed spare receptors. Highly active agonists may occupy as few as 0·1% of the receptors in concentrations just sufficient to produce a maximal response.

spasmolytic drugs Drugs used to relieve smooth muscle spasm of the intestinal tract (intestinal colic), bile ducts (biliary colic) and ureters (uretal colic). Spasmolytic drugs include **atropine-like drugs**, and smooth muscle relaxant drugs such as papaverine, mebeverine, alverine, isometh-eptine and flopropione.

species tolerance *See* **tolerance.**

spectrin The principal protein of the erythrocyte cytoskeleton. Actin is also a component. The cytoskeleton controls cell shape and the disposition of proteins within the membrane.

spermicidal agents   Agents that kill spermatozoa, or that hasten their degeneration by impeding their passage through the cervical canal. They are applied in the form of vaginal creams, pastes, jellies or foams. Agents that cause mechanical occlusion include **surfactants** such as sodium lauryl sulphate and lauromacrogol 400. Agents used to kill spermatozoa directly include phenylmercuric nitrate, chlorindanol, cyoxylate, hexylresorcinol, ricinoleic acid, **hydroxyquinoline**, chloramine and sodium borate. Propranolol has a spermicidal action when given intravaginally. The effect is unlikely to be the result of β-**adrenoceptor** blockade and it is not manifested after systemic administration.

spermidine   *See* **polyamines**.

spermine   *See* **polyamines**.

spinal anaesthesia   *See* **local anaesthetic drug**.

SRS-A   Slow reacting substance of **anaphylaxis**. A smooth muscle contracting substance released from **antigen**-sensitized lung tissue. It is now known to be almost entirely composed of **leukotrienes** C_4, B_4 and E_4.

starch blocker   A drug or plant extract that prevents pancreatic amylase from catalysing the hydrolysis of starch with the formation of dextrins and maltose. Such products are manufactured from certain legumes, such as the red kidney bean (*Phaseolus vulgaris*), and are believed to possess α-amylase inhibiting action. Since starch blockers prevent the digestion of starch, they might be expected to reduce energy absorption and thereby aid in weight-reducing regimens. However, there is little evidence of efficacy in this respect (*see*, for example, Bo-Linn *et al.* (1982) *New Engl. J. Med.* **307**, 1413). Presumably the pancreas secretes more amylase and so overrides the effects of the inhibited enzyme.

steroidogenesis inhibitors   Drugs that inhibit the biosynthesis of steroid **hormones** by inhibiting one of the enzymes in the synthetic pathway. They include mitotane, amphenone B, metyrapone and aminoglutethimide. Several other drugs may impair steroidogenesis by an indirect mechanism (e.g. **morphine, antidepressant drugs, heparin** and inhibitors of protein synthesis).

Straub reaction   A characteristic reaction to **morphine** and related **drugs** in mice, first described by Straub. The tail of the mouse becomes elevated and held rigidly across the back of the animal in an S-shape (also called the Straub tail effect). The effect is a consequence of an action of morphine in the spinal cord which results in contraction of the sacrococcygeus dorsalis muscle.

Straub tail effect *See* **Straub reaction**.

streptozotocin A water-soluble nitrosourea produced by the fungus *Streptomyces achromogenes*. It is used in experimental pharmacology, rather like **alloxan**, to produce a diabetes mellitus in experimental animals. It selectively damages the islets of Langerhans, probably by producing **free radicals** which cause a severe depletion of pyridine nucleotides, NAD and NADH. Pretreatment with nicotinamide prevents this effect.

In human therapeutics it is used to control islet cell tumours and carcinoid tumours.

Student distribution A distribution derived from the Gaussian distribution (*see* **binomial distribution**) by a man named Gossett who originally published under the pseudonym Student, and this has remained the generally used name for the distribution and for statistics pertaining to it. The Student distribution takes account of the fact that although the means of large samples have a Gaussian distribution, the means of small samples have a slightly different distribution in which the curve is flatter at the peak and more elongated at the tails. The Student distribution contains the term t in place of the standardized deviate, $(x - \mu)/\sigma$ of the Gaussian distribution, and it contains the term n (degrees of freedom).

sublingual administration Administration, usually in tablet form, under the tongue. Absorption takes place through the surrounding mucous membrane, and the liver is bypassed on the first pass.

substance P Von Euler and Gaddum in 1931 obtained a substance from tissues by acid–alcohol extraction. They were able to dry it to a powder, and simply named it substance P to indicate this. It produced an atropine-resistant contraction of all gastrointestinal smooth muscle, including the rat duodenum (which relaxes in response to **bradykinin**). Most smooth muscles contract in response to substance P, but vascular smooth muscle relaxes. Substance P also stimulates salivary secretion, and it stimulates some nerve cells.

Substance P is now known to be an undecapeptide. It and related naturally occurring but non-mammalian undecapeptides (e.g. physalaemin, kassinin and eledoisin) have been called tachykinins because responses to them occur more rapidly (Greek: *tachys*, swift) than responses to bradykinin.

$$[\text{N}]\text{Arg–Pro–Lys–Pro–Gln–Gln–Phe–Phe–Gly–Leu–Met–NH}_2[\text{C}]$$
$$1 \quad 2 \quad 3 \quad 4 \quad 5 \quad 6 \quad 7 \quad 8 \quad 9 \quad 10 \quad 11$$

Substance P

Substance P is present in the terminals of first-order afferents in the dorsal roots and may serve a neurotransmitter function in pain pathways. It is also present in some parts of the brain.

There may be two substance P receptor subtypes, as defined by the order of potency of the tachykinins. At the SPE receptor, eledoisin and kassinin are equipotent with each other and more potent than substance P and physalaemin. At the SP receptor, the rank order of potency is physalaemin > substance P > eledoisin > kassinin.

Substance P antagonists are available. They are analogues containing D-amino acids. The compound (D-Pro^2–D-Phe^7–D–Trp^9)SP is an example.

sudorific drug *See* **diaphoretic drug** (Latin: *sudor*, sweat).

suicide substrate An enzyme substrate that is converted by the enzyme into an irreversible inhibitor of that enzyme. The enzyme may therefore be thought of as having committed suicide. The advantage of the mechanism is that the irreversible inhibitor is produced only at the required sites.

Suicide substrates have been designed and developed for **GABA** transaminase (e.g. vinyl GABA and 4-aminohex-5-ynoic acid), for peripheral **dopa decarboxylase** (e.g. difluoromethyldopa), for **monoamine oxidase** A and monoamine oxidase B (e.g. pargyline and segyline), and for a number of other enzymes including formylglycinamide ribonucleotide aminotransferase, 5α-reductase, serine proteases and hydroxylases.

Penning (1983) *Trends pharmacol. Sci.* **4**, 212

sulfonamides *See* **sulphonamides**.

sulphate conjugation A hepatic (also kidney and intestine) non-microsomal conjugation reaction in which sulphate is transferred from phosphoadenosine phosphosulphate to substrates containing a hydroxy or a primary amine group to form ethereal sulphates or N-sulphates (sulphamates) respectively. The reactions are catalysed by sulphokinases or sulphotransferases. *See also* **drug metabolism**.

sulphonamides (sulfonamides in USA) Compounds containing the sulphonamide group ($-SO_2NH-$) in their molecules. The term usually refers to the antimicrobial sulphonamides, of which the now obsolete sulphanilamide was the first to be discovered (1933). However, a number of other drugs also contain the sulphonamide group and strictly speaking are therefore sulphonamides (e.g. the oral hypoglycaemic **sulphonylureas**, the **carbonic anhydrase inhibitor** acetazolamide and related drugs, and the **thiazide** diuretic drugs).

The antimicrobial sulphonamide drugs inhibit folic acid synthesis and consequently impair the formation of DNA and RNA in those micro-organisms that cannot absorb folate. Organisms that can absorb folate (including some micro-organisms and all higher animals) are resistant to sulphonamides. The sulphonamides are structural analogues of para-aminobenzoic acid which is essential for folate synthesis. The sulphonamides act as **antimetabolites** by competing with para-aminobenzoic acid for the enzyme dihydropteroate synthetase.

Examples of the many antimicrobial sulphonamides include sulphapyridine, sulphasomidine, sulphamethoxazole, sulfadoxine, succinylsulphathiazole and mefinide hydrochloride. They have the general structure:

$$R' - \overset{H}{N} - \text{(ring)} - \overset{O}{\underset{O}{S}} - \overset{H}{N} - R''$$

sulphones Any compound containing two hydrocarbon radicals attached to the radical $-SO_2-$, but generally restricted to mean 4,4'-diaminodiphenylsulphone (dapsone) and derivatives of it. These substances were first synthesized during the flood of research that followed the discovery of the sulphonamides. They were eventually found to be effective against acid-fast bacilli including *Myobacterium leprae*, the causative organism of leprosy, and they remain (especially dapsone) of use in this disease. Their mechanism of action probably resembles that of the **sulphonamides**

$$H_2N - \text{(ring)} - \overset{O}{\underset{O}{S}} - \text{(ring)} - NH_2$$

Dapsone

sulphonylureas A class of oral **hypoglycaemic drugs** of use in maturity-onset diabetes mellitus. They act mainly by stimulating the release of **insulin** from the islets of Langerhans, and they are therefore ineffective in the total absence of functional islet tissue. The sulphonylurea group of oral hypoglycaemic drugs include tolbutamide, chlorpropamide and glibenclamide.

$$CH_3 - \text{(ring)} - \overset{O}{\underset{O}{S}} - NH - CO - NH - CH_2 - CH_2 - CH_2 - CH_3$$

Tolbutamide

sulphydryl inhibitors Agents that combine covalently with $-SH$ groups in enzymes and coenzymes. Group III metalloids (arsenic, antimony, bismuth) and a number of heavy metal ions (copper, silver, mercury, gold) have this action and their toxicity is a consequence of this.

$$\boxed{\text{Enzyme}} + Hg^{2+} + \boxed{\text{Enzyme}} \rightarrow \boxed{\text{Enzyme}} \quad \boxed{\text{Enzyme}} + 2H^+$$
$$\underset{SH}{|} \qquad \qquad \underset{SH}{|} \qquad \qquad \underset{S-Hg-S}{|}$$

209

sun-screening agents Agents that block the access of solar radiations to the skin. They are applied in lotions, creams or ointments to protect the skin from excessive sunlight. They may simply be opaque materials, blocking or reducing all radiations (e.g. zinc oxide, talc, titanium oxide). They may block the ultraviolet component by absorbing radiations in the range 250–350 nm, thereby preventing tanning as well as the erythematous response (e.g. benzophenone derivatives). Selective absorption of the erythema-producing wavelengths may be achieved with para-aminobenzoic acid and derivatives which absorb wavelengths below 315 nm. **Salicylate** esters absorb radiation in the 290–330 nm waveband.

superinfections Many different micro-organisms live commensally on or in man, each competing with the others so that a harmless balance is maintained. Antimicrobial drugs may kill some groups of the natural flora as well as the pathogenic organism. This may free some of the non-susceptible organisms from competition. Consequently, they multiply excessively to create what is termed a superinfection. The yeast-like organism *Candida albicans* is often responsible for superinfection.

superoxide dismutase An enzyme that removes superoxide by catalysing the reaction

$$\overset{\cdot}{O}_2{}^- + \overset{\cdot}{O}_2{}^- + 2H^+ \rightarrow H_2O_2 + O_2$$

See **free radicals**.

suppository An easily meltable medicated mass for introduction into a body orifice, commonly the rectum.

surface anaesthesia Anaesthesia of an area of skin produced by application of a **local anaesthetic drug** (e.g. hexylcaine, lignocaine).

surfactants Surface active agents that reduce surface tension. They are used as skin cleansing agents (e.g. soaps and detergents), as antiseptics and disinfectants, as adjuncts to **laxatives** for the treatment of flatulence (e.g. activated dimethicone), and they are included in some contraceptive vaginal **pessaries**.

    Lung surfactant is a mixture of lipoproteins (lecithin and sphingomyelin) secreted by the type II alveolar cells into the alveoli. It reduces the surface tension of pulmonary fluids and thereby contributes to the elastic properties of the tissues. Deficiency of lung surfactant in the newborn gives rise to respiratory distress syndrome.

surgical anaesthesia A state of reversible unconsciousness that permits surgical operations to be carried out. *See* **general anaesthetic drug**.

surugatoxin A toxin isolated from the ivory shell *Babylonia japonica* which selectively binds to and blocks **nicotinic cholinoceptors** on sympathetic ganglia. (It does not block nicotinic cholinoceptors at the neuromuscular junction.)

Hayashi & Yamada (1975) *Brit. J. Pharmacol.* **53**, 207

sympathin A term coined by the American physiologist R. B. Cannon in the 1930s to denote the chemical transmitter released by sympathetic nerves. It had properties that differed somewhat from those of **adrenaline**, and at that time it was not known that it was in fact **noradrenaline**. To explain why released sympathin could excite some tissues but inhibit others, Cannon and Rosenblueth proposed that the sympathin combined within the effector cells with one or other of two hypothetical substances (E or I substance) which imparted excitatory or inhibitory actions, not only on the innervated tissue but subsequently, after circulating around the body, on remote **autoindicator tissues**. The released sympathin was said to be converted to sympathin E or sympathin I by the innervated tissue. Their misconception arose because of the autoindicator tissues that they happened to choose.

sympatholytic drug A drug that blocks responses to stimulation of sympathetic nerves. Objection has been taken to the suffix '-lytic', since it conveys the sense of destruction. In any case, the term lacks the precision necessary to classify the actions of modern drugs.

sympathomimetic action Sympathomimetic is a term introduced by Barger and Dale to denote drug actions that mimic those of stimulating sympathetic (noradrenergic) nerves. *See* **sympathomimetic drug**. At the time it was not known that the transmitter of these nerves in mammals is usually **noradrenaline**, but in fact Barger and Dale were referring to **noradrenergic nerve fibres**.

sympathomimetic bronchodilator drugs Drugs that dilate the bronchi by directly or indirectly stimulating the β-**adrenoceptors** of the airways. Such drugs include non-selective **agonists** at α- and β-**adrenoceptors** such as **adrenaline**, partially **indirectly acting sympathomimetic** amines such as ephedrine, selective β-adrenoceptor agonists such as isoprenaline (isoproterenol in USA), and selective β_2-adrenoceptor agonists such as salbutamol and terbutaline.

sympathomimetic decongestant drugs Drugs that cause vasoconstriction in, and therefore shrinkage of, congested mucous membranes by directly or indirectly stimulating α-**adrenoceptors** in the arterioles. Such drugs include ephedrine, cyclopentamine, phenylephrine, methylhexaneamine, oxymetazoline and xylometazoline.

sympathomimetic drug Drugs that produce **sympathomimetic actions**. Most are amines, and the term sympathomimetic amine is commonly used. Many, but by no means all, are **catecholamines**. Sympathomimetic drugs include the endogenous compounds **noradrenaline**, **adrenaline** and **dopamine**, and numerous synthetic or plant derived compounds that mimic some or all of the actions of noradrenaline.

Sympathomimetic drugs are classified into directly acting **agonists** on α- and/or β-**adrenoceptors**, and indirectly-acting drugs that cause the release of stored vesicular noradrenaline. Examples of directly acting sympathomimetic drugs include noradrenaline, oxymetazoline and isoprenaline. Tyramine is the prototype of an **indirectly acting sympathomimetic** amine; its direct actions are very weak. Some sympathomimetic amines exert both direct and indirect actions to different but appreciable extents; ephedrine and amphetamines are examples.

sympathomimetic mydriatic drugs   Drugs that dilate the pupil (mydriasis) by directly or indirectly stimulating α-**adrenoceptors** on the dilator pupillae when applied in eye-drops. They include **adrenaline**, phenylephrine and ephedrine.

sympathomimetic pressor drugs   Drugs that elevate blood pressure by directly or indirectly stimulating α-**adrenoceptors** in the arteriolar smooth muscle, thereby producing vasoconstriction. Such drugs include **noradrenaline**, **adrenaline**, metaraminol, methoxamine, phenylephrine and methylaminoheptane.

synergistic action   A drug action that increases the effect produced by another drug. A synergistic action may involve potentiation or may be simply an additive effect, or may be neither.

The diagram below (after J. H. Gaddum) represents the combination of two drugs, both of which produce the same effect. The axes represent concentrations of the two drugs. The distance OA represents the concentration of drug A that produces the effect in the absence of drug B, and the distance OB represents the corresponding concentration of drug B. If the effect is produced by combinations of the two drugs represented by points inside the rectangle OACB, the two drugs are synergistic in their actions. If the effect is just produced by combinations represented by points on the line AB, the effects are simply additive. If the effect is produced by points in the triangle OAB, there is potentiation, which means that the drugs produce the effect in a combined concentration that is less than can be accounted for by simple addition. If the effect is produced by points in the triangle ABC, the combined effect is less than additive, but synergism is still present because the given effect is produced by a smaller amount of each drug than would be necessary if only one drug were given.

If the effect is produced by combinations of the drugs represented by points above the line AC, then drug B is antagonizing drug A. Similarly, if the effect is produced by combinations represented by points to the right of CB, then drug A is antagonizing drug B.

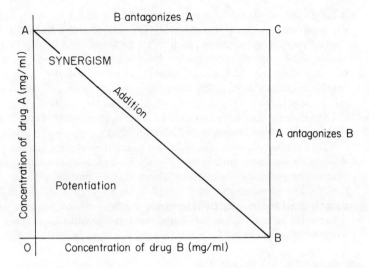

Lines joining up points corresponding to drug combinations that produce equal effects (e.g. the line AB is one such) are called **isobols** (Greek: *isos*, the same; *bolos*, effect).

There are of course many cases in pharmacology in which drug B, though without effect by itself, nevertheless potentiates or antagonizes drug A. For example, drugs that inhibit inactivating enzymes (e.g. **anticholinesterase drugs**) potentiate the enzyme's substrate (i.e. **acetylcholine** in this instance), and drugs that block **receptors** (e.g. atropine) will antagonize the effect of the specific **agonists** (e.g. acetylcholine in this instance). In these instances, the concentrations of drug A necessary to produce a given effect are less (potentiation) or greater (antagonism) than would be the case if drug A were used alone.

2,4,5-T (2,4,5-Trichlorophenoxy) acetic acid. A herbicide of the defoliant type. 2,4,5-T has been used as a defoliant in 'jungle warfare', for example by the British in Malaya and by the Americans in Vietnam. The defoliant known as Agent Orange in Vietnam (because of the orange ring painted around the containers) was a mixture of 2,4,5-T and 4-(2,4-dichlorophenoxy) butanoic acid (2,4D). The main problem with 2,4,5-T is that it contains minute traces of dioxin, a powerful toxin that produces severe skin eruptions (chloracne), birth abnormalities and probably cancer. Dioxin was accidentally released into the environment after an explosion at a northern Italian chemical factory at Seveso in 1976.

$T_{1/2}$ The half-time; that is, the time taken for the concentration of **drug** in the blood or plasma to decline to half of its original value.

If the log plasma concentration (log C_P) against time graph is linear (i.e. a single-**compartment** model), then $T_{1/2}$ is the same over the whole time-course. For example, the time to fall from C_0 (concentration at start) to $C_0/2$ is the same as the time to fall from $C_0/2$ to $C_0/4$. In multi-compartment models (see **compartments**) this is obviously not so.

From the calculations under **elimination rate constant** (K_{elim}) it will be seen that for a linear log C_P v. time graph, $T_{1/2}$ is given by $0.693/K_{elim}$.

tachykinins   *See* **substance P**.

tachyphylaxis   A rapid diminution in response to each of a succession of repeated doses of a drug (Greek: *takhus*, quick; *phulakterion*, a protection). The derivation of the word suggests that the drug protects against its own action in some way. The term tachyphylaxis does not imply any particular mechanism, but possible mechanisms include **receptor desensitization**, the drug may be self-blocking because it is a **partial agonist**, or the drug may act indirectly to release an endogenous mediator which becomes exhausted by repeated doses (cf. **tolerance**).

taenicide drugs   Drugs used to kill intestinal tapeworms (cestodes). Examples of such drugs are niclosamide, dichlorophen, male fern and derivatives, mepacrine, paromomycin and hexylresorcinol. Drugs that paralyse tapeworms rather than kill them are called **taenifuge drugs**.

taenifuge drugs   A drug that paralyses (but does not kill) tapeworms so that they are expelled in the faeces. Such drugs are largely obsolete. An example is an extract of pumpkin seeds called fugitene; it is still used in some countries. More modern drugs are referred to under **taenicide drugs**.

taipoxin   A polypeptide **neurotoxin** from the Australian taipan snake, *Oxyuranus scutellatus*. It acts to prevent the release of **acetylcholine** from **cholinergic nerve fibre** endings.

tardive dyskinesia   A syndrome of irregularly repetitive involuntary movements that may occur during treatment or after withdrawal of certain **neuroleptic drugs** (e.g. fluphenazine), that block **dopamine receptors**. It is thought to be a consequence of dopamine receptor hypersensitivity. It is characterized by abnormal writhing movements or protrusions of the tongue with lip-smacking, puckering and chewing movements and facial grimaces. Choreoathetoid movements of the extremities, or repetitive movements of the neck or trunk, may accompany the orofacial dyskinesia, or may occur alone. The syndrome is common among patients treated with moderate to high doses of **neuroleptic drugs** for prolonged periods and may prove irreversible, particularly in patients over the age of 50.

Although the adjective tardive implies that the dyskinesia is late in appearing, the syndrome has in fact occasionally been produced after only low doses have been administered for a short period.

tartar emetic Antimony potassium tartrate. *See* **antimonials**.

taurine The most abundant free amino acid in the animal kingdom. It is formed from cysteine by oxidation and decarboxylation. There is some evidence that taurine may function as an inhibitory transmitter or modulator in the brain. It is a central depressant with antiepileptic activity, and attempts to make analogues that might serve as useful **antiepileptic drugs** are underway. Taurine may also be involved in the control of Ca^{2+} fluxes in cardiac muscle cells.

$$HO-SO_2-CH_2-CH_2-NH_2$$
Taurine

tear gas *See* **incapacitating agents**.

teratogen A substance that produces abnormalities of the fetus (Greek: *teras*, a monster). Hence, teratogenicity, the capacity to produce fetal abnormalities and teratology, the study of teratogenicity.

teratogenicity *See* **teratogen**.

teratology *See* **teratogen**.

tetanus toxin A protein **neurotoxin** produced by the Gram-negative bacterium *Clostridium tetani*. It blocks inhibitory synapses in the spinal cord, thus producing the characteristic spastic paralysis of the disease tetanus in man and animals. In addition, it exerts a slowly developing **botulinum toxin**-like action on peripheral **cholinergic nerve fibre** endings so that the initial spastic state is eventually followed by a flaccid paralysis.

tetracyclic antidepressant drugs A class of antidepressant **thymoleptic drugs** used to elevate mood in depressive illness. The molecule contains four fused rings. Mianserin is the main example. The mechanism of action is uncertain. Tetracyclics do not block amine re-uptake as do the **tricyclic antidepressant drugs**.

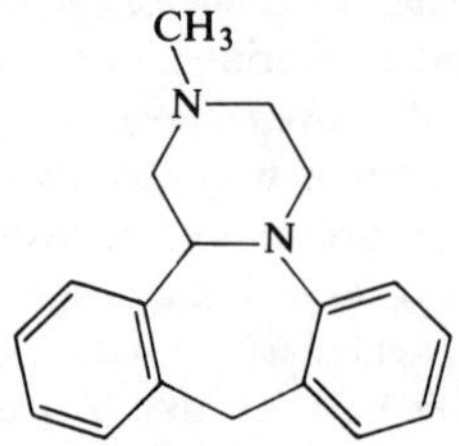

Mianserin

tetracyclines   A group of **antibiotic** drugs with four ring structures in their molecules. The first tetracyclines (chlortetracycline, oxytetracycline and demeclocycline) were obtained from *Streptomyces* species. The remaining members of the group (tetracycline, rolitetracycline, methacycline, doxycycline, clomocycline, lymecycline, minocycline) are either prepared from the naturally occurring compounds or are totally synthetic. The tetracyclines are broad-spectrum antibiotics with a wide range of bacteriostatic activity. They act by binding to the 30 S subunit of the bacterial ribosomes and to mRNA.

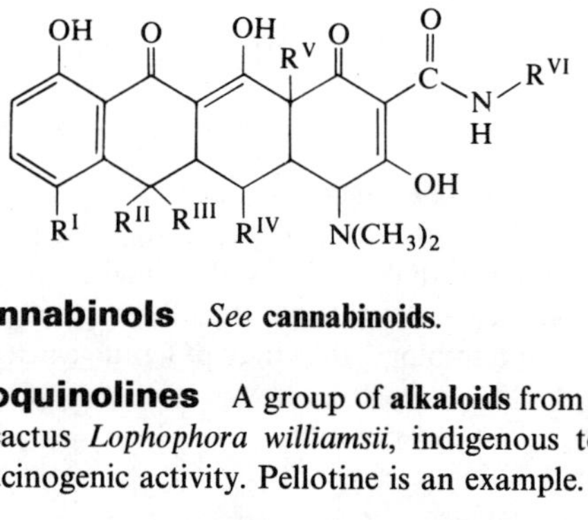

tetrahydrocannabinols   *See* **cannabinoids**.

tetrahydroisoquinolines   A group of **alkaloids** from peyote (the dried top of the cactus *Lophophora williamsii*, indigenous to Mexico). They possess hallucinogenic activity. Pellotine is an example.

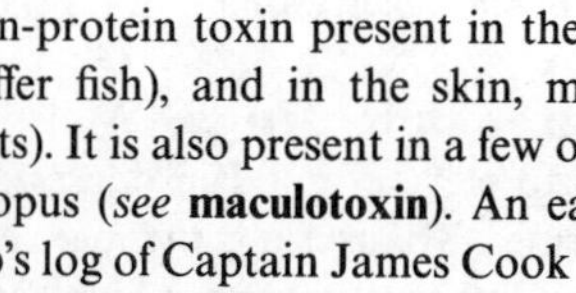

Pellotine

tetrodotoxin   A non-protein toxin present in the ovaries and liver of the *Tetroadontidae* (puffer fish), and in the skin, muscle and blood of the *Salamandridae* (newts). It is also present in a few other species, for example the blue-ringed octopus (*see* **maculotoxin**). An early case of poisoning is described in the ship's log of Captain James Cook (1774) in which he refers to eating 'blow-fish' in New Caledonia.

Tetrodotoxin selectively blocks voltage-dependent Na$^+$ channels in nerve, skeletal muscle and cardiac muscle, and can be used as an affinity label to count such channels. It is much more potent in blocking conduction in nerve than in muscle, and it does not affect most smooth muscles at all, since the action potential in most smooth muscles does not depend on an inward Na^+ current. Tetrodotoxin is used as an experi-

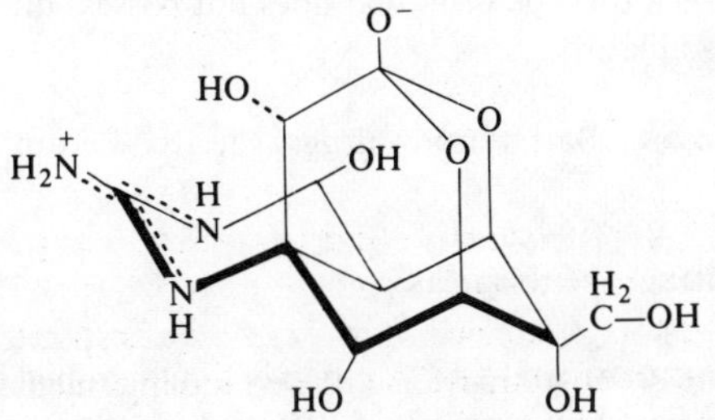

Tetrodotoxin

mental tool by physiologists and pharmacologists to provide evidence as to whether a particular effect is or is not dependent on Na^+ channels. The molecule contains a guanidinium group which is essential for its activity. Its actions are similar to those of **saxitoxin**.

THC Tetrahydrocannabinol. *See* **cannabinoids**.

therapeutic index Sometimes called therapeutic ratio. The concept was devised by Paul Ehrlich, as the maximum tolerated dose divided by the minimum curative dose, to give an idea of the safety of a drug (Ehrlich used it for antimicrobial drugs).

Nowadays, the therapeutic index is calculated (from animal data) as the ratio LD_{50}/ED_{50}. The concept obviously has limited usefulness since it cannot be calculated for man, and data relating to one species cannot reliably be transferred to another. Also called **Gaddum's chemotherapeutic ratio**.

thiazide drugs A group of drugs containing a thiazide nucleus in their molecules and most of which, but not all, are **diuretic drugs**. The thiazide diuretics possess a **sulphonamide** group and, like other sulphonamides, they are **carbonic anhydrase inhibitors**. However, the main component of their diuretic action is a consequence not of carbonic anhydrase inhibition, but rather of inhibition of Cl^- (and hence of Na^+) reabsorption in the

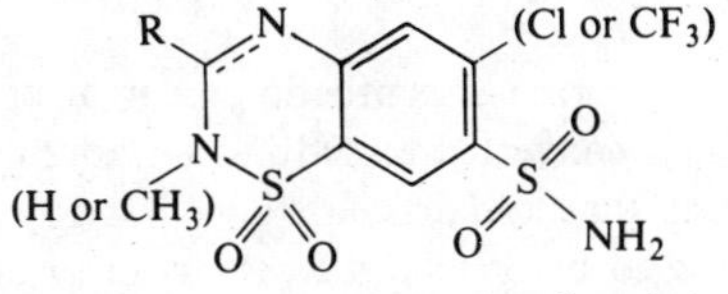

General structure of thiazide diuretics

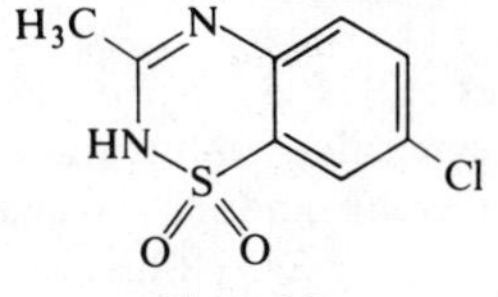

Diazoxide

217

ascending limb of the loop of Henle and the distal convoluted tubule. Thiazide diuretics also possess a vasodilator action and are used in the therapy of hypertension. Examples of thiazide diuretics include chlorothiazide, bendroflumethiazide and cyclopenthiazide. (There are many more.)

Diazoxide is a thiazide drug that does not possess diuretic action. It is used as a vasodilator.

thiobarbiturates Barbiturate drugs derived from thiourea. *See* **barbiturates**.

thiocarbamides *See* **thioureas**.

thiosemicarbazone drugs A group of antimicrobial drugs, the first of which was prepared by Domagk in 1946 and found to be effective against the bacterium responsible for tuberculosis. Compounds of this type were subsequently found to exert some antiviral activity. Methisazone is an example.

Methisazone

thiouracils A class of **antithyroid drugs**, including iodothiouracil, methylthiouracil and propylthiouracil, which inhibit the formation of thyroxine.

thioureas A class of **antithyroid drugs** whose molecules are based on thiourea ($H_2N—CS—NH_2$). They are also known as thiocarbamides. They include carbinazole, methinazole and the **thiouracils**. They act by inhibiting thyroxine formation.

threo-DOPS *Threo-d*ihydroxyphenylserine. A synthetic precursor of **noradrenaline**. On decarboxylation it is converted directly to noradrenaline, thereby omitting the **dopamine** step that is characteristic of levodopa.

Threo-DOPS has been reported to be beneficial in the control of socalled **on–off effects** in patients with Parkinson's disease.

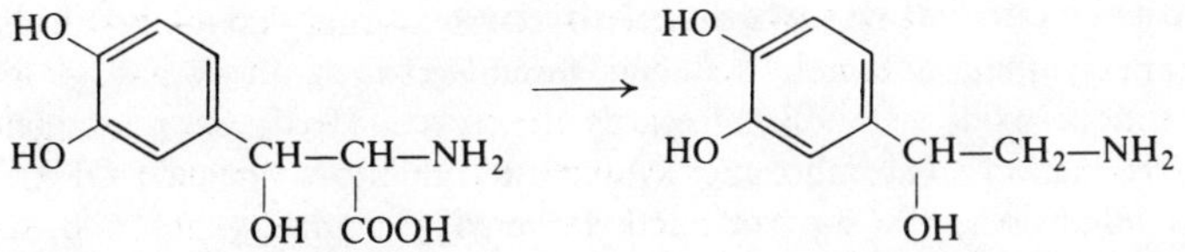

Dihydroxyphenylserine → Noradrenaline

thromboxane antagonists Drugs that block the actions (vasocon-striction, bronchoconstriction and platelet aggregation) of **thromboxane** A_2 and related **thromboxane mimetics**. The antagonism is probably competi-tive. Thromboxane antagonists include the compounds coded EP 045, EP 092, EP 116, AH 19437, SC 23536, ONO 11105, SKII-144 and BM 13177. The structures of three examples are:

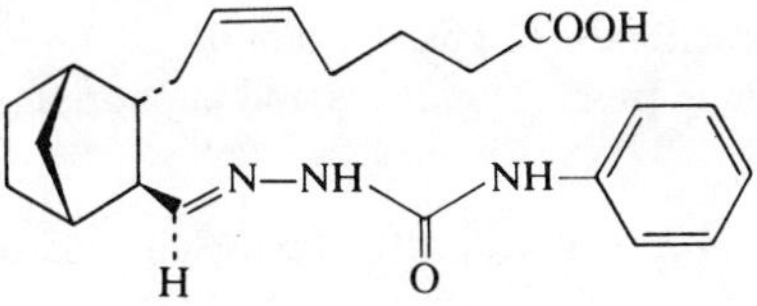

EP 045

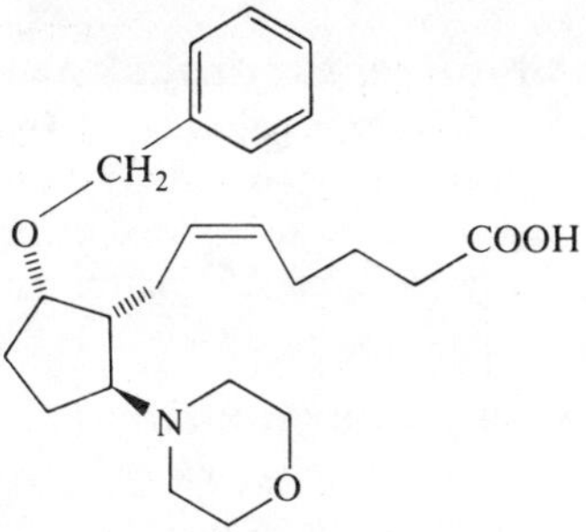

AH 19437

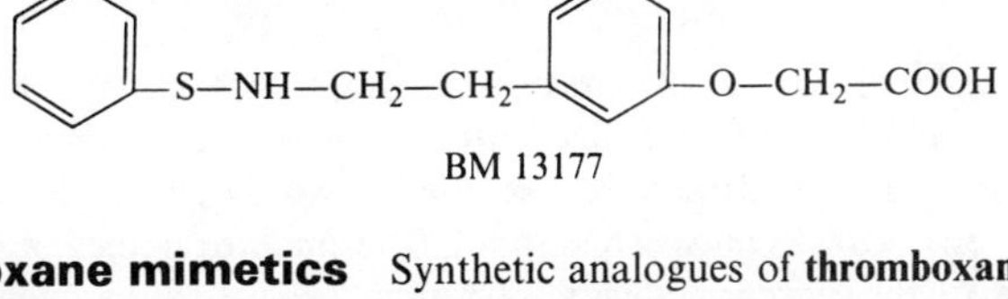

BM 13177

thromboxane mimetics Synthetic analogues of **thromboxane** A_2 that are relatively stable and in most cases full **agonists**. They include U-46619, CTA_2 and EP 171.

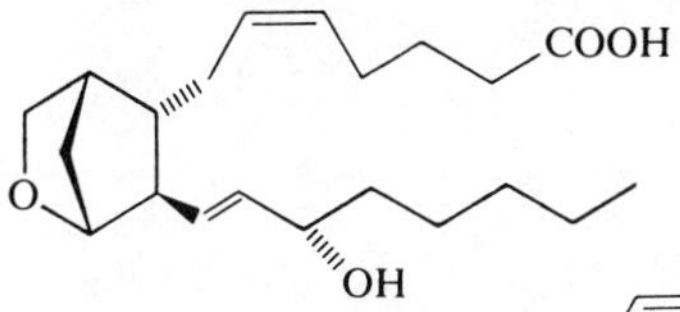

U-46619

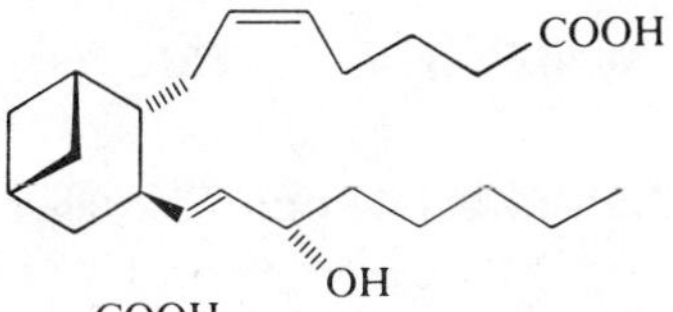

CTA_2

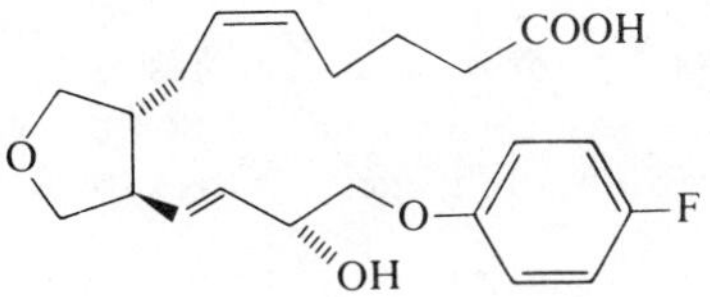

EP 171

thromboxane synthetase inhibitors Drugs that inhibit thromboxane synthetase, thereby reducing **thromboxane** synthesis and so forcing endoperoxide metabolism towards prostacyclin (PGI_2, *see* **prostaglandins**) production. Thromboxane synthetase inhibitors include OKY 1581 (sodium (E)-3[4(-3-pyridylmethyl)phenyl]-2-methacrylate) and dazoxiben (4[-2-(1-H-imodazo-ol-1-yl)ethoxy] benzoic acid).

thromboxanes Metabolites of the PGG_2- and PGH_2-type **prostaglandin** endoperoxides that have the cyclopentane ring replaced by a six-membered oxygen-containing ring. They have a thrombus-forming potential, hence the name (*see* **prostaglandins**). The highly active thromboxane A_2 (*see* **prostaglandins**) has a short half-life and is quickly converted to the biologically inactive thromboxane B_2.

thymerectic drugs Antidepressant drugs belonging to the **monoamine oxidase inhibitor** class. The term is derived from Greek words signifying that the mood (Greek: *thumos*, emotion) is maintained. Drugs in this class are used to control depressive reactions. A typical example is tranylcypromine. Alternative names include psychoenergizers and euphoriants.

thymic hormones Hormones synthesized within the epithelial cells of the thymus gland and released into the general circulation, affecting the development and maintenance of the immune response. The hormones include thymosin, *facteur thymique serique* (FTS), and the thymic humoral factors.

thymoleptic drugs Antidepressant drugs that elevate mood from a depressed level, yet that have little stimulant effect when the mood is normal. The term is derived from Greek words meaning support of the emotions (Greek: *thumos*, emotion). The main examples of this class of **drugs** are the **tricyclic antidepressant drugs**, such as amitriptyline, which are used to control psychotic depression.

thyroliberin *See* TRH.

tissue tolerance *See* tolerance.

tocolytic agent A drug that suppresses premature labour. β_2-**Adrenoceptor** agonists, such as salbutamol, are examples. They act by inhibiting contractions of the uterus (Greek: *tocos*, childbirth).

tolerance A term applied usually to clinically used drugs when larger and larger doses have to be given to produce the desired effect. Important examples of drugs towards which tolerance develops are **narcotic analgesic drugs** such as **morphine**, **dopamine antagonists** such as haloperidol, **barbiturates**, and certain **antihypertensive drugs** such as **ganglion blocking drugs** (e.g. hexamethonium) and **adrenergic neurone blocking drugs** (e.g. guanethidine). Mechanisms underlying tolerance include adaptive changes such as receptor uncoupling and **up-** or **down-regulation of receptors** (tissue tolerance or pharmacodynamic tolerance), and increased activity of reflex compensatory physiological mechanisms, or there may be stimulated metabolism of the drug through **enzyme induction** (metabolic tolerance). Enhanced reflex compensatory physiological mechanisms or enzyme induction in the liver would mean that tolerance would be demonstrable only in the whole organism. Receptor uncoupling or up- or down-regulation of receptors, on the other hand, is demonstrable in isolated tissues when removed from a tolerant animal. Tolerance to morphine, for example, can be demonstrated in isolated vas deferens or ileum taken from chronically treated animals.

Tolerance to morphine may be a consequence of receptor uncoupling. Tolerance to various **agonists** or antagonists may be due to down-regulation or up-regulation of receptors respectively. Tolerance to barbiturates is largely the result of enzyme induction.

Individual tolerance is a term applied to the insensitivity or relative insensitivity of individual members of a species to a particular drug or class of drugs. For example, a few human beings are tolerant to (i.e. resistant to) the **neuromuscular blocking drug** succinylcholine, because they possess a genetically determined abnormally high level of plasma cholinesterase activity (the so-called $E_{cynthiana}$ variant), which inactivates the drug. Another example is the genetically determined tolerance to the anticoagulant action of warfarin that is exhibited by some human beings.

The term species tolerance refers to the resistance to a drug that is exhibited by all or most members of a particular species. For example, most rabbits are much more resistant to atropine (and hence belladonna) poisoning than most other species, because they have evolved with an enzyme in their plasma (atropinase) that hydrolyses atropine.

The tolerance of some micro-organisms to certain **antibiotics** is described under **antibiotic resistance**.

tranquillizer A term introduced in 1953 to describe the psychotropic action of reserpine, but now more commonly used to describe drugs with sedative and anti-anxiety actions for use in anxiety neuroses. Alternative names include minor tranquillizer, tranquillosedative drug, psychosedative drug, ataractic drug, anxiolytic drug, antineurotic drug. Examples of such drugs include chlordiazepoxide, diazepam, benactyzine, benzoctamine.

tranquillosedative drug An alternative name for **tranquillizer**.

transfer factor A dialysable polypeptide–polynucleotide (mol. wt. < 10 000) from sensitized leucocytes that converts non-immune lymphocytes to immune lymphocytes. Some immunodeficiency states associated with cancers and chronic infectious diseases are associated with a deficiency of transfer factor. Transfer factor was discovered by H. S. Lawrence who has also demonstrated its remarkable ability to control certain diseases consequent upon immunodeficiency.

tremorine A drug used in experimental pharmacology to produce an animal model of parkinsonism. It produces tremor, hypokinesia, and rigidity by a central muscarinic action, and peripheral parasympathomimetic effects by stimulating peripheral **muscarinic cholinoceptors**. It is in fact a **prodrug**, the active metabolite being **oxotremorine**. The similarity to parkinsonism is limited but it has proved useful in detecting **antiparkinson drugs** of the atropine-type.

Tremorine   Oxotremorine

Trendelenburg preparation of guinea-pig intestine A segment of guinea-pig ileum set up in an organ bath in such a way that both changes in volume and changes in length are recorded simultaneously. The peristaltic reflex is triggered at regular intervals by increasing the pressure within the length of ileum. In the original method, drugs can be applied only to the external surface (Trendelenburg (1917) *Arch. exp. Path. Pharmak.* **81**, 55), but in a modification of the method drugs may be applied to either surface (Bülbring *et al.* (1958) *Brit. J. Pharmacol.* **13**, 440).

Treppe   *See* **Bowditch staircase phenomenon**.

TRH   Thyrotropin-releasing hormone (also called thyroliberin); a tripeptide (pGlu–His–Pro–NH$_2$) which stimulates the release of thyrotropin and prolactin from the pituitary gland.

tribulin The name given by M. Sandler and colleagues to an as yet unidentified substance extracted from human urine obtained from anxious patients during withdrawal of **benzodiazepines** or alcohol, or from patients with panic disorder. Production of tribulin appeared to be suppressed by benzodiazepines or alcohol.. The main pharmacological property of tribulin that has been demonstrated is its ability to displace benzodiazepines from the **benzodiazepine receptor**. It appears to act as a so-called **inverse agonist**, rather after the manner of β-CCM (*see* **benzodiazepine receptor**), and it may be an endogenous anxiety-producing agent.

Tribulin is associated with an endogenous **monoamine oxidase inhibitor** but it is unlikely that both properties are exerted by the same molecule.

trichothecene mycotoxin A powerful toxin isolated from *Fusarium* species (e.g. *F. nivale*). Nivalenol is an alternative name. It is a haemorrhagic agent and causes blistering and necrosis. The lethal dose in man is probably very small. It, and related toxins, are said to have been developed as chemical warfare agents—the so-called T-toxins or 'yellow rain'.

tricyclic antidepressant drugs A class of antidepressant **thymoleptic drugs** used to elevate mood in depressive illness. Their molecules contain a three-ring structure, hence the group name. Their mechanism of action is not fully understood, but they exert the common property of blocking the **neuronal re-uptake of noradrenaline** and **serotonin**, and most theories to explain their antidepressant action depend upon this property exerted in the limbic system. Examples include imipramine, desipramine, amitriptyline, nortriptyline, protryptiline and doxepin. *See also* **tetracyclic antidepressant drugs**.

General structure of tricyclic antidepressant drugs.

triple response A series of events produced by intradermal injection of **histamine**. The immediate effect is a local *flush*, due to dilatation of the nearest blood vessels. Then more distant blood vessels dilate to produce a *flare*. The flare is not a consequence of the histamine diffusing through the tissues to reach the blood vessels but is thought to be a consequence of an axon reflex evoked antidromically in sensory endings which retrogradely release some vasodilator substance (perhaps ATP or **substance P**). Thirdly, a **wheal** develops in the flushed area due to local oedema consequent upon increased permeability of the capillaries.

tropolones Compounds containing a tropolone nucleus in their molecules. Tropolones are isosteric with catechols and are competitive inhibitors of **catechol-O-methyl-transferase**.

4-Methyltropolone

trypanocidal drugs Drugs that kill trypanosomes and which are used in the treatment of trypanosomiasis. Only three trypanosomes are pathogenic to man: *Trypanosoma gambiense* and *T. rhodesiense* which cause African sleeping sickness, and *T. cruzi* which cause Chagas' disease in South America. Trypanosomal infections are spread by insects in which part of the life cycle takes place.

Drugs used in African sleeping sickness include pentamidine, suramin, melarsoprol and tryparsamide. Drugs used in Chagas' disease are primaquine and puromycin, but there is no reliable therapy.

tryptaminergic nerve fibres *See* **serotoninergic nerve fibres**.

tryptophan hydroxylase inhibitors Drugs that inhibit the enzyme tryptophan hydroxylase (EC 1.14.16.4) which catalyses the conversion of tryptophan to **serotonin**. Such drugs include α-methyl-paratyrosine, dopacetamide, 6-fluorotryptophan, parachloramphetamine and parachlorophenylalanine (fenclonine) and its methyl ester.

T-toxins *See* **tricothecene mycotoxin**.

tuftsin A tetrapeptide (Thr–Lys–Pro–Arg) which is part of a parent carrier molecule γ-globulin, leukokinin. Two enzymes serve to free tuftsin from the carrier molecule: a spleen enzyme, tuftsin endocarboxylpeptidase, nicks the heavy chain to free the arginine end of tuftsin, and a membrane enzyme in the phagocytic cells, leukokininase, cleaves it at the amino end of threonine to release tuftsin. Tuftsin stimulates all functions of phagocytic cells: phagocytosis, pinocytosis, motility, immunogenic activity including processing of the **antigen** and augmentation of the number of **antibody**-forming cells, bactericidal activity, and tumoricidal activity.

tumour necrosis factor A cancer toxin with some similarity in its amino acid sequence to lymphotoxin (about 30% homology between the two). It is derived from activated macrophages and, like **lymphokine**, it has cytotoxic activity against tumour cells, but little or no activity against normal cells.

tumour promoter An agent that increases tumour incidence when administered after a sub-optimal dose of an **oncogen**, but which is not itself oncogenic. Croton oil and its constituent **phorbol esters** are well known tumour promoters.

type I hypersensitivity reaction *See* **immediate hypersensitivity reaction**.

Tyrode solution A **physiological salt solution** originally devised by Tyrode in 1910 (*Archs. int. Pharmacodyn.* **20**, 205) for bathing isolated mammalian smooth muscles. It has the following composition (mmol/l): NaCl 137, KCl 2·7, $CaCl_2$ 2·2, $MgCl_2$ 0·1–0·5, NaH_2PO_4 0·4, $NaHCO_3$ 11·9, glucose 5·5. It is bubbled with air, oxygen or 5% CO_2 in oxygen.

ubiquinone A lipophilic electron carrier which is a component of the mitochondrial respiratory chain. It is also called coenzyme Q. (*See also* **electron transfer inhibitors**.) The quinone portion of its molecule is alternately oxidized and reduced. The number of isoprene units in its side-chain ranges from six to ten depending upon the source of the coenzyme Q. The side-chain renders the molecule lipid-soluble. Coenzyme Q_{10} is of particular interest to pharmacologists because it has been used as a drug to improve cardiac function in heart failure. An **inotropic action** of coenzyme Q_{10} can be demonstrated in *in vitro* preparations of cardiac muscle, but only when contractions have been depressed by hypoxia. It presumably acts by increasing ATP synthesis in the hypoxic cells.

Coenzyme Q_{10}

ulcerogenic drugs Drugs that may give rise to peptic ulceration of the stomach or upper duodenum, or exacerbate an existing ulcer, as an unwanted effect. Such drugs include **non-steroidal anti-inflammatory drugs**

(NSAID) such as aspirin and indomethacin, **glucocorticoids**, reserpine, **histamine** (including endogenous histamine released, for example, after a burn injury), vasodilator drugs and possibly caffeine. The mechanisms of action involve inhibition of **prostaglandin** E_2 formation (by NSAIDs and glucocorticoids) which normally negatively modulates gastric acid secretion, depletion of **serotonin** (by reserpine) which normally plays a role in terminating the intestinal phase of gastric secretion, direct stimulation of oxyntic cells to release acid (histamine acting on **histamine H_2-receptors** and possibly caffeine via a Ca^{2+} mechanism) and indirect stimulation of oxyntic cells as a consequence of increased blood flow (vasodilators such as nicotinic acid and tolazoline).

uncompetitive inhibition A type of enzyme inhibition that arises when the inhibitor cannot combine with the free enzyme, but is capable of combining only with the substrate–enzyme complex.

The following equation may be derived in relation to uncompetitive inhibition.

$$\frac{1}{v} = \frac{K_m}{sV} + \frac{1}{V}(1 + iK_i)$$

where v = reaction rate, V = maximal reaction rate, K_m = Michaelis–Menten constant, s = original concentration of substrate, i = concentration of inhibitor, and K_i = the dissociation constant for the inhibitor-enzyme complex. Graphs of $1/v$ against $1/s$ and $1/v$ against i have the following form (cf. **Linweaver–Burk plot**).

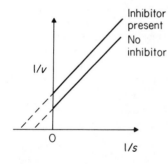
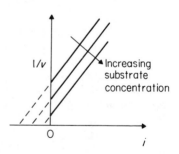

uncouplers of oxidative phosphorylation Substances that act in the mitochondria to uncouple the production of ATP from electron transport. (*See also* **electron transport inhibitors**.) ATP synthesis therefore ceases, but electron transport and oxygen consumption continue, and metabolic rate and body temperature increase markedly. Examples of uncoupling agents include 2,4-dinitrophenol, **salicylates** (in high concentrations), and substituted phenylhydrazones (e.g. carbonylcyanide-*m*-chlorophenylhydrazone, CCCP).

up-regulation of receptors The capacity of a cell to increase the number of functional **receptors** in its membrane in response to diminished activity of the specific **agonist**. Many types of receptors are synthesized on the ribosomes and are stored, possibly in the Golgi body, until required. If the receptors already in the membrane are chronically blocked by an antagonist, or if the quantity of agonist in the region of the receptors is chronically reduced below normal (e.g. through denervation), the cell can compensate by inserting new receptors into its membrane. Up-regulation of receptors is one process that contributes to **tolerance** to an antagonist, and to supersensitivity to agonists after chronic denervation (*see* **denervation supersensitivity**). The signals that trigger the process of up-regulation of receptors are not yet understood. However, there is evidence that the protein **fodrin** and the enzyme **calpain 1** are involved at some sites. *See also* **down-regulation of receptors**.

uptake 1 *See* **neuronal uptake of noradrenaline**.

uptake 2 *See* **non-neuronal uptake of amines**.

uric acid synthesis inhibitors Drugs that impair the synthesis of uric acid. The main drug in this class is allopurinol which interrupts uric acid synthesis by blocking the enzyme xanthine oxidase, which catalyses the conversion of hypoxanthine to xanthine, as well as xanthine to uric acid.

uricosuric drugs Drugs that produce an increase in the urinary excretion of uric acid. They may be used to control hyperuricaemia, including that occuring in gout. The main examples of uricosuric drugs are probenecid and sulphinpyrazone which, in large enough doses, block the active reabsorption of uric acid in the proximal tubules of the kidney, and hence increase the quantity excreted. In small doses these drugs may actually reduce uric acid excretion by competing with the acid carrier involved in the proximal secretion of uric acid. *See also* **uric acid synthesis inhibitors**.

vaccines Preparations of micro-organisms (viruses, bacteria and some protozoa) used to produce active immunity against disease caused by the same or a closely related micro-organism. The micro-organisms are either killed, or, if they remain alive, they are modified in such a way that they are no longer capable of causing the disease. The terms vaccine and vaccination come from the Latin word for cow (*vaccus*) to commemorate the first successful immunization programme initiated by Jenner, around the beginning of the 19th century, when the relatively harmless cowpox was used to produce immunization against smallpox.

Vagusstoff   The name coined by Otto Loewi (1921) to denote the substance released on stimulating the vagus (parasympathetic) nerve to the frog heart. Vagusstoff is now known to be **acetylcholine**. Loewi showed that when the vagus was stimulated, the heart slowed and a substance (Vagusstoff) was released into the perfusion fluid. When this perfusion fluid was passed over a second heart, it too slowed. Loewi's experiments on Vagusstoff and **Acceleransstoff** were fundamental in the development of the concept of neurohumoral transmission.

variant angina   Also called Prinzmetal's angina. Angina thought to arise from intermittent coronary vasospasm rather than from intraluminal obstruction.

vasoactive intestinal peptide   Also called VIP. A highly basic polypeptide containing 28 amino acids. It is present throughout the gut. It inhibits gastric secretion, stimulates electrolyte and water secretion by the pancreas, stimulates lipolysis and glycogenolysis, stimulates the heart, and produces vasodilatation (hence its name). Many of these actions are mediated by the **adenylate cyclase–cyclic AMP** system. In addition, VIP is present in a number of nerve fibres and may serve as a transmitter or a **co-transmitter** at some sites both in the brain and in the periphery. It is present in high quantities in nerves in the human penis and may be responsible for the vasodilatation underlying erection.

vasoconstrictor drugs   Drugs that reduce the calibre of blood vessels, especially arterioles, by producing contraction of their smooth muscle. Examples include **agonists** at α_1-**adrenoceptors** and vasopressin and its derivatives (e.g. felypressin).

vasodilator drugs   Drugs that increase the calibre of blood vessels, especially arterioles. They may act by interrupting the sympathetic vasoconstrictor tone through an action on the vasomotor centre, the sympathetic ganglia, the **noradrenergic nerve fibre** endings or the **adreno-ceptors**, or they may act directly on the smooth muscle of the blood vessels to impair Ca^{2+} influx, to hyperpolarize the membranes, or to enhance Ca^{2+}-binding through increased cyclic nucleotide formation (**cyclic AMP** or **cyclic GMP**). Some act by releasing **EDRF**.

veratrum alkaloids   Compounds obtained from plants belonging main-ly to the species *Veratrum album, V. viride, Zigadenus venenosus* and *Schoenocaulon officinale*. They increase the excitability of nerve fibres by lowering the threshold at which voltage-dependent Na^+ channels (*see* **voltage-dependent ion channels**) open and by interfering with their closure (i.e. delaying inactivation). The action potentials are therefore prolonged, and with high concentrations spontaneous action potentials may be generated. They exert a similar effect on the Na^+ channels of cardiac and skeletal muscle, although rather higher concentrations are needed. Their effects are blocked by the Na^+ channel toxin, **tetrodotoxin**.

They have had limited use in hypertension where they are believed to act by increasing the sensitivity of the afferent side of the depressor reflex. They are now almost obsolete.

vermicidal drug An **anthelmintic drug** that kills (Latin: *caedere*, to kill) parasitic worms as distinct from simply paralysing or expelling them.

vermifuge A type of **anthelmintic drug** that causes the expulsion of worms. For example, arecoline (from betel) has been used as a vermifuge in veterinary medicine, and pomegranate seeds may be used to expel tapeworms (**taenifuge**).

vesicants Substances that produce erythema, pruritus and then blistering on exposure to skin and mucous membranes. They include agents developed as chemical warfare gases such as mustard gas, arsenicals ('Lewisite'), nettle gas and dimethylsulphate, and medicinal vesicants such as the obsolete cantharidin and isothiocyanate (from black mustard) and sinapine (from white mustard). The medicinal use is as **counter-irritants**.

Cantharidin (from certain beetles, 'Spanish fly') has a totally unjustified and dangerous reputation as an **aphrodisiac**.

vinca alkaloids The **alkaloids** from the periwinkle plant (*Vinca rosea*). The main alkaloids are vincristine and vinblastine which have some use as antineoplastic drugs. They disrupt microtubules and probably owe their antineoplastic action to disruption of the mitotic spindle.

VIP *See* **vasoactive intestinal peptide**.

VIPergic nerve fibres Nerve fibres that release VIP (**vasoactive intestinal peptide**) as a transmitter. Many nerve fibres, both central and peripheral, have been shown to contain VIP by the use of specific **antibodies**, but evidence that it actually functions as a transmitter or **co-transmitter** is incomplete.

viroid Infectious agents of plants that are the smallest known autonomous replicating forms in biology. They are single-stranded, closed, circular RNA molecules. Unlike viruses, they have no protein.

vitamins Essential organic constituents of diet that in many cases function as coenzymes or as precursors of coenzymes. They were first recognized as essential by the development of deficiency disorders when they were omitted from the diet of man or animals. In man, five major diseases, keratomalacia, rickets, beriberi, pellagra and scurvy, arise as a result of dietary deficiency of one or other of the vitamins. As each vitamin was discovered it was denoted by a letter, A, B, C, D, etc. Most of the vitamins have now been chemically identified, and the letters are therefore superfluous, although they are still retained. The important vitamins in the human diet are A, the B complex, C, D, E and K. B and C are water-soluble; A, D, E and K are fat-soluble.

Vitamins were originally thought to be amines and were given the name 'vitamines' (amines essential to life). Once it was realized that many are not in fact amines, the terminal 'e' was dropped.

Some vitamins have a reputation, sometimes justified, for producing particular beneficial effects over and above their essential dietary role. These include the use of vitamin A (retinoic acid and derivatives) applied topically for certain skin diseases, vitamin B7 (nicotinic acid) as a vasodilator and cholesterol-lowering agent and vitamin C (ascorbic acid) as an antidote to the common cold; vitamin E (α-tocopherol), which is a membrane-bound **free radical quencher**, is said to have a role in slowing down the ageing process.

voltage clamp   A method for holding (clamping) the membrane potential of a cell constant at a level determined by the experimenter, so that ionic currents can be recorded and studied. One method of achieving this is illustrated by the diagram of a set-up for clamping the membrane potential across the motor endplate membrane of a skeletal muscle fibre. Two microelectrodes are inserted into the muscle fibre. One of these continuously monitors the voltage across the membrane and the other passes current into the fibre. The voltage-recording electrode is connected through a feedback amplifier to the current passing electrode, and the arrangement is such that current will be instantly passed to maintain the voltage at the chosen level. For example, it might be decided to clamp the voltage at the

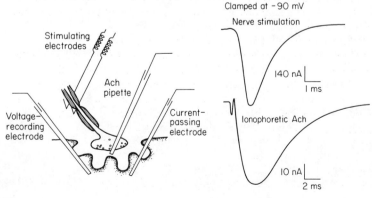

resting membrane potential ($c.$ -80 mV). **Acetylcholine** might be applied to the endplate **cholinoceptors** in two ways: by evoking its release from the nerve with the stimulating electrodes or by releasing it ionophoretically from a micropipette. Acetylcholine will cause an inward, mainly Na^+, current through opened cation channels (*see* **receptor-operated ion channels**) and this will tend to depolarize the membrane. However, this tendency will be instantly detected by the one (voltage-recording) microelectrode and counteracted by the other (current-passing) microelectrode. The current passed by the current-passing electrode is exactly equal and opposite to the ionic current flow caused by acetylcholine. In this way endplate currents (e.p.c.s) and currents evoked by ionophoretically applied acetylcholine can be recorded and studied.

The method is also applicable to studying current flow through **voltage-dependent ion channels**.

voltage-dependent ion channels   Ion channels in cell membranes that are opened to allow the transmembrane diffusion of ions as a consequence of a fall in the membrane potential. It is usual to envisage that the channels are guarded by a gating molecule that can be open or shut according to its degree of activation. A simple view is illustrated in the diagram. The gating molecules are presumably charged, since they are voltage-sensitive, and so they change their state when the electric field across the membrane changes. Their movement must consume electrical energy which is detectable as the so-called gating current at the beginning of membrane excitation.

Examples of voltage-dependent ion channels include the Na^+ and K^+ channels in excitable membranes. The local circuit currents flowing ahead of the action potential depolarize the membrane sufficiently to open the Na^+ channels. Rapid influx of Na^+ then greatly augments the depolarization until the membrane potential is reversed to a point at which voltage-dependent K^+ channels open. Outflux of K^+ rapidly restores the resting membrane potential.

In cardiac muscle cells, another type of voltage-dependent ion channel, i.e. Ca^{2+} channels, are opened around zero membrane potential and give rise to the plateau of the action potential.

With some types of voltage-dependent ion channels, for example the Na^+ channel in nerve membrane, the change in electric field across the membrane consequent upon the reversed membrane potential causes a conformational change in the channel such that it becomes inactivated and non-conducting (see diagram). The membrane potential has to return to normal again before the channel can return to its closed, but not inactivated, state. Inactivation of the channel accounts for the refractory period.

The diagram illustrates:

(a)   The resting state with channel closed.

(b)   The partially depolarized membrane with the voltage-sensitive gating

volume of distribution

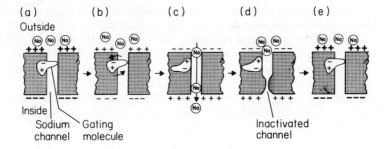

(a)

Outside

Inside

Sodium
channel

Gating
molecule

Inactivated
channel

molecule starting to respond by re-aligning its dipole moment with respect
to the electric field.

(c)   The rotation of the gate results in a small displacement of positive
charge from near the inner surface to near the outer surface so that there is
a reduction in the total charge separation across the membrane. In a
voltage clamp experiment, a small extra outward current (the gating
current) would flow to maintain the voltage across the membrane. The
opened gate allows inward Na^+ current to flow and this reverses the
polarity of the membrane which causes the opening of more sodium
channels in a regenerative manner.

(d)   The large and abrupt change in electric field has caused a conformational change in the channel protein that prevents it conducting the Na^+
current; that is, the channel is inactivated although the gate is still open.

(e)   The restoration of the resting membrane potential, which in some
membranes is assisted by an outward K^+ current (not shown), restores the
channel to its resting closed state.

volume of distribution   The volume of distribution (V_D) is the
apparent volume in which a drug is distributed immediately after it is
injected intravenously.

The graph on the left shows the type of curve usually obtained when
plasma concentration is measured after injection of a drug and plotted

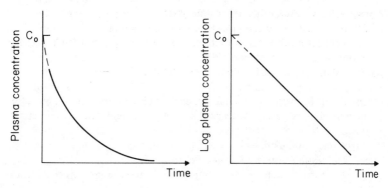

against time. This curve is converted to a straight line, as on the right, when log plasma concentration is plotted. Extrapolation of these lines back to zero time gives the plasma concentration at the moment the injected drug was initially distributed (C_0). The total amount of drug in the body (i.e. the dose injected) at this time should be given by this concentration multiplied by the volume in which it is distributed (V_D), i.e.

$$\text{dose} = C_0 \times V_D$$

or

$$V_D = \frac{\text{Dose}}{C_0}$$

V_D is an *apparent* volume. It does not necessarily represent the actual volume in which the drug was dissolved because it takes no account of drug that may be sequestered in certain tissues. Such sequestration would lower the plasma concentration (C_0) and therefore increase (often greatly) the size of V_D.

war gases   Gases developed as potential incapacitating or lethal agents for use in war. Different types are referred to under **anticholinesterase drugs**, **incapacitating agents**, **tricothecene mycotoxin** (T-toxin) and **vesicants**. The list is not exhaustive.

withdrawal syndrome   A group of abnormal signs and symptoms that arise when a drug upon which an individual is physically dependent is withdrawn. Also called abstinence syndrome. The syndrome is characteristic for a particular class of drugs (alcohol, sedative-hypnotic, anxiolytic, **opiates** and **opioids**, and so on—see **drug dependence**).

Woodworth staircase phenomenon   The increased strength of cardiac muscle contraction that follows a long pause between contractions; i.e. the recuperative effects of a long pause. *See also* **Bowditch staircase phenomenon**.
  Woodworth (1902) *Amer. J. Physiol.* **8**, 213

writhing response   A characteristic response evoked in mice by intraperitoneal injection of certain irritant substances (acetic acid, phenylquinone, benzoquinone, **bradykinin**). It is apparently due to an inflammatory reaction involving **prostaglandin** production, and it is prevented by **anti-inflammatory drugs** that inhibit prostaglandin synthesis (e.g. aspirin). It has been used as a test for this type of drug activity.

xanthine alkaloids   **Alkaloids** derived from xanthine. The main ones are caffeine, theophylline and theobromine present in tea, coffee and cocoa. These compounds are cyclic nucleotide **phosphodiesterase inhibitors** and they facilitate Ca^{2+} flux across some membranes by a separate action. They differ quantitatively in their actions but not qualitatively. They stimulate the CNS, dilate the bronchi, dilate blood vessels, stimulate the heart and produce a diuresis.

Theophylline: 1,3 dimethylxanthine
Theobromine: 3,7 dimethylxanthine
Caffeine: 1,3,7 trimethylxanthine

Xanthine

xenobiotic substance   A chemical foreign to the appropriate biological system (greek: *xenos*, foreigner). Most drugs may be described as xenobiotic (cf. **endobiotic substance**).

yellow rain   *See* **tricothecene mycotoxin**.

Yin–Yang hypothesis   A term borrowed from Chinese Taoist philosophy to describe the idea that **cyclic AMP** and **cyclic GMP** have opposing intracellular actions and that several cell functions are controlled by the balance of the concentrations of the two nucleotides. (*See*, for example, Goldberg *et al.* (1973) in *Proceedings of the IUPHAR 5th Congress on Pharmacology*, Vol. 5, pp. 146–169, Baste–Karger.) In fact, except in a few instances (e.g. frog heart), the hypothesis has largely been abandoned. In many responses (e.g. vasodilatation) both nucleotides appear to act in the same, rather than opposing, directions.

zero-order kinetics   A process (e.g. intravenous infusion) in which the rate of procedure (e.g. change in concentration) does not depend on the amount of the substance undergoing the process is said to follow zero-order kinetics.

The rate of change of concentration of drug D is given by:

$$\frac{dD}{dt} = KD^y$$

but $y = 0$ in zero-order kinetics, hence:

$$D^0 = 1 \quad \text{and} \quad \frac{dD}{dt} = K$$

where K is the zero-order rate constant. Differentiation yields $D = Kt$.